Other Works By Michel Monnot _____

Books

Selling America: Puns, Language & Advertising
  University Press of America, Washington, D.C., 1981.

Articles

American Assn. of Teachers of French National Bulletin
Canadian Modern Language Review
International Review of Applied Linguistics
Le Français dans le Monde
Le Français Moderne
Maledicta: International Journal of Verbal Aggression
TESOL Quarterly
The French Review
The Northfield Magazine
The Parkinsonian

From Rage To Courage

The Road To Dignity Walk

Michel Monnot

St. Denis Press

Library of Congress Catalog Card Number: 88-92596

ISBN 0-9621309-0-7

Designed and produced on a personal computer using Microsoft Word and Xerox Ventura Publisher by:

  Naomi Rubin
  Desktop Systems Corporation
  Denver, Colorado

Reproduced, printed and bound by C & M Press

First printing, September 1988
Second printing, February 1989
Third printing, March 1990
Printed in the United States of America
By Gopher State Litho

Dedication _____

to Janice

Acknowledgments

My thanks:

- to all Parkinsonians, care-givers and facilitators who, by name or not, appear throughout these pages;
- to Naomi Rubin, valued friend of priceless help who designed and produced the book, page by numbing page, assisted by Rusty Eubanks and Robert Dyson of Desktop Systems Corporation;
- to Virginia Marino, dear friend and colleague who edited and shaped the manuscript, valiantly; and to Tom Schmidt;
- to my friend and neighbor Susan Ecklund for the initial editing of my gallicisms and other grammatical shortcomings;
- to Joyce Aimée and readers Jeff Bauman, Penny Cupp, Sidney Dorros, Dr. Roger Duvoisin, Ralph Edwards, Alvin Handelman, M.E. Jarchow, Thorsten Kjelstrand, Dr. Abraham Lieberman, Elliott Rudenstein, Curt and Mary Swenson, Morris Udall, Frank Williams, the father of the Road to Dignity Walk;
- to Zona Meyer whose typing skills avoided the development of incipient ulcers in the impatient author;
- to Carole Wolken and George Melcher of Tucson, Carole and Gérard Pigeon of Santa Barbara, Syng-Yu and family of Pomona, Mike and Beverly Siidmarc of New York, Troy and Ava Crowder of Lubbock, Badrya Al-Ghanin, Dr. Vernon and Linda Shuckhart for their hospitality and generosity;
- to Dean Elveton of Carleton College; to the Arizona Parkinson Institute; to the APDA for their maecenean largesse, and their staffs including Elizabeth Barsness, Corey Pulju, Sherri Regenscheid, Loretta Springer, Nancy Sweeny; Jane and Linda, Mario Esposito, Dr. Paul Maestrone, Fred Springer;

- to Mary Strandness whose hand-picked RV never left us stranded;
- to Madeleine Rodenas for the initial prodding and note taking during the walk;
- to Patrick Monnot, my son, and Sara Cox, his friend, who showed the way to Marguerite and me;
- to Natalie, Gigi and Eric Monnot, for their love and support;
- to the good doctors Alhskog, Boyson, Edwards, Halvorson, Hoffmann, Hutton, Kabat, Lieberman, Melcher, Mellstrom, Montgomery, Nauseida, Page, Snider, Tennebaum, Syng-Yu and Zwiebel;
- to Nelson and Marta Martinez, and Pastor Don Berns for their willingness to share their pioneering experience with adrenal cell brain implants;
- to Nancy Soth, my dear friend who engineered the gift of an IBM-PC when I went on disability;
- to Cachet Frères, Bill Ford, Katarina Harrison, Robb Harriss, Jean Hlavka, Johnny Kamenchuk, Philip Lange and Melody Saunders for their graphic and photographic contributions;
- to Keith Harrison, Sue and Gene Bauer, Christina Harrison, Patti and Loren Haskins, Jean-Luc and Kathy Lahouze, Annalee and Jim Larson, George Mills, Sy and Marilyn Schuster, Toni and Ed Sostek, Bob and Dagmar Tisdale, Paul Wellstone, friends, colleagues and gadflies; for their help and good humor;
- to Jeff Reichel and Dori Tuomi of Carleton College; to Cliff Christiansen, Maxine Lamm, Cynnie Buchwald, Andi Little and Terry Ruane of Northfield Hospital and Methodist Hospital;
- to the memory of Peter Wilder; and to Shawn Ahern, Russ Ahlstrom, Richard Allen, Lupe Beaver, Debbie and Keith Belknap, Natalie Bernard, Leona Bivens, George and Natalie Carr, Diane Cassidy, Joan Claassen, Shirley Cole, Kathleen Cooper, Tim Daggett, Charlotte Drake, Susan Emke, Ruth Fleugel, Paula Folwell, John and Jette Foss,

Zada Harper, Rafer Johnson, Dick Kellow, Ann Kirkland, Milton and Shirley Krims, Charlie Landon, Susan Levin, Phyllis Marks, Rosemary McNamara, Sara Mitchell, Don Moore, Susan Morris, Ellen Moscinski, Neale and Sara Oliver, Liz Parmenter, Jack Perry, Harriet Priore, Bobbie Ross, Diane Rossi, Dick Saunders, Mindy Swartz, Richard Simmons, Peter and Irene Stern, Beverly Stuart, Gladys Tiedman, Bill and Joyce Titchnell, Norm Ufholtz, Barbara Valentine, Irene Vokovan, Ben Warner, Ken Warner, Laura Watt, Mary Willis for their friendship and dedication;

- to Lynn Simross, of the <u>Los Angeles Times</u> as a symbol of the press's responsible coverage of the Road to Dignity Walk;
- to Enduro socks, Etonic shoes, Minnesota Plywood and last but not least of contributors to the Parkinsonian walking movement, Sandoz Inc.

The list goes on...my memory doesn't.

Road To Dignity Walk Route — September 1985 to February 1986

Author's Notes

This book was written to exorcise my body and soul from the evils and encroachments of Parkinson disease; to tender thanks to those afflicted with an incurable disease and to restitute to them a fraction of the immense courage they so readily shared when I so much needed it.

I chose to consider the disease as not belonging to Mr. Parkinson. Hence a consistent spelling of "Parkinson disease" throughout the text.

During my 20 years of teaching at the college level, I have been appalled by the dearth of Latin rooted vocabulary of my students. May they find here a good reason to scramble for their dictionaries.

Any donation or contribution to the Parkinson cause resulting from this book will be turned over to Parkinson research endeavors.

In a small number of cases, I have changed the names of people who appear in these pages, good taste dictating. Any resemblance with reality in such cases is purely fortuitous.

Should any reader be tempted to join and support me for a walk from Vezelay, France where St. Bernard preached the second crusade, to Santiago de Compostella in northwestern Spain—in an international effort to combat Parkinson—s/he should contact me, at the address below.

—Michel Monnot

St. Denis Press
Post Office Box 442
Northfield, MN 55057

September 1988

Table of Contents

Part Three: The Road To Dignity Walk

Appendices

This book is the testimony of a man who exemplifies the true meaning of courage. The author is a professor, husband, father and a Parkinsonian. As of this writing, Michel Monnot is retired from his professorship at Carleton College in Minnesota and devotes his time and energy to raising funds to find a cure for Parkinson disease.

I first met Michel in 1985, when he called my office and volunteered to walk from Minneapolis to Los Angeles, a distance of some 2,000 miles, to generate public awareness of Parkinson disease and raise money for research. My first reaction was negative...that is, until I met Michel Monnot. He is compact and wiry with overt signs of tremor and marked reduction in vocal power, but his inner strength and determination had such a positive effect on me that I knew Michel was ready and able to take on this gargantuan feat.

Michel's entourage included his son, Patrick and Patrick's friend Sara, who took the lead two weeks in advance to promote Michel's arrival in various cities along the route, and Marguerite, the person responsible for driving the van that followed Michel. Hundreds of people turned out to greet Michel, applaud his courage and lend their support. On one occasion during his Road to Dignity Walk, Michel was heard to remark "What can be said to offend us? Parkinsonians of the whole world unite, you have nothing to lose but your shakes." If only that were true!

Michel's personality lends itself to the joyful rather than the sad, the humorous rather than the morose. Consequently, a feeling of camaraderie and joyful celebration was evident in every city and town he entered. When Michel completed his Road to Dignity Walk, weary but happy, he was asked "Do you think you have accomplished your goal?" Michel replied, "Yes, because we have reached out to outstretched hands, arms have been opened, tears shed and hope and faith shared while charity has unfolded its treasures. No, because victory is not yet ours, therefore we must continue this vigil."

Michel Monnot now shows very visible signs of Parkinson disease (a neurological disorder that is progressive and physically destructive). In spite of his disability, Michel continues to champion the cause of 1.5 million Americans who suffer the daily burden of Parkinson disease. He said, "For as long as I can speak, for as long as I can walk, I will fight to conquer Parkinson disease and rescue the lives of my friends and their family members who share their burden. But when I can no longer be heard, I will use a microphone, and when I can no longer walk, I will use a wheelchair."

As national director of the American Parkinson Disease Association, it has been my pleasure to work with Michel Monnot and an honor to have him for a friend. He is indeed a giant among men, and as a single individual, he has made a tremendous contribution to the Parkinson community throughout the United States, and in France.

On behalf of all Parkinsonians whose lives have been touched by Michel and his efforts to "ease the burden and find the cure," we want to applaud his stamina which led him from Minneapolis to Los Angeles, and his mental journey which led him from frustrating rage to positive courage. We thank him and will remain forever grateful.

Frank L. Williams
National Director, American Parkinson Disease Association

Part One

From Rage...

I Am A Parkie

I have Parkinson disease. I am a Parkie. I shuffle and shake, sometimes slowly, sometimes fast, but always arhythmically. I breathe shallow breaths, almost asthmatically. And for a while now, my brain has been playing tricks on me. It is no longer the faithful navigator, the trustworthy informant who used to get me out of predicaments with the same zest it had plunged me into them. The panache is gone. I can now solely rely on what my senses, improbable and inaccurate as they may be, are willing to communicate. My thought process and decision making ability, the vast area between stimuli and appropriate response, between intelligence gathering and pondered reactions, all this network of lightning-speed neural bombardment, goes awry at times, leaving me speechless, mouth agape, clutching at receding threads of memory which vanish into the fog of my muted and engulfing solitude. I become frozen in time, cemented in space, smack in the middle of a sentence.

And all those people in the auditorium who have come to hear my collected twigs of wisdom, how politely patient they have been. For a good 20 seconds of my fumbling and rumbling through the disorder of my mind, they haven't made a sound.... They haven't even fidgeted. But ten, 15 seconds more and they would have started: some would have coughed, some would have squirmed in their chairs or tugged at their collars. I know, it has happened. Oh! God, a minute of blank brain! Not only has the idea you are developing broken off from the mass of its context like the tails of the lizards we'd catch as kids, but the context itself has disappeared like the barely missed bus pulling away around the corner. Moreover, the mere phonemic articulation of any word, the physical mouthing of those very few words that come forward and offer themselves like old faithful servants embarrassed for their master—words like "excuse me" and "I am sorry" have become un-formable, un-shapable, un-articulable. If the shattering of your self-confidence doesn't kill you, the humiliation will.

But all of a sudden, from the depths of nowhere, a little forget-me-not of a voice shoots up: "Shape up, man, remember that old Parkinsonians never die, never die, they just shake away." A twinge of brightness is creeping onto the deserted mental stage, prodded by a last ditch attempt at scraping the last particles of dopamine and adrenaline. I know that this time, the day will be saved, although at the expense of tattered threads of pride on the hooks of an increasingly guilty memory.

Yes, I have been duly introduced by the president of the local Parkinsonian chapter, in the most glowing terms, as "that scrappy, spunky, courageous little Frenchman." All the while, my typewritten speech has been shaking in my hand in a most obvious and obnoxious fashion. "...and now, ladies and gentlemen...."

I have been able to take the few steps to the mike standing on the speaker's table. I have thanked the president and I am reminding everyone that, "I am delighted to be once again among this most generous crowd because that's precisely why I am back: research into Parkinson disease is expensive and I am counting on everyone to participate generously in the latest effort to...to raise funds...I mean, to organize a march to raise funds...and...and...." Blank, everything goes blank except the stark sensation that I am being observed by 150 pairs of eyes, most of them compassionate, certainly, but observing nevertheless. Blank, blank immensity for about 30 to 40 seconds of deafening silence. That is when, blessed among all flowers, the little forget-me-not voice flashes like a semaphore.

On the table next to the speaker's, an overflowing buffet is spread with fanned-out silverware and stacks of trays and dishes piled high. I had noticed it before the official beginning of the program and had directed my steps toward it, only to be advised: "We'll hear your speech first, Dr. Monnot, then we'll eat." And now I was stuck. Totally. Who knows for how long, exactly, when the semaphore flashed its Morse code image to my beaming antennae.

I saw the president flinch as I studiously pivoted on my heels and took five or six hesitant steps past him and to the overflowing table. The flinch turned into a horrified look and a useless embryonic attempt at help, as I grabbed the two-foot tall pile of plastic trays, retraced my steps past the bewildered president and set the pile right in front of me on the speaker's table. The silence was maddening. I picked up the mike with all deliberate Parkinsonian slowness, placed it on top of the trays. My shaking was subsiding. My blood supply must have hit a yet untapped vein of dopamine somewhere. Then I picked up my notes, arranged them comfortably next to the mike on top of the pile, and, having regained the major part of my composure, I simply faced the still tense crowd, and deadpan, I said, "This is what we call in French 'Tray convenient.'"

Part of the audience roared in relief, the other smiled smugly. Who cared? The speech was off and running. The day was saved. If you can humor it, go for it.[1]

But it was a long and circuitous footpath, painfully and not always deliberately followed, that finally set me on the Road to Dignity. Humor did not always play such a large role— at least not at first. During the earliest onset of my illness, the road was steep and rocky indeed.

---

[1] This story first appeared in <u>The Parkinsonian</u>, 1987, I-2.

My Day In Court

The Trial

So big shaking deal. My student Matt Piucci has noticed a tremor in my hand and a slowness to certain of my movements. Now, have I not heard that before, somewhere? That is reminiscent of something. Where was it? Yes, I've got it right there, stuck between two folds of grey matter.

It was at my cousin Monette's apartment in Paris during spring break of 1977. I had come to France for two weeks, wearing my Pau programs[1] supervisor hat, for which I had encountered some flak from all directions: the Pau II program students, their French profs and their host families, all crossfiring at each other. And I in the middle. Obvious as a sitting mallard at mating season. A precarious situation, to say the least. Complaints from the French Dean that American students were in France for a joy ride. Countercomplaints from the Dean of Carleton College, where I had taught for so many years, that Pau was a pitiful pit hole in the Pyrénées. Again, *pourquoi pas Paris?*[2] Complaints from the students that the families were niggardly watchful of the jam jar's contents. Complaints from malcontent families that more than one shower a week was a luxury they could not afford to have on tap. Bitch, bitch, bitch. Bitch that it rains all the time; bitch for this and bitch for that; bitch that the trains run on time; bitch at this and bitch at that.

---

1   Pau I and Pau II programs are Carleton College Foreign Study Programs in Pau, France for which I had been the founder and director.

2   Why not Paris?

Bitch. Let me cultivate my garden! All my diplomatic fi-
nesse had come to its end. I was running ragged, frazzled and
annoyed. T'was time to go home, Yankee!

Monette was sitting in the armchair across the room,
watching me pack my bags.

—"Mais, Michel, tu trembles?"[3] There was no denying it.
Yes, so my hand shook. A real handshake. Caught red-
handed.

But my reflex was still to deny the obvious, "No-o-o-o! It's
nothing. It happens when you are tired and upset. It happens
to everybody."

For the first time, at that precise moment, I linked together the possible relationship between those shaking fits
when tired, upset or hurried and the shaking in my left hand
when straining to go to the bathroom. There had also been
those fits of lightheadedness with the ripples from the forehead to the scalp; there was the fact that I could no longer
drum my fingers on my desktop. Although that did not dis-
turb me too much because I had discovered that I could still
drum if the surface were vertical. When I faced my filing cab-
inet, for instance, I had no problem drumming on the side
panels with either hand. However, I noticed that on occasion,
it was difficult to snap the fingers of my left hand, but not always. That's what made it so strange to analyze: failure and
success, hope and distress, some days no, some days yes; one
day in the morning, the next in the afternoon; some days at
work, some at recess; sometimes when the moon was full,
sometimes during the new moon. I was looking for patterns of
occurrence and recurrence, some indices at least of some regularity, some structure, at least one clue that would put me
on the track of my intruder.

Recently, I had noticed another phenomenon: in the classroom, when pointing at things or at students, my left index
finger did not extend enough: the students were unable to

---

3   —"Hey, Michel, are you shaking?"

discern the object of my pointing. My index finger remained crooked. I pointed to the blackboard. They said "window." I aimed at Gerry. They responded "Gino." It was also at this period that I noticed, again in the classroom, that nodding my head "yes" or "no" was no longer sufficient for communicating approval or denial. I had to verbalize, or else make a genuine effort and tell myself, "OK! Make an effort! Bob your head up and down, up...and down...." Now, the other way, turn your head right...and left, right...and left." Then the students would get the message. Now, if it had been a constant happening, I would have done something about it. But why worry? It happened only once in a while. Besides, all those symptoms were totally painless. Why indeed worry?

I tried to be honest with myself, not to panic. After all, there was always my pedigree I could wrap around myself and use as a security blanket. Nobody in the family ever had had anything drastic. So, I expected heredity to carry the day. But, caution! By the same token, nobody in the family had ever been nearsighted. And there I sat with my -2.5 diopters correcting lenses. In addition, we had been saturated by the American Cancer Society's warning that cancer could strike anybody regardless of their heredity. Say, could it be a slowly developing brain tumor?

I decided not to do anything. All those little problems were not insurmountable. I remembered Prof. Geneviève Delattre, my ex-boss's wife—a woman about my mother's age—telling me ten years before that advancing age riddled one's body with aches and pains. I did not believe her then and why should I have? I hardly knew the meaning of aches and pains. I had even forgotten what a simple headache felt like, the last one having taken place at age 13. For two months these mysterious migraines hammered away and subsequently disappeared as stealthily as they had come brutally.

What I had now, however, were not aches and pains. They were just nuisances, malfunctions of certain muscles, a kind of thief in the night whose sporadic presence was unobtrusive enough to be tolerated. Questioned, yes, but tolerated.

And I spent one more year wondering what my strangely behaving guest was up to and who he was. He certainly had grown into a true companion, not overbearing, not demanding, but here whenever he wished, whether I wanted him or not. Meanwhile, three main activities occupied my time: a) teaching my French I and II students; b) preparing the Pau I program in the spring, which this time, I was going to direct alone since my wife Janice now had her own position at the high school; and c) organizing the hosting of "A Vous la Parole."

AVLP, as it came to be known, is now in its twelfth year and going strong. It is a statewide contest of French poetry recitation. "A Vous la Parole" means, approximately, "Your turn to speak up!" I was worried that our students were receiving too much bookish French to the detriment of spoken French and I wanted them to learn by heart and carry with them at all times, not as a punishment certainly, but as a support, a living example of French literature. The first prize was a free summer trip to France, donated by local travel agencies.

The preparation for such an event was nothing short of phenomenal. There was the publicity; writing or telephoning all the persons and businesses in the region likely to contribute a prize; arranging for the dining hall; fighting to secure enough classrooms to hold all the various sections and subsections of the contest; organizing visits of the campus; renting a French movie; using a room for the display of prizes; reserving the faculty lounge for a teachers' reception; deciding where all the visitors' busses should park; corresponding with all the participating teachers; answering individual teachers' questions such as: "I have in my group a student with diabetes who is on a severe special diet. Can your food services accommodate him?" or "We'll be coming from Two Harbors in a station wagon. Two Harbors, north of Duluth, is seven hours away. Can we stay overnight?" etc., etc., etc., ad infinitum.

Came the day of the event (I forgot to mention name tags and welcoming packets), I was so exhausted that during my introductory speech in the filled-to-capacity chapel, I momentarily forgot the name of the college president, hesitated the length of a stammer or two, and finally managed to come out with "President Ed Robert" when it should have been "Bob Edwards." Shame, shame, shame! There went next year's salary raise.

What made all these activities all the more difficult to manage was that two short days later, I was slated to fly to France to set up, in one week, the Carleton spring term program, called Pau I. For some reason now forgotten, I was flying Minneapolis/Paris via Winnipeg on Air Canada. Since I had a two and a half hour stopover in Winnipeg, I quickly located a sunny table in the airport coffee shop, and, thinking I was already in Paris, I ordered a large café au lait and unceremoniously opened one of my handbags. I pulled out some folders, spilled their contents on the table and on the empty chairs around, and on a space no larger than a 500 Francs note, I proceeded to write a lengthy report on the AVLP day's activities, which was later published in the <u>AATF National Bulletin</u>.[4] I had been writing for a good half hour nonstop when I lifted my head up off the paper to take a quick glance around and reassess my bearings.

At that moment the most bizarre thing happened. I wanted to take a swig of the tepid coffee, so I went for it. Or so I intended. But nothing happened! "Holy mackerel! What is going on here?" My hand was there all right; I could see it. I was not hallucinating. There it was, limp on the table, devoid of life. It might as well have been floating somewhere between Mars and the moon. At a loss for knowing what to do, I got up, but horror of horrors, my hand followed inertly, sliding across the table. It seemed the whole arm was paralyzed.

I gave it a conscious command to move, but it would not budge. My God! What was I to do? Call the waiter and say,

---

4   American Association of Teachers of French newsletter.

"Could you please pick up my arm for me?" or "wipe my hand off the table, would you please?" While debating over what to do next in that ludicrous predicament, a twinge of hope radiated again. I could feel that the same willful command which had scored a zero response a few minutes ago was now making headway on the neural path. Success did not reach the fingers for a few more minutes, but eventually everything returned to normal.

I was exhausted. I did not hear, feel or notice the plane take off for Montreal. That was the first time that fatigue took precedence over fear of flying. Thanks for the fatigue. Thanks for small favors. I've always looked for silver linings.

Two days later I was in Pau, calling Janice on the telephone, describing my visitor's new shape and costume, and confiding that I was depressed, as she had seen me recently on a few occasions. "It's nothing," she was saying. "You have to react. I can't pity you, I won't baby you, and I can't talk you out of those blue moods. Telephoning is too expensive. Besides, there's nothing I can do for you. It's within you that you will find the strength to react and face, or to abandon and lose. If you really think there is something wrong with you, by all means go see a doctor and get this thing behind you. Incidentally, I just talked to Mary Swenson—you remember— she takes classes in Minneapolis to become a counselor—she says most depressions can be undone by sheer force of willpower. Pull yourself up by your bootstraps, and you'll see the light."

That was a very therapeutic conversation. I went back to my apartment at the University, determined that the whimpering had lasted long enough, that I would get to the bottom of this mystery.

* * * * *

—"My dear Mr. Monnot, I will repeat once again: you do not exhibit the symptoms of multiple sclerosis or Parkinson disease or Cushing disease, or Muscular Dystrophy. You must know that there are hundreds of variants in each of these and other neuropathies and myopathies. It doesn't mean that the symptoms that you describe could not be the embryonic manifestations of one of these diseases, but I will repeat," and here he gently, imperceptibly moved his head to look away from me toward the street, "at this point in time you do not have MS, PD, MD or St. Vitus or Huntington chorea." So affirmed Dr. Blanchard.

This Dr. Blanchard had been highly recommended by Sylvie Golvin, one of our local aides and instructors on the program.

Jean-Claude, her husband, swore by Dr. Blanchard, who indeed was an impressive man, a charismatic figure in the otherwise sheepish strata of the Béarnaise intelligentsia. As for me, what counted was the immediate. He had assuaged my fears and given me a mild anti-depressant. I left his office ecstatic. It's a miracle I didn't get clipped by that motorcycle as I crossed the street, light-footed and oblivious to traffic.

I related everything to Sylvie, who was not satisfied with the diagnosis nor the prescription. "Sure," she argued, "you have been a bit depressed, and what he has prescribed may do you a little bit of good for the time being, but it won't provide any long-range improvement. And since the symptoms you describe seem to be progressing rather than regressing, I think you should not wait to see a neurologist. Do you want me to make an appointment with Dr. Jones?"

—"...Jones? Yes...why not? But why the English name?"

—"I don't know either, but does it matter?"

—"No, not at all. In fact, I think it may be easier for me to explain what's going on in English rather than in French." Unbeknownst to me, Sylvie had scheduled an EEG with the office call.

Dr. Jones, as it turned out, was a Britisher who had come to Pau in his adolescence. In the second half of the 19th century, the wealthy English gentry had chosen Pau as their hibernation quarters. The mild climate and even temperatures, combined with native palm trees and luxuriant vegetation, make the town an ideal winter vacation community. To this day, beautiful villas stand as a tribute to the British quest for good taste and gracious living. The epitome in the genre, surrounded by deliriously colorful rhododendrons, is the Villa Lawrence located at the fork of *rue de* Montpensier and *route de* Bordeaux. It has now become state property and the office complex of the president of Pau University.

—"You see," explained Dr. Jones upon my prodding, "there were some difficulties in my family in England, and it was thought best for me and for my education to be raised by my aunt who then lived at the Villa Trespoey."

Dr. Jones took a liking to me, for he went into great details of a personal nature. It must have been the conversation in English! This lack of restraint, indeed, corroborated my very first impression of the man—a flagrant lack of what I considered tact. When first presenting my symptoms to him, I had mentioned, as a parenthesis, that a friend had suggested it could be the early manifestations of a brain tumor.

—"Now, could it be?" I had asked with nonchalance in my voice. When he placidly replied, "The possibility is not excluded," I thought, "What a bore!" I had come to seek help and encouragement and certainly a benign diagnosis to match the mildness of the symptoms, and he intimated that it could be a brain tumor! What kind of quack was he? If he had no more sense, couldn't he at least cultivate a more gentle bedside manner? He must have picked up on my childish inner tantrum and sensed a horribly terrified patient before him, for it was at this point that he finally concentrated all his attention on me.

As he slowly moved my limbs, pushing at the ankles, pulling at the elbows, rotating the hips, flexing the wrists and the fingers, he asked me to describe all the manifestations of my problem.

I remembered one in particular, that affected my left hand and frightened me, because it was one of the oldest of all the manifestations. The best analogy I could find was the movement produced by a cut up chicken leg when you pull on the tendon. The claws open up as you pull and close upon themselves when you release. Indeed, that was the feeling. My hand, which did not seem to be otherwise weak in its grabbing and squeezing functions, seemed to lose the strength to keep itself open. This feeling of folding back upon itself had also been manifest on a few occasions in the shoulders and chest. I had fought it by taking three deep breaths and straightening up.

The neurological exam was one of the most thorough I ever had. All reflexes were checked, all sorts of walking scrutinized (on one foot, on heels, on tiptoe, hopping, shuffling, pigeon-toed, blindfolded while counting back to zero). My hands and fingers were put through all sorts of obstacle courses; reaching wide with the arm extended and bringing it back slowly for the tip of the index finger to come to rest on the tip of the nose; slapping my hand on my knee, palms up, palms down; snapping my fingers in rhythm with a metronome; being given four words to remember and reproduce in order at any time during the consultation (kindness, purple, armchair and autumn).

Contrary to my expectations, the EEG was painless. Conforming to my most ardent wishes, it was also spotless.

—"Well, let us recapitulate. As I said, your EEG is clear. We can thus eliminate the possibility of a brain tumor." He straightened up. "I can hear you breathe better already," he teased. "No, what you seem to show is a little striatitis, a slight dysfunction of the corpus striatum, the part of the brain that produces certain neurotransmitters. You do have a mild hypertonia in the left side, not so much in the leg, but noticeable in the arm, hand and fingers. It's nothing serious at this point. I would just advise you to watch it. Yours sounds like a very slowly progressing striatitis. What is unusual is for this to happen at your age. You are so young to have it. But I have seen it happen. Can you repeat the four words?"

—"Kindness, purple, armchair...euh, Septemb...? No, autumn."

—"Very good." he wrote in my file.

—"So what do you recommend I do? Are there any drugs or exercises or something?"

—"Well, as I said, there's no reason to panic. But, tell me, how long are you going to be in Pau and the vicinity?"

—"Another month, then back home to Burgundy for two weeks and finally back home to the U.S."

—"I could give you some medication called Madopar,™ but I would want to be able to follow your progress and be present should you not tolerate the drug. But you said you live in Minnesota?"

—"Right."

—"Do you live far from the Mayo Clinic?"

—"Rochester is one hour away from Northfield."

—"Well then, what I recommend is that you enjoy the completion of your program in Pau and your vacation in Burgundy, and when you get home, if you feel like it, that you go to Mayo for a more comprehensive diagnosis. In the meantime, I would rest as much as possible. I'd bet you haven't taken a vacation in years."

—"Right you are."

—"Well, you try to live without pressure for a week or two. You won't believe the good it'll do you. You let me know how things develop. Good luck."

—"Thank you, doctor, you've been very kind."

That's when I turned all my deductive and inductive faculties to the service of folk physiology. I reasoned that if a twisted spine or a crooked vertebra or a deformed disk could pinch a nerve—like a Doberman the calves of an intruder—there was no reason why the repercussions should be felt only downwards affecting arms and legs. Why not upwards, affecting certain motor parts of the brain, especially the lower primitive brain stem? All that was needed after that was a precise diagnosis, therapeutic exercises, appropriate manipulations and everything would fall back into place and I would be all right. Dr. Jones had remarked that I was in excellent physical shape. 'Tis true. I was athletic. I exercised regularly, playing squash with my friends and colleagues Ted Hunt and Wolf Chamberlain. I very seldom had a cold or the flu. I never had a headache. I certainly possessed stamina to come to grips with a mild striatitis!

The Verdict _____

Janice came to France at the beginning of the summer with a group of her students from Northfield, Rochester and Minneapolis/St. Paul. I met them at the airport in London. It was good squeezing Janice in my arms, although I sensed a certain reticence: she was exhausted. She had fended for several weeks all by herself, worried sick about what was happening to me, hardening herself against a possible dramatic outcome to the situation.

The brunt of the organization of a novel summer program for French and American students—another Monnot first in the world of efficient foreign language teaching—was on her shoulders. This latest venture was an exchange whereby the American kids spent three weeks in a French family and returned home with the French students as their guests for three weeks of American immersion. Such a program would double the length of cultural and linguistic exchange, while cutting the cost by half. I am sure the idea itself was not new, but I soon understood why no one, to my knowledge, had ever implemented it before. To coordinate the exchange of 40 students on each side of the Atlantic is a phenomenal undertaking that only a superwoman like Janice would have the guts to tackle and the *savoir faire*[5] and stamina to accomplish.

Lest we kill ourselves at the grind, either separately or conjugally, we established a pact. We were going to sit down, jot down all the activities we were pursuing, be they for academic advancement or financial reward. We were going to hack at those two lists jointly. We agreed Janice should have help with the household (we would hire a Carleton student several hours a week); I would not take the Carleton Pau program next spring as I was slated to. She was not going to lead

_____
5   Know-how.

another exchange next summer; I was giving up the Minnesota AATF presidency. We would eat dinner at the Carleton food services (after all, students ate there; we wouldn't be eating *coq au Chambertin*, but what difference would it make?). I was going to apply for the one-term sabbatical leave I was entitled to instead of waiting another two years before being eligible for the two-term leave (yes, we would go to Hawaii and Egypt). She was going to get some help with correcting papers; I would offer and limit the summer bicycle trips to the students of the Experiment in International Living (not give it up, but curtail it); we never knew what the future held in store.... And I was going to make an appointment with Erwin Kabam in Providence in mid-August on my way back to Minnesota.

Erwin Kabam was the guru of the Carleton faculty who jogged, ran, and who more generally, suffered from backaches. Erwin had been Professor of Physiology at the University of Minnesota and was now retired and living in Providence, Rhode Island.

Janice and I recalled that for a number of years now, I had been suffering from back pains which I attributed to a fall I had taken from a tree about ten years before on a nice Sunday afternoon at El Capitan Beach near Santa Barbara.

It was the Fourth of July. We had been celebrating our daughter Natalie's fourth birthday. The Fishers, the Simmons, the Genzlers, the Pigeons were there. We had spent the morning on the beach delimited on one side by the receding waters of an unusually low tide. Shiny, slate-colored beds of mussels were exposed helplessly stuck against the seldom dry rocks and totally defenseless against the predations of two ethnic groups: the Japanese, who crushed the crustaceans to use as fishing bait, while the tiny society of French graduate students and professors at UCSB delicately picked pails of medium sized shells to steam and serve in a fragrant *marinière* sauce of onion, white wine and bouquet garni.

This was at a time when the waters of the Santa Barbara Channel were not so arrogantly polluted as they are today by the demands of the oil-starved society we have become. Then one could still sit with his children on top of the shoreline cliff watching the waning whales spewing their misty plume in search of warm water mating grounds, or stroll in the young avocado groves without risking one's life at the hands of some paranoid, gun-toting minuteman landlord.

Natalie, Patrick and I had wandered off into the vegetation away from the beer-drinking and frisbee-throwing birthday crowd. I was showing off in the branches of a small live oak, performing feats of acrobatics for my kids' adoring eyes, explaining how you must always keep three secure points when climbing a tree, when, all of a sudden—was it an excessive amount of beer I had consumed?—I lost my balance and fell to the ground, hitting some branches as I came down.

Subsequent X-rays showed nothing was broken; chiropractic manipulations proved in the long run that pain could be partially and temporarily alleviated, but never eradicated. So that in the Minnesota winter of 1973-74, when I noticed that my left arm did not swing as freely as it had before, I made a mental note that sometime, if and when time ever permitted, I would take a trip to Providence and have Erwin take a look at my back, arm and shoulder. In the meantime, it was probably the cold that was stiffening my arm muscles. It must indeed be a slipped disk.

The elaboration of this plan of joint action, including my seeing Erwin Kabam, brought Janice and me closer than any counselor could have. So, it was mid-July when I made two transatlantic direct-dialed telephone calls. The first was to Erwin Kabam's office. Yes, he would see me with pleasure, any time on Monday morning, August 18. And what seemed to be the problem? Oh, probably just a slipped disk that is causing some funny sensations and weird movements. Yes, he would take a look at it, and who recommended him to me? Well, of course, our good mutual friend Jerome Olson, anthropology professor at Carleton.

Erwin Kabam was now being regularly visited by a fervent retinue of colleagues who hailed him as nothing short of a miracle worker, so that it was not rare to see an English prof

walking through campus pushing up on his chin with both
thumbs turned up, shoulders flat, head held back; or in the
faculty locker room one would hear of the improvement
Erwin's prescribed exercises had produced on previously un-
manageable migraines.

The next phone call was to Ann Pellicano, an old Carleton
friend who had moved to Providence a couple of years before.
Yes, it would be good to see each other again and yes, she
would put me up for a couple of days. She would show me
Newport, we would go out for lobster, we would go to the
beach at low tide, and I would fix *mussels marinière.*[6]

At Carleton, Ann had been Howard Swearer's secretary.
She had followed him as his private secretary up the American education ladder from his post at the Ford Foundation, to
the Carleton presidency and now to the presidency of Ivy
League Brown University. Upon his latest nomination,
Howard Swearer had grandly asked Ann to follow him to his
new post to perform her functions which she described as
those of "office wife."

Staying at Ann's, in addition to affording us a chance to
reminisce about people and events at Carleton, would enable
me to see Howard again, perhaps chat with him for a few precious minutes, at any rate, give me enough time to thank him
for having been, in my book, a great mentor.

Howard had always supported—and funded—all my proposed endeavors, often dipping into his own discretionary
budget to fund proposals which myopic committees had rejected. Howard had flair, and while I had never confronted
him with the issue (-ance) of cyanide pills for the asking—I
had requested that he approve some pretty far-out proposals
that became academic or financial boons for the college. He
had that quality of recognizing his limitations and leaving
the details to the experts, while being able to discern the pho-
nies from the genuine—regardless of their flamboyance, or

---

6   Mussels in white wine sauce.

lack thereof. Among the proposals rescued from sclerotic committees by Howard's flair and pragmatic intelligence were the Summer Institute for Secondary School Teachers of French, the two programs in Pau running concurrently, the reopening of French House and the A Vous la Parole contest.

I was not to meet with Howard on that occasion, for he was busy that Monday having lunch with Harry Lovinger at the State Department. Ann presented me with his most sincere apologies...and best wishes for my health.

Erwin Kabam, however, was punctual to the rendezvous. I liked him immediately. His deep brown eyes expressed care and kindness. Besides, he was agreeing with my self-diagnosis, "Yes, from what I can see and feel so far, you have a slightly displaced disk between the fifth and sixth cervical, causing motor disturbances." (There he mumbled something to his secretary. It sounded like gibberish to me, the only word I could make out was "eyelid" repeated two or three times.) "And I'd like to do one more test to show you what I mean and explain how you can heal the condition yourself."

I was beaming inside. What a great doctor! A real miracle man, indeed. When I get home, I'll buy Jerome Olson a bouquet of roses. The test in question seemed ludicrous. Erwin had me sit on the side of his examination table, and with his right index finger, he lightly tapped once on the top of my head.

—"Now," he said, "I want you to hold my wrist in your hand with all your might. Squeeze, don't let go, squeeze harder, don't let..." pop! His wrist slipped between my thumb and tightly squeezing fingers with no effort.

—"OK! Now I'm going to lift your head, gently, like that...good! Now, squeeze my wrist again, hold fast, squeeze, squeeze. Bravo." He could not pull his wrist out. Once again, he tapped my head with his index finger; once again his wrist slipped through my fingers; he lifted my head in his cupped hands; I could hold his fist; again and again. It was uncanny. I thought he was joking. I asked him to do it once more. I had never seen anything like that.

—"Now," he said, "I'll give you these two sheets of explanations. It describes how you can reestablish your disk flexibility—it takes 24 hours—and how you can maintain it in good condition. Now that's one thing that bothers you and we have taken care of it. The other thing," and here, he pivoted to face me and sink his deep brown eyes into mine, "the other thing is that YOU HAVE PARKINSON DISEASE."

—"Park...what?"

—"Yes, Parkinson disease. You are indeed a little bit too young to have it. It's very rare at your age, but it does happen." I was livid. He glanced at me and quickly added, "But don't worry. There are now some wonderful drugs available to control it. If you had come in here five years ago, for example, I would have told you to brace yourself with patience, that a drug was on the way. Well, the drug is here today and let me repeat and assure you: it does wonders...for 95% of the patients."

—"Hew! And you expect me to believe that? Please, where are my shirt and my glasses?" Did he know what he was talking about? Here I had come to see him regarding a slipped disk which was causing my muscles to stiffen, and he comes at me with this ludicrous answer? Surely there were better doctors around. So thank you and good-bye. I left the office and sat on the steps of the Cape Cod style house. What was I to do? My life-long achievements and successes flashed through my mind.

KABOOM—YOU HAVE PARKINSON DISEASE.

Kabam, comes the echo. Kaboom, Kabam, kaboom, kabam. Where do you go from there?

3

Coping 101

Three Memories

So there I sat, on Erwin Kabam's doorsteps, crying, dejected, shaking my fist at an unjust god, bitter, beaten, defeated, experiencing my first Waterloo. I had to do something. I could not stay there indefinitely. I had to go somewhere. But I did not know yet in which direction. So I waited a bit longer.

I could call Ann. But she had dropped me off at Erwin's on her way to work, saying good-bye and wishing me luck. It would be awkward. Besides what could she do about it? I didn't even know what Parkinson was all about, what caused it, what the prognosis was, if there were ways to combat it.

So the first idea I focused on was: But what is Parkinson disease? What do I know about it? Not much at all. The search command I sent to my memory bank was producing only two images and one verbal French expression.

The first image to appear was that of Dr. Reese (my classmate Les Reese's father). He had been Professor of Chemistry at St. Cloud State College, was now Professor Emeritus, and still occasionally shuffled his way in and out of Stewart Hall. Les had told me in a whisper during class that his father had Parkinson disease, an incurable and degenerative disease, against which modern medical science was totally helpless. So the next time I passed him in the hall, I took a good look to appease my conscience and I wrote in my mind's file: Parkinson disease, shuffling, unsteadiness, trunk bent forward; arms hanging stiff; red, scaly skin; scalpful of dandruff; and I added as a reminder: Why would a man want to be seen in such a condition? Why did he not stay home? By

Jove, if I ever had anything like that, no way would I want to be seen in public. I would probably kill myself.

The second image to surface from the depths of oblivion was a much older, much less clear picture. The reds have turned to rust, the greens veered to browns, and the blues become a melancholy smoky grey. But whatever brilliance was lost in the chromatic scale has been more than made up by the sharpness of the pain that comes with it, by the mental anguish it conjures. It is a spring Thursday afternoon in Digoin, France. No school on Thursdays. A half dozen boys of the neighborhood, my age and a bit older, are playing by the canal. Mémé is about 150 yards away, bent over the laundry that she beats to a pulp between the washboard and the paddle.[1] The paddling echoes crisply on the warehouse wall, back and forth across the opaque greenness of the canal.

So busy are we with our ricochet contest, that we have not noticed the arrival on the scene of the Père Chandioux.[2]

—"Eh! guys, look!" says André, the leader of the canal rascals, "Here comes the Père Chandioux. Let's follow him." But as soon as he has registered our voices, Père Chandioux takes an oblique away from the canal. There's no telling what these little good-for-nothings will do next. And he saunters away, hands a-shaking and white cane a-flying, little anxious to hear the limerick composed in his honor, and even more afraid of the stones that the meanest among us have been known to throw at him on occasion.

—"Not true, not true," they would counter. "We were only ricocheting stones on the canal."

Mémé has kept a vigilant eye on the situation and when the taunting threatens to degenerate, she stands up from her kneeling position forcefully bringing us back to reason by making it clear that if she catches one of us, she will gladly

---

1   Mémé and Pépé Semet, my maternal grandparents who lived in Digoin, my hometown.

2   Old man Chandioux.

replace her laundry by that someone's *derrière* at bat! We disband, our limerick petering out in the thick foliage of the nearby plaza's sycamores (to the music of "Cadet Roussel"):

> Vieux Père Chandioux chasse l'écureuil
> Mais comme ses mains tremb' comme une feuille
> Au lieu d'tirer sur l'écureuil
> Il se fout le fusil dans l'oeil
> Ah! oui, ah! oui vraiment
> Il est encore plus borgne qu'avant.[3]

Indeed I had overheard Mémé and Pépé Semet, and my parents explain that besides being almost blind, Père Chandioux had wildly shaking hands due to shell shock on the front lines, and that this condition was called "la maladie de Parkinson."

The third memory, for some reason, was the most indicting. While talking about his immediate supervisor who had just been diagnosed with Parkinson disease, my father had used the pejorative expression, "Il sucre les fraises,"[4] aptly describing the pill rolling motion one uses to spread a teaspoonful of sugar over a bowlful of strawberries. That was considered the hallmark of incipient senility. "Il sucre les fraises." Would my father ever apply that damning expression to me?

---

3   Old man Chandioux goes squirrel hunting
    But since his hands shake like a leaf
    Instead of shooting the squirrel
    He crams the gun in his eye
    Oh! yes, there's no denying it
    He's now blinder than before.

4   "He sugars his strawberries."

What Could I Tell Them?

All this became a different story when I tried it on myself. Let's see: Michel Monnot, Parkinsonian, how did that sound? The cloak of gloom and inevitability was too oppressive to endure. But what to do? Call Janice, talk to the kids, write a letter to my parents? What would I tell all of them? Even if I had been more knowledgeable about the disease, how could I have broken the news to Janice? "Guess what, love, I have picked up a companion. His name is Parkinson." (News of having contracted syphilis would not have been more humiliating to announce.) "From now on, he will be with us on our life's journey. Day after day, month after month, year after year, every second of every day of every year, we will walk with him. His presence shall be more and more noticeable and inescapable. We will no longer be able to enjoy carefree time together, watching TV, dining out. Parkinson is forever and everywhere. It has an unbreakable lease on your life. Yes, even in our most intimate moments, he will be between us, robbing us more and more of these moments."

And how would I have presented it to the children? "Now kids, your dad is not going to be the same as he used to be. He has an incurable disease which is not too noticeable now, but which will become worse. His shaking will increase, he will become more prone to anger, his movements will slow down considerably, he won't be able to do many things for himself anymore, you will have to help him clothe and feed himself, you will have to speak for him when he stutters and cannot project his voice, you will have to wipe the drooling off his chin, you may even have to fight for his and your own dignity when people, especially children in school, make fun of him. And like the promises he has made to your mom of hiring a cleaning woman and taking her on carefree cruises around the world, the promises he has made to you to play tennis and soccer or to play Risk™ and Boggle™ more often, will not be fulfilled. Eventually, he will also have to resign, quit his job, go on disability, take unanticipated retirement, get a much reduced salary, and no longer be the figurehead and patriarch of the family."

And what could I tell the folks? Incongruously, a Ferlinghetti litany was coming back to mind, "What could she tell brother and what could she tell mother and what could she tell the cat with future feet." Just a short week ago, Maman and Papa were bidding me farewell at the train station in Digoin, crossing their fingers for that mild case of striatitis to disappear, hugging my shoulders as if to exorcise the ominous pervader, wishing me Godspeed to get back home (to Janice and the kids, first, for the academic year; then to France for the summer again). Could I tell them that this only child of theirs, this heir of theirs, was going to fall short of the mark? To be frank, I had never let them down, be it at the *lycée*[5] where I snatched the excellence prizes, or at the university where I fulfilled (almost) my mother's dream: I became a "doctor" albeit a Ph.D. instead of an M.D. Neither had I let them down in their affections: I had filled their solitude by bringing to them a daughter-in-law they admired and three grandchildren they loved. What was this unexpected monkey wrench thrown into the family path?

What do you do? You hash and rehash. You take it personally and you deny. But one day, one week, a light shines. You go from rage to courage… but the road was poorly lit at first, and I found myself lost and panicked in a strange place several times. I searched my memory for a signpost I might have missed, some warning; or for some possible reason that this could be true. I remembered that once an acquaintance in Santa Barbara had convinced me, against my better judgment, to open my palms to him. He had predicted some seri-

---

5   French secondary school including junior and senior high school.

ous health problems at age 40. Well, hell, I was now only 38; I had two years to go!

I searched my memory for at least a familiar harbor at which to anchor my sinking heart. Could I really have come this far only to find this curse at the end of the road?

4

Born To Be American

The Pedigree

When I survey my genetic antecedents, I find nothing at first glance that predisposes its progeny to anything drastic except longevity and death by natural causes at an average age of 81. On my maternal side, Maman is now the 68 year-old envy of any 48 year-old. Up at 5:00 every morning, she is continuously active in the house and in the garden until 9:00 in the evening. Aside from some migraines which have disappeared with the onset of menopause, Maman is in perfect health. Her penchant for homebodyness keeps her from restaurants, pâtisseries and gastronomic excesses. Even though she is a marvelous cook—friends and strangers alike whom I have gathered over the years around her table have attested to this—she is a model of frugality and discipline. I was born when she was 20, and ever since, she has remained a coquettish 100 pounds. The only *péché-mignon*[1] Maman indulges in is a particular brand of champagne discovered while making her yearly round of the provinces. She is very proud of her find, which she now buys by the case at the producer's and with which she delights all her guests.

Of her two sisters, Raymonde—Monette's mother—is the more cosmopolitan. Married to a military career man who was promoted to the rank of General upon retirement, she has lived in a multiplicity of contexts, from the jungles of Indochina to the refined gardens of the Black Forest at Baden-Baden, via the high plateau of the Algerian Atlas. Unfortunately, in the majority of cases, she found herself on

---

1   Petty vice.

the wrong side of history, a fact she and her husband have never been able to reconcile. That, of course, might account for their behavior being similar at times to that of the disillusioned GI returning home to a thankless public.

Edith is the youngest of the three sisters, totally selfless, a bit eccentric. She was a convert to vegetarianism before the wheel was invented, or at least before Gaylord Hauser invaded the French health food market. I must confess, Edith is somewhat of a nutty, wacky, and altogether delightful scatterbrain. Thanks to this last character trait of hers, I can boast two birthdates.

A few days after de Gaulle's London appeal of June 18, 1940, German troops invaded Digoin, our home town. Tales of horror and mutilation of newborns preceded the arrival of the enemy, and fed the imaginations of expectant mothers and attending aunts and grandmothers. And so, with unabashed perversity, I chose that very day to grace the world with my first cries.

The men, among them my father and grandfather, had retreated south, according to Pétain's grand plan of accommodation with surrender. Left in the house to greet the welcome arrival and ready to stab, bite and eviscerate anyone who would dare touch the baby were Maman, Mémé Semet (her mother) and Tante Edith, a pert but scared-silly 17 year-old. A midwife also helped Dr. Pignal, the only physician left in town, who, because of his age, was not required to retreat— simply to treat. Mémé and Edith were hysterical. But my *chère* Maman, I believe, had other things in mind and body to worry about.

—"Edith," said Mémé the next day, "il faut que tu ailles à la Mairie déclarer la naissance du bébé."

—"Mais ça va pas, tu es folle, tu me vois m'aventurer toute seule dans les rues? Il y a des 'boches' partout, à tous les coins de rue. Il paraît même qu'ils ont établi leur quartier général à la Mairie. Ah! Non, non, non, pas question; j'y vas pas!"[2]

A few days later, Mémé finally prevailed. But by then Tante Edith, still frightened and even more confused, had forgotten the date and given the 23rd, when the actual event had in fact occurred on the 22nd. This may seem an insignificant error in my destiny, but the event places me on the cusp between Gemini and Cancer, an embodiment ably described by a once-good friend as a double-faced crab. On the plus side, however, my star-crossed identity makes for two servings of Maman's hand-picked and foot-squashed birthday brew.

Pépé Semet was the patriarch of the clan. Life had molded him into a modern-day wise man, laconic, sought after for his realistic and philosophical approach to life. Upon his turning 75, someone asked him, "Eh! Joanny, how does it feel to be three-fourths of a century old?"

—"OK! The hardest is yet to be done."

A born athlete and graceful gymnast, he had become champion of Burgundy when WWI abruptly interrupted his career. He spent a full four years at the front, in and out of trenches, but mainly out since he was in charge of distributing the food to his cohorts. In other words, he was a prime target. Some would call it luck: in four years, he did not get a scratch. In the photo album of my mind, Pépé's picture appears in the very first pages. I see him in the half-light of the living room in that modest third-floor apartment where Maman was born and where 20 years later I was born: eyes half shut, enjoying his after-dinner one-a-day cigarette, listening intently with one ear focused on the low volume

---

2   —"Edith, you've got to go to City Hall to register the baby's birth."
    —"Are you crazy? I'm not about to venture out on the streets alone when there are 'krauts' on every corner. I've heard they've even set up their headquarters at City Hall. No way! I'm not going out there!"

BBC French broadcast while the other was straining for the noise of a possible collaborator/informant at the door. For the French language BBC broadcast was prohibited, and a few scums made their living by denouncing their neighbors.

So Pépé sits center stage, an immovable anchor of strength and wisdom. From his return to civilian life through WWII and until retirement, Pépé will satisfy his sense of self-worth by turning dinner plates on the wheel of a commercial pottery. His health is phenomenal. He will not have seen a doctor in his life when suddenly one morning while going to the farm for the daily quart of milk, he is overcome by a massive coronary thrombosis. A week short of 80, he has taken everyone by surprise, including Raymonde and the Général, who, used to planning things and ordering people around, had had the audacity to taunt the gods by reserving exclusively for Pépé a room in the house they had built, so sure was everyone that Mémé would precede him to the grave.

The three sisters had suddenly to face the unthinkable, the unforeseen, the unthought of, really. The need to care for Mémé remained just as real, but the competition to provide it became much less vigorous. They ultimately reached a not-so-gentlewomanly agreement whereby Mémé, an invalid by now, spent most of her remaining years in Maman and Papa's care. Maman was indeed the eldest, the closest to Mémé, and her house was probably the best suited to meet Mémé's special needs. Mémé died at 86 after a brief stay in the hospital. That was four years short of bridging a five-generation span which would have included Mémé, Maman, myself, my daughter Natalie and my grandson Eric.

Because of the geographical distance which separated us, I am much less close to the paternal side of my family. The 60 mile drive is nothing today with modern cars and highways, but in the forties it was a different story. In the first place, there was no traveling during the war years. After that, between the Liberation and 1951, my parents were saving for, but did not yet have, a car. There was a train, however, which allowed us to take the few journeys I remember to my grandparents.

One trip in particular stands out most vividly in my mind. It was just after the Liberation and the Monnot clan had decided to celebrate the event by convening at Pépé and Mémé Monnot's in Chagny-en-Bourgogne.[3] Gathered there were Uncle René, from whom I inherited my middle name, his wife Tante Yvonne, and their son, my cousin Jean-Pierre, three years my senior. They had come from Romans-sur-Isère where René was director of the technical *lycée*.[4] We were all taking an after-dinner stroll—to help with the digestion of Pépé's famed *lapin chasseur*[5]—and we were merrily coming back from Pépé's vineyard when horns started blaring behind us. It was a convoy of Jeeps filled with hilarious GIs draped over the fenders, the windshield and the hoods, and those marvelous creatures—yes, some were painted all black with big white teeth in the middle of their faces—were throwing a shower of chewing gum packs and candy bars at us. I am not sure I knew what their presence meant for the country, but from that moment on, the fuzzy notion that some day I would thank these heroes by becoming an American, began to germinate.

In the meantime Jean-Pierre and I were waging our own fierce battle in the grassy ditch and shoulder to see who would retrieve the most goodies from that unexpected liberation hunt. Although he bullied me on those rare occasions when we met at our grandparents', Jean-Pierre was a sort of hero figure for me, perhaps the incarnation of the big brother I never had. I was proud that he was my cousin, pride which never quit to this day as Jean-Pierre became a judo black belt, champion of Savoy for the 100-meter free style, a ranked

---

3   Mémé and Pépé Monnot, my paternal grandparents who lived in Chagny-en-Bourgogne.

4   Vocational-Technical high school.

5   Rabbit cacciatore.

tennis player in France, a 50 year-old wind surf master and, most recently, one of the eight coaches of the French Olympic ski team. This capacity for physical prowess he inherited from Uncle René and Tante Yvonne, avid hikers, who know the French Alps, all the trails, all the refuges, like the back of their hand. Now skirting his 80s, a sprightly Uncle René still bikes 20 kilometers (12 miles) every morning.

Mémé's and Pépé's names were Marie and Joseph; but there stops, on the family tree, any brush we may have ever had with sainthood or even religiosity. For Pépé belonged to the Free Thinkers Association and as such was buried, upon his request, with only a civil ceremony. As for Mémé, daughter of a fanatical Voltaire admirer, who had changed his family name from "de Givry" to "Degivry"[6]—more proletarian and less dangerous—she fervently espoused the ideas of the revolutionary leaders for whom things religious were not of primary importance. On the contrary, Pépé Joseph and Mémé Marie formed a solid couple anchored by deep mutual respect and a healthy dose of earthy gusto. I will always remember Mémé, withered-apple-faced and with mischievous eyes aflame, telling us a dream Pépé had once had:

—"You see, it was at the time your father had some problem at the Food and Wine Co-op. Perhaps you remember, Adrien Roburat was challenging his effectiveness as Co-op President. That evening's board meeting must have been quite turbulent: your father came to bed late, tossed and turned for a long while before falling asleep. But even his sleep was agitated. He kept talking, saying things like, 'Adrien, you can't do this to me; I'll make you pay for it.' And as a definitive statement, he turned his back, said very clearly, 'Tiens, voilà pour toi, vieille vache,'[7] and let out a gigantic fart."

---

6   A *de* before the family name indicates a title of nobility. However the *de* attached to the name indicates a family of common origin.

7   'Here's to you, bastard!'

Mémé died in 1960 at age 80, of liver blockage, probably due to the excessive intake of goose fat covered toast which, during the lean years of the German occupation and rationing, was the only culinary delicacy she could afford.

Tante Louise was the sole member of the clan who did not enjoy superb health. A bout with rheumatoid arthritis damaged her heart. She lived in the shadow of her two successful brothers whom she adored. She married late and was never able to have the child she so much desired. She derived most of her life's pleasure from working as receptionist for the Lameloise Hotel in Chagny, which boasts one of the ten best restaurants in France.

Her younger brother Georges, my father, was born when she was five and from that time on she deferred to his doubly superior status as male and as baby of the family. The baby grew into a handsome, tall, strong, intelligent, earthy, healthy man who to this day works tirelessly in his garden, lavishing T.L.C on his baby leeks, lettuce, peas and other assorted legumes. But his true title of glory stems from his passion for trees.

For the 22 years they lived in the schoolhouse of the little village of Uxeau, near Digoin, Papa never tired of improving the garden, which, like the schoolhouse itself, belonged to the municipality of Uxeau. When the weather was bad he spent most of his free time in his wood workshop making cabinets and storage shelves for his vegetables and fruit. When the weather was good, he would be outside pruning, fertilizing, grafting, spraying, babying his prize-winning pear and apple trees. Then in 1967, with retirement age lurking on the horizon, he and Maman began looking for a suitable lot whereupon to build their dream house. They finally settled on a fairly large piece of land, a cow pasture located on the outskirts of Digoin—approximately half a kilometer from the banks of the Loire River and half a kilometer from the Canal Latéral à la Loire. The lot, in the shape of a capital T, was bare; the soil sandy and not very rich, but ideal for certain varieties of trees. The house was designed by an architect friend inspired by copious notes and sketches copied from my first American home: the house of Dr. & Mrs. Vernon E. Shuckhart, my American Field Service foster parents in Park Rapids, Minnesota.

My parents' house, itself T-shaped, sits in the crux of the T. The vertical—or south—branch of the T has the driveway lined up by a row of leafy maples, paralleled by an orchard. When the time came to choose the trees, Maman and I convinced Papa of the necessity of having a majority of plum trees, juicy Mirabelles and golden Reine-Claudes, but there is also a wide assortment of cherries, peaches, apples, pears—even a quince tree which every year is so loaded with fruit that Papa has to prop up the branches with long fork-shaped supports. All around the rest of the property Papa has planted over 150 yews whose fast growth soon discouraged the curious looks of the neighbors.

The right (east) part of the horizontal branch of the T was turned into a garden which produces vegetables all year long, in spite of the unexpectedly gigantic growth of a cedar which casts more shadow than there should be for optimum garden productivity. But its majestic presence is worth fewer pea pods and a somewhat curtailed carrot harvest.

Nestled at various strategic locations in the maze of alley-ways, delineating the asparagus mounds from the potato patch, the baby Boston lettuce rows from the temporarily stocked maple nursery and the winter bean furrows from the endives growing under glass boxes in a white sand pit, grow various medicinal and aromatic plants whose leaves and flowers Maman picks and dries to add to the family phytotherapeutic pharmacopoeia: lusty green spearmint and peppermint; cleansing and refreshing citronella; purple heady lavender tufts alternating with clumps of sage and thyme, not to mention the gastrophiliac chamomile and verbena plants. It's summertime, and a treat to visit.

—"Oh Georges, le dîner est prêt," shouts Maman.

—"D'accord! Cinq minutes, je finis d'arracher les patates."

—"Cinq minutes, pas plus. J'ai des oeufs en meurette sur le feu!"

—"Ah! des oeufs en meurette! Alors j'arrive tout de suite!"[8]

Papa has worked all morning outdoors. I've watched him and kept track of his activities. He has not stopped once, busy doing half a dozen projects. Completed them all, too, except the last one where Maman interfered: You just don't make *oeufs en meurette* wait. You have to know your priorities! So he started at 9:00 AM after a copious breakfast of herring, salami, Camembert cheese, café au lait, croissants that Maman got fresh from the bakery at 7:00 AM, and fresh fruit from the garden. Also, religiously, three almonds.

He started by straightening out the basement so that he could move freely with the wheelbarrow. This morning he will make 35 trips with the barrow loaded with gravel from the front of the house down to the basement prone to flooding. At one point, I magnanimously offered my help. Five trips and my back was begging for mercy. He downs a glass of lemonade, shakes his head with an ironic smile and a gentle nudge for me to rest and give him back the arms of the wheelbarrow.

When I come back, his concentration is riveted on the spinach seeds which he dispenses evenly from the pack into the furrows, by a short staccato flip of the wrist, accompanied by a light drumming of the index finger on the side of the pack. Then, with a wide bulb digger, he takes a scoopful of humus and repeats the same wrist motion, this time covering the seeds with a thin film of the intensely black, rich, essential nutrients. Finally, by short pulls and pushes with the side of the hoe, he returns the little levee of earth standing on either side of the trench to the furrow.

---

8 —"Lunch is ready."

—"OK, give me five minutes to finish digging up the spuds."

—"Five minutes, no more. I have eggs Burgundy on the stove."

—"In that case, I'm coming right away."

Straightening up, his right hand on his hips, his left hand holding the hoe on which he leans for a second, he sighs with satisfaction. He's happy for my company too, which is, alas, too rare and sporadic. He looks at me.

—"Say, Michel, I'm going to wash up, tell your mother that I have dug up the potatoes. She might want to get a couple of shelves ready. OK?"

—"OK. See you in a minute."

In the west section of the T's horizontal bar, Papa gave free rein to his imagination, indulging in his sculptural sense of esthetics. He planted over 20 varieties of trees. All year long, the living room's gigantic wall window is an insured front row seat for the symphony of shapes and colors deployed by this exotic mixture of varieties. It frames Ponderosa pines, Norway pines and a Colorado blue spruce; there is a weeping willow shedding its tears on a decorative red flowering plum tree; there is a *sangre de Christo* sumac bush that stays quiet until fall and then suddenly explodes into a carmine bouquet just before dying; there are half a dozen Lombardy poplars, a joyful crab apple and a golden rich liquidenbar; and there is the ginkgo, also known as the 40 gold coin tree.

This tree is Papa's despair: in 20 years, while the poplars quickly shot up from a man's height to their present 60 feet, his ginkgo has grown a measly two feet, sprouting a tentative new twig every other year. Almost. On numerous occasions, out of sheer frustration, Papa has threatened to chop it down. But Maman has always been vigilant enough to discover and thwart such machinations before it was too late. To everyone else's delight, the ginkgo's crown-shaped leaves still dress each branch as a gold spun sleeve covers an arm.

After lunch, sitting on the living room sofa, watching a roaring fire and admiring the ever-changing hues of his trees' foliage, Papa is fond of reciting—almost as a vindication—the first few lines of La Fontaine's well-known fable. He puts his feet up and starts:

Un octogénaire plantait.
Passe encore de bâtir,
Mais planter à cet âge...[9]

And very soon, overcome by heaving waves of strength-re-building sleep, Papa abandons us—with no need to dream of greener pastures—for the few hours of his daily siesta. Mean-while, Maman has tirelessly cleared off the table, done the dishes, shaken the tablecloth free of crumbs, swept the floor, fed the cat, selected the menu for dinner, prepared the vegetables, written a letter to her granddaughter. She is radiant. Her only son and only child is home. Today she fixed one of his favorite dishes. Tomorrow, it will be another spe-cialty: *andouillette grillée.*[10] I wish I could tell her, them, how much I admire them and how grateful I am for the training they gave me and the example they set for me.

Thirty And Immortal

Thus genetically equipped, carrying my pedigree around my neck like a protective St. Joseph amulet, I embarked joy-ously on my life's journey. Joyously indeed! I had beaten all the odds: conceived within two weeks of the declaration of war, on one of those hot August nights of 1939 when the air smelled of summer storm and the earth shook in fear of storm troopers; then born nine months later, the precise day the German troops invaded the town; the men gone to war; my difficult birth in difficult circumstances; I had quite a begin-ning.

---

9   "The 80 year-old man was planting a tree. I would understand it if
     he were building something, but to plant a tree at his age...."

10   Grilled tripe sausage.

No one so fervently desired was welcomed in so gloomy a background. Could the situation get any worse? There was only one way to go, and that was up. I was the symbol of hope. The sunshine boy shedding his radiance on my feminine entourage, Mémé, Maman and Tante Edith. And under the conditions stipulated by the Pétain surrender, Pépé Semet and Papa soon came back to town, one to resume his work as a potter, the other as a teacher.

The Loire River was the demarcation between free and occupied France. Digoin, was on the wrong side of the river, so the whole family joined hands, forces and wits with neighbors and friends to infiltrate the German lines and come back home from the free zone with fresh eggs, flour and milk. Some stories recounted years later, about the artifices used to elude the German patrols or about the way this neighbor or that got captured and executed for his illicit crossing of the demarcation line are models of the epic narrative genre.

Stories of bravery, bravado and bravura, titillating stories of the victory of brains over brawn, tragic stories of oppression and torture, of massacres and reprisals, heartwarming stories à la David and Goliath, heartrending stories of mistrust and denunciation, real-life stories of man's bestiality and of man's sacrifice, stories to keep to oneself or to unload upon our grandchildren, stories by which to live better.

But could a story of Parkinson really fit among them? If indeed I had the disease, would I be able to weave a tale worthy of those I remember? I spent hours reminiscing, seeking strength from my family past, retracing my roots to see where the road was meant to lead, and what preparations had been made for my journey.

Only one episode during those early years takes the form of a cloud: at six months, a severe bronchial pneumonia pushed my temperature up to the danger point. My attending court nearly gave up, I am told, but I must have had the right genetic stuff, for even without the benefit of being breast fed, I pulled through to cast again my aura of hope and my sense of innate enthusiasm.

So I grew up healthy; short, but healthy; no flus; few colds; yes, short, but solid and healthy. Then a finely shaped body, small but graceful, began to emerge and if it had not been for two months of migraines at age 13, I would have reached adolescence and adulthood untouched by doctors' hands.

The Liberation came, with more GIs and more candy bars. The GIs went home with all the pretty "war brides." The Marshall Plan rebuilt the bombed cities and the shattered economy. After five years of suffering, introversion and paranoia, the purifying breeze of liberty never wafted so heady an aroma. The black curtain of tyranny, drawn shut for so long, opened up again on a world that, this time around, was going to be better; a world in which you could spread your wings; a world you could sink your teeth into; a world pulled impetuously by the chimera of American capitalism. Hope was permitted once again. I subconsciously felt this attraction and drive; I could sense it in the air; it was an almost global phenomenon; the world was a ripening plum and that plum was going to be mine: I knew I was walking with history. I was born to be American.

No more gossip and rumors, no more "no, no, no, you can't." But instead, a home on the range where you can if you want to, where tradition does not interpose itself like an obstacle at every whim of your way, where you are free to try—free to break your teeth too—but free to fly, even if it is to burn your wings. Dedalus, Icarus.[11] Never heard of them! All the better. I had the guts, the willpower, the brains and especially, if not the luck to *be* an American, at least the energy to *become* American.

---

11 Dedalus: the architect who designed and built the Labyrinth; Icarus: his son, who burned his wings by flying too close to the sun as they escaped out of the Labyrinth.

Energy Galore

I first discovered this on a cloudless Sunday morning in the late spring of my sixteenth year. It was the last Sunday of the school year when, all throughout France, all school children are either busy playing cards behind the windows of a bus, totally oblivious to the pedagogical message, or are busy setting up stands, booths and a stage on the school grounds for the annual school festival.

The first graders will show off the songs they have learned during the year, the second graders will—oh so cutely—misstep to a folkloric *gavotte* or *bourrée*;[12] big brother will spend all his savings at the shooting gallery stand, trying to win a bottle of cheap champagne by hitting three out of four dancing balloons with five bullets—but he won't, because the shooting gallery is weighted against him; the local aspiring Lily Pons and Maurice Chevaliers will ruin everybody's ears by singing too close to the mike and send the overloaded, precarious public address system into waves of screaming feedback; Susan will have spent the whole afternoon making herself up, hoping to attract Pierre's attention and if all goes well, perhaps parlay this attention into an invitation to twirl at the dance.

This year in Uxeau, a cup will also be presented by the mayor, Mr. Poiseau, to the winners of the soccer game. For the school festival was also an opportunity for the youth of the neighboring villages to compete in a very loosely organized soccer contest. Loosely organized, because no one was in charge; and that is because no one knew any better, because the passive status quo was by far preferred to the unknown, risky business of taking chances. Tradition!...I see myself as

---

12 Folk dances.

a fresh breeze in this sclerosed atmosphere. I had no money, but I had the energy to make a difference, and I was not going to let this chance go by. Loosely organized, because of primitive premises which no one ever questioned. Loosely organized because "what was good enough for the previous generation was good enough for the present one too."

So we operated on a soccer shoestring, with a pasture for a field, borrowed from a farmer; with individually purchased jerseys for shirts—so much for uniforms!—blue and white were the "official" colors; sky blue, navy blue, light blue, blues of all hues were the result; with all sorts of kickable things as an excuse for a ball—I remember we once practiced with a plastic bucket, kicking said bucket to its own demise.

But for this special school festival, we had managed to raise enough money to buy a brand-new soccer ball, and genuine soccer goal posts, discounted at cost, as it were, through the generosity of the local carpenter. Shoes and socks were left entirely to the individual fancy, taste and ability to provide. Some of us at times played barefoot, thus emulating, more often out of necessity than choice, the players of the Indian Olympic team whose pictures and exploits we had seen in a sports magazine.

That afternoon, our invited competition would be the team of Vendenesse-sur-Arroux. It is in this strategically located valley of the Arroux River that Julius Caesar conducted his conquest of my ancestral Gallic tribes. Uxeau, on the contrary, is perched on a hill with a 360-degree panorama, and for this reason, the inhabitants have always felt superior to the more urbane but less independent valley dwellers. Would we be able to maintain that superiority on the soccer field?

9:00 Sunday morning I hear through the open kitchen window, "Hey Michel." Our apartment is on the second floor of the schoolhouse, with most windows facing the plaza with the memorial monument to the war dead.

—"Salut."[13] It is one of my teammates, Hervé Tillier, all decked out in his Sunday mass best. He lives in Bassenier, five kilometers away, one of the village's hamlets. His hair is a mess, his face all red. He's visibly upset.

—"What's the matter?"

—"Come on down! Hurry up!" He pushes his bicycle against the school yard wall, wipes his forehead with his sleeves.

—"Quick! Get a move on! Get down here!"

—"Well, what is it, man?"

—"Get down here, I can't shout it out! For Christ sake, hurry up!"

—"Well, you come on up. I'm not dressed; I haven't even had breakfast." I dash off to my room to put shirt, shoes and socks on.

—"M'man, you want to pour me a café au lait and also one for Hervé Tillier? Thanks." He must have climbed the stairs three at a time. He's already here, his footsteps in the hallway rapid and determined.

—"Come in, come in, what is it?" I ask, one knee up, hands tugging at one sock, teeth clenched on the other. He catches his breath. "What is it? Grab a chair and sit down."

—"Well, I don't have much time, I have to serve mass this morning, but I thought..."

—"Ah! Bonjour, Hervé." Mother waltzes in with two huge bowls of café au lait and Sunday croissants. "You seem upset. Have something to eat, and you can..."

—"Bonjour, Madame! No, thank you, I am sorry, I can't, you see, I..."

—"Well, man, you're gonna tell me what's on..."

—"Oh," interrupts Maman, "it'll be good for you, or would you prefer some brioche? I baked two loaves last night..."

—"No, really, thank you, I can't. You see, I'm going to take Communion..."

---

13 —"Hi."

—"OK, M'man, thank you, but please let him speak. Leave us alone."

—"All right, I'm going, but Hervé, I won't let you go back home all the way to Bassenier without anything in your stomach."

—"Mother, please, don't..."

—"You come back after church! I'll re-heat this for you."

—"Yes, I will, thank..."

—"And you, Michel, will you have something, you've hardly eaten anything..."

—"Mother, please, Hervé is trying to say..."

—"I am leaving you two alone. Good-bye!"

—"Good."

I spin him by the shoulder and sit him down.

—"So will you tell me what's going on?"

—"Yeah, I don't have much time, but since you are not going to church, I thought," he sits closer to the edge of his chair, "I thought you might want to go take a look at Grand-claude's. I took the short cut by Faviole's Lake to come up here. And I couldn't see from there the goal posts that we had put up Tuesday evening on the Grandclaude's field."

—"You didn't look right, obviously. We sank those posts in two sacks of cement."

—"I hope you're right. I did go to bed very late last night, but you know the old Jean Grandclaude. He can be pretty bizarre at times. His dogs didn't even bark. I wish you would go take a look. It seemed a little spooky." And as if he needed to gather his courage and muster his premonitions, he takes a great gulp of café au lait. He is about to take a huge bite of one of the begging croissants when his arm stops in midair and he yells, *"Merde!"*[14] which even a quick hand cupped over the mouth is too late to cover.

—"Now what? You startled me."

---

14 —"Shit!"

—"Now I have to serve mass and I can't take communion. I just drank some coffee. The priest is going to be so mad."

As my parents have raised me a free-thinker, the subtleties of the Catholic rituals elude me almost completely, and I am totally baffled when Hervé winks at me, saying, "Sweet Jesus will forgive me, won't he?" and tilting his head back, pops into his mouth that piece of croissant which had been waiting in midair.

—"OK! Now, to work. I'll see you after church. Good luck!" And, like two frisky colts savoring their first spring, we rush downstairs, laughing at our prankish carefreeness.

The small country road, the shortcut to Grandclaude's, is the very picture of full-blown spring. The hawthorne which replaced the wild plum blossoms a week before is now slowly being overtaken by the bridal gown of the acacias which, in due time, will yield to the cherry blossom, before the white umbrellas of the elderberries. The turtle doves are treating each other to a coo concerto; and the cottontails hop ahead of me as if they had spring-loaded toes. Even my curiosity to discover what's going on at Grandclaude's cannot compete with the wonder of the scene. Still, I'm pedaling fast. Up Jacob's hill, there's a turn to the left. From there you can see Faviole's Lake and if you stretch a bit, you can see part of the Grandclaude's farm. I'm half way up the hill and starting to lose my momentum when, coming out of nowhere and gaining momentum, a cyclist plunges down the hill past me, hair a-flying and eyeballs flattened by the wind. I recognize the shirt as the cyclist whizzes by.

—"Eh, Alain! Slow down and come here," I shout over my shoulder. But he is too thrilled by the speed of the downhill, and probably also carefully anticipating the patch of sand accumulated on the non-tarred pavement at the bottom of the hill. He may also not have heard me. Alain Dubrion is our goal keeper and must be informed immediately if there is a problem. So, without another thought, I turn my bike around and start the chase. Of course I come down too fast on the patch of sand, my back wheel starts sliding. Heavy jamming of the back brakes with the right hand which accentuates the sliding although, fortunately, reducing the speed, for it is now head first into a soft—if stinging—bed of nettles.

Alain heard me yell as I lunged in the nettles. When I regained my aplomb and climbed out of the ditch, he was already at my side, readjusting my twisted handlebar. Knees? check, not a scratch; head? check, thinking, President of the Republic? Edouard Herriot, check, memory functioning; hands? dirty, a few bloody scratches on the palms, burning sensation; but what in...Could I have broken something in my elbow? It hurts fiercely. Left elbow. I move it slowly, pain; agony; but it does move.

—"Good, listen Alain, we have to go to Grandclaude's to check on something," and I tell him of Hervé's premonition.

—"Did you notice anything strange?"

—"Well, I did not come the same way, but let's go back up Jacob's hill and we'll take a look from the bend." Alain is worried about the goal posts. As the team goalie, he feels a proprietary responsibility. And he would be crestfallen if for this formal occasion we had to host the Vendenesse team with jerseys for goal markers—as we did for practice—instead of real official posts. Our hillfolk mentality and honor are at stake.

In spite of all the burning sensations, let alone the itching, I have no problem following Alain to the top of the hill. As a matter of fact, I feel impetuous. Must be an adrenaline reaction to the nettles. Alain is panting because we came up too fast. I am panting because we are not moving fast enough. I want to get this thing cleared up, and the faster, the better. We hop off the bikes, leave them on the spot, climb over the big wooden gate and walk a few yards. The lake down below is smooth as a Corian counter; no sign of activity at the Grandclaude farm. Everything seems to be enjoying this Sabbath rest. As if to perfect the harmony of the scene, the church bells are starting to ring.

—"Sounds like Hervé's having fun swinging on the bell ropes," and I can imagine him in his altar boy surplice, pull-

ing down hard on the ropes, the higher to be lifted off the
ground on the upswing.

—"And it looks like I'm not gonna make it for church, because do you see what I see?" asks Alain as he points past the
farm to the soccer field. He's livid: one set of posts is lying,
dismantled, on the ground. Wood chips around the still anchored stumps: the posts have been axed down. The other set
of posts stands, visibly untouched. But what remained of the
bag of lime which we brought at practice Tuesday evening to
draw the lines on the field has been strewn all over the far
end of the playing field.

—"Who could have done such a thing? And why? As a team
we have no enemy." We look at each other.

—"You don't think the guys from Vendenesse…" I venture
with hesitation. He turns his head and laughs, but it's a
funny sort of laugh. I turn toward him, curious. But he is
looking into the distance as if musing.

—"No, no," he says, "it's not the guys from Vendenesse;
they want to play as much as we do, but it's…oh, forget it, you
wouldn't understand." His face becomes somber.

—"Try me, what is it? Do you know who did it?"

—"You wouldn't understand, because you don't go to
church, you don't believe in our old wives' tales. It sounds so
silly, you're going to make fun of me. It's a superstition.

—"I won't make fun of you if your superstition tells us who
did this." We get back on our bikes and instinctively head for
Grandclaude's.

—"Well? You gonna tell me?"

—"Well, as I left the house this morning, my grandpa said
to me, 'Alain, there's trouble by the lake. I heard the female
owl hoot in that direction all night long and old man
Laureau's peacocks have seldom been so restless. Be careful!' "

—"You're right. I don't see the connection between sav-
agely axed down soccer goal posts and a hooting female owl
and crying peacocks."

—"You see, I told you, you would make fun of me. Sure, you go to the *lycée*, you're educated, you know more than all of us here in Uxeau, but man, you're losing your roots, it's as if you didn't belong here anymore. You'll probably end up in some faraway place like America."

—"Whoa! Whoa!, just a minute. What's got into you this morning? I can see you're upset by the sight of your goal posts, but we can do something about that before the game starts at 2:00. Why attack me? Cool off a bit, won't you?"

A couple of bends further appears the Grandclaude's farmhouse. Circumspection is in order. We both slow down and dismount from the bikes which we lean against the old pail-worn well sill. The courtyard is eerily silent. At the far end, by the cellar door, one of Grandclaude's dogs observes our entrance. He's lying down, front paws extended in front of him, his head resting flat on them. A timid, hesitant tail-wagging registers our approach. No barking. The other dogs must be sleeping in the straw hangar. It's starting to get warm. A hummingbird flutters on a morning glory. We are subconsciously closing ranks—two young sleuths in suspense walking carefully lest we upset this unreal calm.

—"Look," I whisper, and point to the living quarters entrance. On each side of the double hinged door—the solid oak bottom half and the glass-paned upper half, each of which opens and closes independently—five or six geranium plants writhe on the ground, soil spilled about, in a heap of pottery shards and debris.

—"Something really weird is happening. You see, my grandpa was not so far off. There's trouble all right." And I am sure that in Alain's head, as in mine, visions of an ax-wielding madman push the adrenaline production level as high as our decibel production level sinks low. My throat is dry in spite of furious swallowing contractions. At the same time, a strange impression of shaking and paralysis invades me. It requires all my strength to take the few steps to arrive at the door. We both flatten our noses and faces against the

windowpane, with hands cupped to better pierce the secret of
the obscurity within.

—"Oh, my God!" I can hardly believe my eyes. The floor is
littered with broken dishes and glasses and way at the far
end of the huge room, behind the stove, stands Mrs. Grandclaude, holding the baby in her arms, while the older child is
hanging to her skirt. She brings her free hand to her lips and
I wonder if it is to tell us to be quiet or to repress or contain
the expression of surprise that our apparition certainly
caused her. Once again, Alain and I look at each other to find
mutual reassurance that what has to be done coincides with
our instinctive but inexperienced reaction. We are agreed.
We must not break the silence for fear of attracting any evil
attention lurking on the premises. Alain tries the door handle. Locked.

—"Try the handle to the upper half. If it doesn't work we'll
break a window pane." Locked too. But the woman has recognized us by now. She is inching her way toward the door,
loaded down by the two leech-like children, navigating carefully on her bare feet among the pieces of broken glass and
avoiding a large black puddle between the stove and the
table. She tugs at the upper lock for a few seconds and the
window half of the door swivels open in our faces. An
awkward silence betrays our total lack of social graces. My
sensation of blockage has returned. It's as if, for a few seconds, I were cast in concrete.

The woman speaks in a whisper, "Alain Dubrion et Michel
Monnot! Mais qu'est-ce que vous faites là?"[15]

I haven't seen her for a long while, but I recognize her immediately. She's the daughter of the municipal caretaker. I
especially remember her wedding procession, when the
whole party walked from the farmhouse to the village—city
hall first, then the church. It was another perfect day in early
June. A friend and I had made up several bouquets which, ac-

---

15 "What are you doing here?"

cording to custom, we had placed at strategic locations along the route to be picked up by the wedding party in exchange for a few coins. I remember how pretty she had appeared that day in her wedding gown and I am wondering if she ever suspected such a change of fortune in such a few short years.

—"Mais, qu'est-ce qui se passe?" Alain wants to know. "Il a bu un cannon de trop? Mais pourquoi il a saccagé nos poteaux de goal?"[16]

—"Did you see him anywhere?" she asks.

—"No," I say, "but now that I see the broken wine bottle, I'm wondering whether he might be in the cellar. Let's go take a look. But tell us what happened."

—"Wait a second. I'll put the baby in the crib. And you, Serge, you are a big boy, you wait for Mommy on your bed, so you don't cut your feet on the broken glass."

She has regained some of her composure and I see her bristle when Alain asks again, pointblank, "Did he have too much to drink?"

—"I don't know. It started yesterday afternoon, when the cattle dealer came by. He sold him a heifer for a good price. So they had a glass of wine to conclude the deal. But for some reason he kept drinking and towards evening he became violent. I tried to reason with him; he grabbed the dishes off the table and threw them all down. Then he left. That's when I bolted the door. I could hear him fume, go to the cellar for more wine, curse the dog."

—"He chopped down my goal posts on the soccer field," mourns Alain, "and we're playing Vendenesse this afternoon."

In front of the cellar door, the dog is still keeping its reluctant guard. She shoos him away unceremoniously and flings the door open. In the darkness, gradually lightening, we

---

16 —"What's going on here? Did he drink too much? But why did he ruin our goal posts?"

make out Grandclaude's body, spread-eagled, head under the
barrel spout. He is snoring most forcefully.

—"Let's let him sleep it off," I suggest. "In the meantime,
Mme Grandclaude needs some help and you and I, Alain,
need some goal posts. So why don't you stay here for company, and I'll go for help as fast as I can." Which brings the
question into my mind: am I a coward or am I convinced that
I can move faster than Alain? Number two prevails. I want to
show it. Back on the bike, I almost make the same mistake
again at the bottom of Jacob's hill. My heart skips a beat as I
feel my back wheel beginning to slide, but somehow I clear
the sand trap. And it's uphill to the village plaza, with build-
ings neatly arranged around the marble monument, the
schoolhouse that doubles as city hall and refectory building,
the two cafés, the bakery, the church slightly recessed on top
of the hill, a few habitations. In anticipation of the afternoon
and evening festivities, a "Sunday-fied" crowd has already
assembled at the *café d'en bas*[17] more homey but less
cosmopolitan than the *café d'en haut*.[18] Many of the players
on the team are there; the rest are still in church. I have
hardly set foot on the ground when I am assaulted by an excited crowd, surrounded like the hero that I nurture in my
imagination.

—"Okay, guys, here's the scoop. Maybe Hervé's already
told some of you before he went to church, somebody chopped
down one set of our goal posts, so if we want to be credible in
the eyes of the Vendenesse team, we have to erect a new set
before 2:00. You, Maurice, why don't you plead with your
Uncle Dauvergne to let us have the wood? I'll pay him out of
my own pocket if I have to. Henri, since you live not too far
from Grandclaude's, could you bring that new tractor of
yours? We need to pull out the two stumps. We also need a
couple of rakes and brooms to clear the lime off the field, a

---

17 Café down the street.

18 Café up the street.

couple more people to go over the lines, especially the goal lines, two more people to set the goals in cement once Henri has pulled up the stumps. I'll ask my Dad for a bag of cement from the school stash. Maybe you, Gérard, could take it on your motorcycle. Okay, everybody? Et maintenant buvons!"[18]

—"Jannine, un Perrier, s'il te plaît![19] Meet all you guys on the field at 1:30. Don't drink too much. Easy on the Pernod. We'll celebrate AFTER the game. Hooray for Uxeau. And hey! guys, I forgot, with all this confusion. The road signs to the soccer field are in the school yard, under the shed. They need to be put up. There are 12 of them. How about three of you guys each taking four? Jean-Paul? André? And let's see somebody who lives in Dardon...Christian, could you, would you? Yes? Great. Let's go pick 'em up. I'll walk over with you. I have to go home anyhow."

Maman has fixed something light. Papa, who has been working on the booths and a last rehearsal of the one-act play, is in the kitchen, drinking a glass of water.

—"Since my two men are here, I suggest we eat right now. I didn't fix much, thinking that you would want to supplement at the sandwich booth."

—"That's OK, M'man, I wouldn't have time anyway."And I proceed to tell my parents what has happened.

In their careers as school teachers in a small village in Burgundy, this is not the first case of alcoholism they have been faced with. Normally, they go to the farm themselves and talk with the couple, their only interest being the welfare of the children. But given today's special circumstances, Maman offers, "Michel, I would like you to go back and tell Mme Grandclaude to come over with the kids. Poor woman, she probably hasn't had anything to eat since yesterday

---

18 —"Let's drink."

19 —"Jannine, a Perrier, please!"

noon. I'll whip up a salad; there's still a whole dishful of strawberries and we have lots of bread and cheese. But, *zut alors!*[21] Hervé! I told Hervé to come for something to eat after church."

—"Oh, don't worry, M'man. I forgot to tell you. I just saw Hervé at the café. He told me to thank you, but he wanted to go straight home.

—"P'pa, another thing I forgot. I asked Maurice Dauvergne to get new posts at his uncle's for the goals, but we have no way to get them to the soccer field. Could you give me a quick ride to Dauvergne's: we'll put the posts on the top carrier and we'll drop them off at the field. Also, is it okay if Gérard takes one bag of cement from the mason's stash so we can sink the posts firmly in the ground like we did Tuesday?"

—"Boy, you sure choose your days! But that's okay, I want to talk to Grandclaude anyway. He should be awake by now. I certainly don't want him to start drinking again and come at the spectators with his axe or a pitchfork. But let's go right away; I have a lot to do before the public arrives."

—"In that case," interrupts Maman, "why don't you bring Mrs. Grandclaude and the two kids back with you in the car? She must be exhausted too; that will save her the walk and, I am sure, the embarrassment of meeting people along the way."

—"Okay, Son, where to first?"

—"To the sawmill."

—"Sounds like you had quite a day!..."

—"And it's only the beginning. We have to beat Vendenesse this afternoon. But I feel good. Except for some funny little quirks, I feel in great shape and I'm pretty sure I can last both halves. Oops, could you stop, please? I think I saw Gérard in the café. Back up a little bit, please. Yeah! Gérard, it's okay for the bag of cement. You know where they are; take your pick and see you on the field."

---

21 —"Shoot!"

—"I'll be there in about half an hour. Do you have the posts?"

—"On our way to get them." A couple of miles down the road, we meet a jubilant Maurice.

—"My uncle gave us the posts. No need to pay him; only problem, he has only enough four-by-fours for the two vertical poles—nothing for transversal except a kind of crooked piece of birch."

—"Leave your bike in the ditch and hop in, we're going to get whatever he's got. No more time to be fancy."

Of the rest of the day I have only a blurry recollection, except that we beat Vendenesse by something like five to two, three of the five points bearing my signature. I remember being carried in triumph by my teammates, being given a "most valuable player" trophy and collapsing on my bed, prey to an overwhelming attack of "charley horse" spasms in my calves. One of my last memories of the day, when I woke up late in the evening, was of Pépé congratulating me for being a worthy successor to his physical prowess. The other was at the dance—Cécile Midel beaming, across the room, an immense smile at me.

Coming To America _____

One year later, on August 13, 1957, I was walking down New York's Fifth Avenue, barefoot, holding my shoes in one hand and Katarina Moberg's hand in the other. Mysterious Katarina! So Swedishly beautiful! I often reflected on the symbolism of this scene: bare feet, meaning freedom, liberty, the bearing of good news; shoes in hand representing the Old World traditions, which have been shed but not totally discarded nor rejected, and kept in the hand for fail-safe measure; Katarina's hand symbolizing gregariousness, companionship; like Ariane's thread in the labyrinth of the New

World; serene light leading the way to the place where roots must be sunk; living illustration of St. Exupéry's words: "To love is not to look in each other's eyes but to look in the same direction." And for the past week that direction had been indelibly stamped: WEST! Go West young man! I was not yet an American but becoming one was inevitable. After six years of life as a boarder in an all boys' *lycée*, literally as prisoner behind high walls, my captivity was finally over. We had just come ashore from a week-long voyage crossing an ocean, and that fact alone insured keeping a healthy distance between today and yesterday.

Yes, we had just spent a week crossing the Atlantic, 800 of us from every country of Europe, plying the waters on the *Arosa Sky*; 800 bright and eager young minds, fed at the Old World trough and champing at the bit to drink the New World's youth potion; 800 carefully selected recipients of an American Field Service scholarship gathered on this nutshell of a boat to make waves that would be felt all over the world. I was not yet an American, but becoming one was only a matter of time. This was the Statue of Liberty! This was New York! It was not yet known as the Big Apple, but I already had my teeth firmly planted in it for the biggest bite I could take. This was Manhattan! This was America! And I was now, physically at least, part of it. I remember the smell of the harbor, I remember the jagged and spirited skyline of the city, the multicolored taxicabs; yes, cars of all colors, so smooth and silent, so shock absorbing. I remember the team of reporters from WOR-TV who came on board to interview us, the vast hall where we had dinner that night before heading off to our individual destinations.

All these tangible images of the reality that I was now discovering were worthy of the fantasies I had elaborated. Not one was disappointing. I knew I had left home in order to come home. This brought on some spells of sadness about my poor parents, now all alone, but I survived these episodes without too much difficulty.

Two days later, at the end of an epic Greyhound bus ride, during an afternoon of festivities organized in my honor by my new American parents, Dr. and Mrs. Vernon E. Schuckhart, I was at a Minnesota lake cabin, with a gargantuan meal on the table, while in front, on the lake, a speedboat constantly churning was pulling an armada of accomplished water-skiers gliding over sky blue waters. It wasn't long before I joined them. I soon forgot that, back at the AFS selection interview in Lyon, I had requested to be placed in California! At least until the first spell of cold Minnesota weather came.

My first priority took on a direction that was not particularly popular with the AFS organization. The official idea was that we were in this country as temporary guests serving as grassroots ambassadors for our own country. From the beginning, I had felt differently. In my American English class at the *lycée*, I had had the good fortune of being the student of an extraordinary teacher. Professor Robert Silhol was one of those rare dynamos who could communicate feelings and sensations, and make limpid sense out of a recalcitrant foreign text. Viewed through his enlightened exegesis, arcane passages of Whitman, Dos Passos and MacLeish, Faulkner and Steinbeck disclosed all their meaning, and in my young eyes and intrepid mind, America became sensuously desirable.

So when I arrived in Park Rapids, Minnesota, I had already decided that for me, this was going to be a year of total immersion, of intense Americanization. To my delight, my first name changed from the musical "Michel" to the more rugged macho "Mike." Two months of winter passed without my uttering a word of French. At school I had selected classes unheard of in a French *lycée*, classes like typing, choir and business. The rest were American history, social problems and an American literature class where the lacunas in the teacher's preparation drove me insane with impatient smugness. The very first week, for instance, he argued that RSVP were the initials of four Latin words.

—"Sir," I interjected, "I sink zere is a mistake. Zis is an acronym made up of the four French words *Répondez s'il vous plaît.*"

After that, I noticed we never again covered words in italics or words that were underlined.

Socially, I rapidly became a butterfly. I was at all the dances, the life of most parties; I learned the jitterbug, my favorite songs were "Honeycomb" and "Wake Up, Little Susie," and on the altar of the stars, my devotions were distributed equally between Elvis and James Dean. I saw the movie East of Eden two dozen times and I bemoaned that, unfortunately, the French translation of Rebel Without a Cause, La Fureur de Vivre, was more appropriate. For this was indeed what I was feeling: a rage, a fury, a burning thirst, an uncontrollable desire to live fully, positively, to live at my measure, at my tempo, with speed and gusto. "Soon" was not enough, only "now" would do; "local" was a derision, an aberration, "global" was my vision; not "something sometimes" but "everything always." Born to be American, to remain young like the country, to become immortal. Everything was possible; nothing could, nothing would stand in my way.

I made Emperor Cinna's motto my own: "I am in control of myself as of the universe. I want it so. So I am." Very seldom indeed did any obstacle appear to curb my delirious enthusiasm. What I did not know then was that for each door that opened in front of me, a bridge was being burned behind me. And doors kept opening. It started with the understanding attitude of my American "parents," Dr. and Mrs. Vernon E. Shuckhart. Vernon was a successful dentist: athletic, direct, in tune with the cosmos; Linda was a true mother for me. She filled in the blanks left in my adolescent formation due to six years of the socially crippling *lycée* incarceration.

Then, the most significant door of my life opened when I met Janice that 9th of March 1958. It was love at first sight, for me anyway. A thunderbolt, whose rumblings are still felt in sweeping waves of emotion.

Staples, Minnesota. The winter had started to show signs
of weakness. Patches of sunny blue appeared in the tundra
shroud. Bumpy bogs resumed breathing at the rhythm of
light: freezing in the night, thawing during the day.
Throughout Hubbard and Todd counties, the farmers were
burning the dead, dried grass to fertilize and make room for
the new shoots underneath.

Tom Tjepkema had come from Staples, 60 miles southeast
of Park Rapids to pick me up. The Staples AFS club, of which
he was president, had invited a score of foreign students from
central Minnesota towns for an extended weekend of fun and
games and cultural exchange.

My host family was going to be the Sellnows, with Gerry
and Ron, high school senior and sophomore. Tom dropped me
off at their house. Gerry and Ron complemented Tom's
sketchy briefing. We'd spend the whole day at school the next
day, Friday, and go to an all school dance in the evening.

In the meantime, if I wanted to see the 10:30 PM news, we
would watch the segment reporting on the statewide Future
Homemakers of America convention held in Minneapolis.
The song leader was a local senior with a golden voice. Her
name was Janice Bienusa; she lived three blocks up the
street. She was also the soprano soloist for the high school
choir which had consistently earned superior ratings under
her leadership for the past three years. She also sang at all
the weddings and funerals in town. Not bad looking either....
I was intrigued.

Lily Pons was my idol. Janice Bienusa was the town's pride
and celebrity. And when the camera zoomed in on her and
she belted out "God Bless America," all the goose-pimples I
had ever felt from the former's performance were nothing
compared to the visceral havoc wrought by the latter's velvet
and fire. Very pretty face too.

—"Tell me more, tell me more."

—"Well, good student, National Honor Society, good friend
to some of the more popular girls in the class, best friend of
Elena Rodriguez, the AFS student from Spain...Yes, good

Catholic girl. No...no boy friend that she could be associated with...."

I slept fitfully, obsessed by the refrain "Younger than Springtime."

The next day at school lasted forever. The FHA convention was to be over at 5:00 PM. But the return trip from Minneapolis would take another three hours. Janice would probably be very late, if she would make it at all to the dance.

When she finally showed up Gerry pointed her out coming into the far door of the gym, while Ron, subtle and perceptive to my too obvious *mal d'amour*, was engaging her in conversation and guiding her steps in our direction. As I extended my hand to greet her, I had a moment of emptiness: the black and white image of the TV segment had not revealed the limpidity and the depth of the blue of her eyes. I was impaled. She was much less impressed. It would be an uphill proposition.

Together, we made it through college in three years. Those three years at St. Cloud State College, in St. Cloud, Minnesota were another proof of Janice's and my own unusual energy levels. I started in Business Administration, but when, in the spring of the first year, my grades for Accounting 101 read: C for the first quarter, D for the second quarter and an F was about to be cast for the third, I quickly reconsidered my options. Janice and I had decided to marry and, since neither of us had any money, we agreed that graduating as early as possible was most laudable. We would become secondary school teachers of French and Spanish. After all, we were already used to a marginal existence....

The tack was to major in French and Spanish, thereby having the possibility of earning a year's worth of credits by passing comprehensive examinations in those two languages. We had to contend with the Administration. We proposed. They opposed. We argued. They relented. It was not quite as easy as that, but with a lot of studying for the special exams, with lots of pluck and fast talking, we convinced the powers that be that we were capable and worthy of the exception.

Besides, ever since the Sputnik launch, Uncle Sam had been looking for a few good teachers, the NDEA Act had been passed and Science and Foreign Language teachers were at a premium. If the U.S. needed good French and Spanish teachers; two were right here, ready to answer the call. So, please, stand out of the way, we're walking down the aisle to pick up our diplomas. And what if it is a year early? Never again would we have the opportunity to work 60 hours a week while going to school. Yes, 60 hours a week! Five jobs, for six months preceding the wedding!

Up at 3:30 AM, braving the central Minnesota winter temperature, bracing against the windchill, I load my old Chevy with bundles of the freshly printed Minneapolis Star-Tribune. Half blinded by the raging blizzard or half-awake by the toll of three hours' sleep a night, I grope my way through the snowflakes and the streets of St. Cloud and vicinity in search of paperboys' driveways. I am a spotter. The back seat is loaded with bundles of fifties: two on the front seat, one on the floor. The bundles are tied with steel wire. I cut them with a heavy duty wire cutter. The bundle next to me is open. A flashlight beams on the route list taped on the dashboard: Andy Sevcik, 1005 5th Ave. South, 21 newspapers. Ah! There's a change. Two drops and one new customer. Twelve, 14, 16, I let my fingers do the counting, 18, 20, 21. I reach for a piece of precut twine, squeeze it around the sub-bundle as hard as I can, tie the knot, and through the open window, plop, I drop Andy's daily crop.

There are variants. Sometimes, on nice spring mornings, when the paperboy's route is light, like five to ten papers, I use the parachuting method. I tie the twine while driving, then hold the bundle in the left hand outside the window. The trick is to calculate distance and speed accurately to know at what precise moment, before going past the driveway, to throw the hook shot over the car that will land the papers right smack on the doorsteps. It does take practice. Here goes,...whiz,...splat.

—"Oh! Shit, that was the tulip patch! I bombed."

No time to verify or to remedy. I have to be at the gas station at 7:00 AM to open up. Just enough time to grab a cup of coffee at the Greyhound Bus Depot. Or maybe a Coke.... A Coke for breakfast!... That used to be one of the components in the panoply of my American fantasies, a symbol of liberation from the inescapable tradition of the tyrannical three-meals-a-day French routine, a symbol of the fast-paced life, of this rage to live, to experience and savor everything before the Fates snip the thread from their destiny-casting hands.

Fred Klein was the gas-war gadfly in the St. Cloud area, and, as such, the target of bizarre practical jokes and anonymous phone calls in the middle of the night. By the time I came to work for him, he was thoroughly paranoid. It's three minutes to seven. From his dining room window, Fred has been eyeing the punctuality of my arrival. Ever since my first day at work when I showed up five minutes late, Fred and I have had a pact: to give me a second chance, and in counterpart, to fire me on the very first failure to be at work at 7:00 AM. I pumped gas at Fred's for two years. From 7:00 to 10:00 AM Sundays, Christmas and the Fourth of July.

Classes, I squeezed in between: 11:00 to 12:00 and 1:00 to 2:00. Noon to 1:00 was sacred—lunch hour. Sacred, because I had discovered that I could simultaneously earn and save money. Simple. I free-lunched off the trays and tables I was bussing in the cafeteria. And I mean good lunches. Having grown up subject to food rationing, I could not believe my contemporaries' abject wastefulness. Glassfuls of milk, untouched hamburgers, unspoiled desserts. A bottomless cornucopia. "Bless us, O Lord, and these Thy gifts which we have just received, through Thy bounty.... Amen!"

At 2:30 PM, it's back to the Star-Tribune office for the afternoon deliveries of the Star-Tribune. Until 5:00 PM—a little rest, maybe a beer, socializing a bit with Janice and friends, dinner, then tutoring. Did I forget studying? Bedtime never came before 11:30 PM.

Such a schedule was probably the sowing ground for ills and ailments to come, but I would not have wanted it any other way. Besides, was there any other way?

And on those weekend days when I left the gas station in late afternoons and the sky was wide open and flamboyant over the Mississippi, I would shiver with the jejune and romantic notion that I was walking in Chateaubriand's footsteps discovering the New World's immensity—from sea to shining sea.

Then it was graduate school in Boulder, Colorado where the door to the nursery was opened by Natalie's arrival. There also, the professional door was pushed open when I worked as a Research Associate in Pierre Delattre's Speech Synthesis Laboratory. This led to a move to Santa Barbara, California. In the spring of 1970, I had a lot to celebrate and be thankful for:

- I had become an American citizen and took great pleasure in waving the miniature flag offered by the Daughters of the American Revolution.
- I had passed my Ph.D. oral exams. Only the dissertation remained.
- I had been offered two jobs—one for the summer at an institute in Rennes, France, the other for a one-year appointment at UCLA.

Janice had her own parallel meritorious achievements, but she will have to tell her own story.

So, a fine Saturday morning in May, a friend and I dug a huge hole in the front lawn, lit up a bed of charcoal, set up a rotisserie and proceeded to roast a pig and a lamb. We hired a band, barricaded the streets two blocks away, stocked up on beer, and all afternoon and night, neighbors, colleagues, friends, relatives and crashers feasted and danced most regally.

Two miles away, in distant Isla Vista, the student quarter of the University of California-Santa Barbara, they were shooting students near the burnt out carcass of the Bank of America. During the band recesses, we could hear the crackling of gunfire.

During our six years in Santa Barbara, both Janice and I had been longing for the greenness of Alpine meadows, for a year divided into four seasons, for the warmth of family and relatives at Thanksgiving and Christmas and on the Fourth of July at the lake.... Janice was tired of freeways and polluted beaches. I was tired of commuting between UCSB and UCLA, and of "no trespassing" signs in avocado groves.

Making a decision was easy when in January 1971, after I had attended the Modern Language Association Convention to deliver a paper on French phonetics, I was invited by two Minnesota schools to join their faculties: we would return home to Minnesota. The more difficult decision was to choose between the two schools. Would it be the University of Minnesota—Minneapolis campus, or Carleton College in Northfield, halfway between Minneapolis and Rochester of Mayo Clinic fame? How does one choose between Yin and Yang? How does one answer the (stupid) question: "Who do you love most, your Mommy or your Daddy?" How do you pick, eenie, meeny, meiney, moe? Carleton it was, and we have never regretted it.

*Living In Northfield*_____

Carleton College is a microcosm, an island of intense living where all social fads and fashions are fervently sought and espoused, refined to their paroxysm, then discarded like so many ephemeral moths on a summer night, only to be replaced by the newest craze.

When I joined the faculty in 1971, fishing was the current fad. Each colleague was the holder of esoteric secrets on the subject. One knew—but would never divulge—where to fish for trout only three miles from town; another spent his vacations researching and practicing the almost extinct art of fly-tying; cocktail parties were replete with budding Hemingways, abuzz with tall tales of wide-mouth bass and other assorted crappies. In a word, everyone was hooked.

Fortuitously, vasectomies came next. Everyone became unhooked, so to speak, off the hook. I unfortunately do not have figures or statistics on the legions of Ph.D. material spermatozoa which went down to their demise, but I venture to guess that one half of my colleagues submitted to the neo-barbaric custom, only after thorough forays, however, into the currently available literature on the subject. So that before becoming thus diminished, each member had become a walking encyclopedia of testicular physiology. All pertinent articles had been read, statistical studies were quoted *ad libidum*, sperm was counted, then discounted, local surgical hands were watched closely for dexterity and results were invariably praised with near cocky satisfaction.

When the clamor subsided and scalpels fell silent, when all the ligations turned into irreversible knots, the faculty then turned its *summa cum laude* attention to the arcane delights of gastronomical premières. First, the introduction of the morel into the menus and dishes of Friday night dinner parties produced a mushrooming interest into the surroundings of local ash trees, interest which spread to all areas of the community and to all strata of the professorial ladder.

It is ironic, however, that in the frenzy for the fashionable morel, the succulent and omnipresent girole was totally overlooked, unheralded by the golden trumpets of the local taste and fad makers.

The same was true of the lowly Kir. It has become a household word in Northfield, but its origin and the variants in its preparation still remain an enigma to many. For those who always wanted to know but were afraid to ask, the name is derived from that of the past mayor of Dijon, the reverend canon Kir who served Burgundy's interests for two decades in the chamber of deputies in Paris, and served Burgundy wine, of which he was so proud, to all his guests. Unfortunately, on celebrated and well-chronicled occasions, he would overdo his homage to Bacchus under the form of the ancestral "vin blanc/cassis" a natural mixture of the driest *aligoté*[22] and spiritual black currant cream liquor.

A native of Burgundy myself, whose father is something of a connoisseur and whose grandfather produced wine in Chagny-en-Bourgogne, I was a bit nonplussed when in the heart of the wineless Midwest winter I was ever so condescendingly smiled at and diplomatically ridiculed for having served—gaffe of gaffes and faux-pas of faux-pas—what is considered at home, and even preferred by the old-timers, a most common variant: a mixture of red Moroges and cassis— also known as a *Jacobin*.

This constant search for the *nec plus ultra*,[23] this fastidiousness sometimes bordering on the ridiculous is nevertheless a credit to my colleagues' intellectual honesty and perspicacity, and I must say that while I never bit at the Collegiate Fishing Society, and I bristle at the dogmatism of the gastronomical experts, my wife and I do appreciate and are thankful for the benefits of my newly found sterility. It is because the zeal deployed by my colleagues on their hobbies parallels the energy lavished on their professional field of specialization that I decided to join in the collective wisdom and partake in the next faddish pursuit that eventually led me straight to Dr. Erwin Kabam's door.

* * * * *

Another spring had landed. The April smell of hyacinths invaded the front porch like a fragrant tide and there was not one cubic inch of the open structure that did not bear witness to this aromatic invasion. It took me by surprise as spring

---

22 A type of dry white wine.

23 Latin phrase meaning, "Of which there is nothing better."

has a tendency to do here in Minnesota. So conscious is it of its delayed arrival and so aware of summer's impatience lurking in the wings that it just jumps at you one morning, leaping, yapping and licking, like a puppy sweetly drooling, gnawing at his master's hand.

I pushed the porch gate open, took the four steps in one leap, walked a few yards towards the neighbor's house, and still accompanied by slowly regressing waves of quintessential perfume, continued on for my daily two-mile hike. It was one of those spring mornings that makes one feel triumphant.

I had let Janice go back to sleep for a few more hours; the children would gradually emerge in their own time from under the blankets, cast first one tentative round eye at the rectangular boob tube, then the second. Then, firmly hooked onto their cultural and not so comic fare, they would huddle for a while in moronic stupor before realizing that a better fare was being prepared by Dad in the kitchen.

—"What is it this morning?" Gigi asked. "Manhole covers or bituminous pancakes?"

Natalie made a studied effort at pretending to object to seeing Dad in the kitchen. She is a creature of habit and everything that is not according to plan or custom is, by definition, suspicious. She just does not like to be surprised.

Patrick, dreaming of becoming the decathlon champion of the cereal box or the Robin of Batman fame, came to the table for the length of a commercial break, virile and physical, pushing his sisters around and devouring his pancakes plus two more I was saving for his mother.

—"Dad, thank you, these were good pancakes. Did you by any chance mistake the bag of cement for the bag of flour?"

He ducked just in time to avoid my flying slipper, and before he left the house, I heard him say, "Dad, I'll be at the computer center with Kevin and Doug. If your colleague the chemist bumps us off the 'games' program again, I'm going to tell him that man doesn't live by iodine alone."[24]

"Sounds reasonable. Have a good time. What about you girls? What have you got cooking for the day?"

—"Unfair, Dad!" said Nat. "Just because we're girls, you should not take it for granted that we're planning our weekend in terms of cooking. What really infuriates me is that you consider us as...as...I don't know...as kitchen objects, there!"

With Natalie, it is hard to know if she is truly upset or whether she's royally putting you on. But she was at that age when (regardless of her motives) I should humor her rather than meet her head on.

—"Eh! young Ms., who's being unfair? Who is it who cooked the pancakes?"

—"There you go again, implying that it's not your job or any man's job, for that matter. You should really examine your motives and your prejudices!"

—"Okay, okay, Nats. I am in a good mood. I don't want to change it, so let's cool it. What about you, Gi? Anything special that I can help with?"

—"Yes! Oh, thank you, Dad! Can you take us to the zoo in Apple Valley? Helene went last week and she says they have a brand-new baby gorilla that's really smart and funny. Can you, hey? Dad, will you?"

—"Okay, bun! How about 3:00 this afternoon?"

—"Oh, great, thank you, Dad. Can we take Chris along?"

—"Sure, but make sure you tell her mom, though. See you for lunch."

I thought life would thus be a long succession of Saturday mornings, when, after having made love to my lady and prepared pancakes for the crew, I would have the rest of the day to wallow in contentment, in the euphoria of a well-deserved

---

24 Reference to the licence plate of a Chemistry Department colleague which spelled out IODINE.

and uninterrupted sabbatical span of time when I could clean up my desk at the office, or write up that last bit of research, or catch up with the correspondence, or read the students' evaluations of a colleague up for tenure decision.

I would never learn....

However, by working constantly, I escaped the insidious gnawing feeling, the vague premonition that perhaps something was wrong. I had not verbalized those sensations yet. It was really nothing that could be pinned down. It was more a malaise, a slight nausea, a mildly depressed attitude, perhaps the result of an unfounded fear that the time was coming to atone for the fast living I had done and for all the arrogant displays of energies I had flaunted. There was, of course, that slight stiffness in my left arm. Did it have something to do with my strange mood? For the past few winters, or portions thereof, I had noticed that while walking, my left arm did not swing quite so freely as before. But since that stiffness seemed to disappear with the return of warmer spells, I simply stuck to my self-diagnosis: it all stemmed from my original fall in Santa Barbara, when I must have hurt some disk or vertebra, resulting in a pinched nerve, all easily fixable by any good back specialist. Someday I'd go see Erwin Kabam.

And indeed, I had not felt the pull in my shoulder for the past two weeks. I should have felt relieved. I felt anguished instead. The nasty, nagging thought refused to be swept back under the rug. It popped its head up at the most unexpected places and times, frightening vision of a protruding phallus in a field of chaste and delicate forget-me-nots.

Yes, as it did recently at the Hunts' New Year's bash. When Janice and I arrived, the party was in full swing, a gargantuan spread was being attacked by 120 gigantic appetites all whetted and spiced by the one-upmanship of social intercourse.

—"Ah! enfin, voilà les Monnot. Qu'est-ce que vous atten-diez pour venir?"[25]

—"Nous étions simplement à la recherche du temps perdu...[26] We do that every year at this time, don't you know? But we've never met with any luck yet."

—"Come on in, my friends, and search for the divine bottle instead."[27]

"Happy New Year, Ted. I like that idea."

For about ten years now, Joni and Ted Hunt have thrown a huge party for the occasion and the celebration has almost become a social must. Faculty spouses cattily try to find out from each other whether they have been invited and who else shares in this year's roster. Will the Sociology Department chairman's wife again make those grossly greasy 'rillettes' (rendered pork delicacy?). Will May Okada fly over from across the street with her enormous kettle of delicately per-fumed chicken wings? What about Liz? Will she have re-covered enough from her hysterectomy to be able to make it? And if not, who will replace her as the official community clarion?

I had inched my way to the table, reached for a glass, backed up into the crowd, shuffled my way to the liquor cab-inet and poured myself a hefty serving of Joni's special treat she had brewed up just for me. It was my very own stash of cherries-in-brandy that Joni made with my mother's recipe. I love them. So we have decided to keep them in her house to prevent too hasty a consumption. I was playfully holding a stem with thumb and index finger pretending to drop it into my mouth, when I heard behind me:

—"Hi there, Michel!"

—"Well, hello, Don! Haven't seen you in a long time."

---

25 —"Finally, the Monnots are here. What took you so long?"

26 —"We were just searching for lost time..." (literary allusion to Proust.)

27 Literary allusion to Rabelais.

—"Yes indeed. Denise, the kids and I just got back from Dresden last week, just in time for the beginning of winter term."

—"Great! How was the program? You'll have to tell me all about it before Janice and I embark on the Pau I program this coming spring term."

And before he had time to say anything, the nagging thought surfaced again from the most visceral depths, implacable, inescapable. My head felt light, my chest oppressed; I felt a sudden hot flash. Who are all these people? I know they are my colleagues, but I have nothing to tell them. I've got to get out of here, right now, or I'll pass out. A vestige of civility forced me to stammer a few incoherent syllables in Don's direction as I quickly turned my back on him. He can think whatever he wishes. I don't care. All of a sudden, I felt different from all the revellers. My God, what is wrong with me? What is that weird sensation? It started just at the base of the forehead, just above the eyebrows, and like a ripple in a piece of velvet, moved up toward the hairline, to peter out in the scalp, like a wave beaching itself on the sand. Quick, the door!

—"Excuse me, please."

Some people were just leaving. Ted was by the door.

—"I am sorry, Ted, I don't feel well. I don't know what's wrong with me. I can't breathe. Please tell Janice I am walking home; the keys are in the car. And thank you for the party, and, oh yes, Happy New Year."

I literally ran past him, without a hug, without a handshake. Ted knew me well enough not to take umbrage. He's a true friend.

Walking in the melting snow toward 609 Ottumwa Street was instantly salubrious. I breathed better and tried to reason with myself.

—"Now, Monnot, let's not panic. Deep down, you know it's nothing serious. A little stiffness and a little mental confusion. The stiffness, you've already figured out. The mental confusion, the surge of irrationality is due to your excessive working hours...Oh, hogwash! Hogwash nothing. Can you tell me when you last took a day off, including sick leave? Can you remember when you last were on a beach getting a suntan? You need to rest, man. You're not 18 anymore, not even 28. Take a good look. You are 38 years old. And the stiffness is probably the result of all those activities, too. So take a rest, go on a vacation without taking your brief case along, isolate yourself for a period. That way the stiffness will disappear."

The problem is that it has disappeared. Disappeared...and returned...disappeared...and returned, and each time a little more noticeably. Add to that that for some time I had had a slight tremor in the left hand each time I strained to defecate, that I had difficulty drumming my fingers and, on some days, holding my fork in a position where I derived most efficiency.... When viewed panoramically, all signs pointed to a greater and greater encroachment, both physical and mental. Coincidence? Maybe. Progression? Surely.

At Larson's

As the bus pulled into the Minneapolis Greyhound depot, I snapped out of my reverie to find my whole family—Janice, Natalie, Patrick and Gigi—waiting for me. Shielded by the tinted glass of the bus, I could see them lined up by height against the dark grey hue of the station wall, looking more incredulous than resigned, heavy-hearted for me as much as for themselves.

All I seemed to feel was guilt at that moment. Guilt toward Janice for abandoning her, guilt toward the children for the opprobrium they would have to suffer. And guilt toward the whole family, my parents especially, for my failure to conquer the shimmering vision they had of a social Everest...

The door opened. The crowded aisle started to empty, slowly, while an unmistakable mid-August Minnesota mugginess diluted the air-conditioned coolness. A few more steps and there was Janice with her warm, solid embrace.

—"Welcome home, darling! Chin up! We're going to make it."

Natalie, as she's wont to, stepped out of the line-up formation to avoid a hug. Is it simply because it's just not cool to embrace your father when you're a teenager? Or is she (subconsciously?) angry at me for possibly having contracted a disease, the ramifications of which she cannot even begin to get hold of?

—"Hello, Nats, sweetheart! No, it's not a contagious disease. You don't have to worry about it. Do I get a smile at least?" I asked a bit defensively. Slowly she lifted her head, her eyelids, the nicely shaped lips cracked a hesitant smile. She looked at me. I risked a step. She returned the advance, then took one more step and placed her head on my shoulder, arms glued to her body, for a second.

Gigi could not contain her excitement, "Oh! Daddy, daddy, daddy! I love you!" and she scratched my head. She has always loved to play with my hair and I have never brushed aside this mark of affection. "I'm so happy you are home! Did you have a good..."

Patrick interrupts. He, too, had a hard time hiding his emotions, mixed as they were between fear and jocularity.

—"Hi, there, Parkie! How was your trip?" he asked aloud in front of everyone. And as he spinned me by the shoulder and took me towards the baggage compartment, he whispered, "Dad, is it hereditary?"

—"No, it's not." I replied almost too hastily. "But we'll talk more about it."

In the car going back to Northfield, the conversation sagged. I sensed an uneasiness among my family.

—"Listen, guys, let's not mope around. I am not substantially worse than when you last saw me, am I? So, I don't think I can frighten you that much. Besides, it's not even a sure thing that I have Parkinson disease. Erwin Kabam's disk exercises may do the trick."

And I think I really believed that at the time.

We had just walked in the door, home from the bus depot, I with Erwin Kabam's declaration still sizzling in my innards, when the phone rang. It was Annalee inviting us for dessert to catch up on our respective summer activities.

As expected the conversation quickly veered toward the Northfield Arts Guild productions of the season. Would the world première of Jesse (James), the musical in which Patrick was to play one of Jesse's children, be the smash hit everyone expected? Both Janice and Annalee, noted local sopranos, had been involved in previous productions. As expected, factual considerations quickly gave way to gossip-a-gogo.

So James and I slowly shifted our rumps on the couch, grunted, and turned our backs to our spouses and our attention to our frosted mugs of Grain Belt beer, studiously sipping on our brew between rapidly diminishing topics of common interest: job search for Jim who was wanting advancement in the architectural world; for me advances I had made on my research project of gathering puns in American and French advertising. We also took note of each other's current endeavors on the jogging/running scene. Perhaps we could go out together some morning, etc. But my heart was not in it. So I let an ear drop to the ground to skim over our ladies' tidbits and pick up a cue for Jim and me to rejoin the foursome.

I was far from imagining that this particular sort of behavior—social slowness and dullness, impaired desire for speech activity, counting on Janice to step in on my droning conversations, expecting her to plug up and cover up the expanding vacuum and premature exhaustion of my social intercourse—was another one of Mr. Parkinson's disguised presence revelations.

And sure enough, it was not long before Janice was uttering the new word of the day, "striatitis."

—"Yes," she was telling Annalee, "that's what Michel says the French neurologist told him, 'a little striatitis,' that's all."

—"And do tell what 'a little striatitis' means," said Jim as he took a great gulp of beer. Annalee got up and disappeared for a few minutes. I was surprised to see her come back, not with the dessert as I expected, but with a stack of medical dictionaries and encyclopedias. In its index, one volume mentioned "striatum, *Corpus striatum*" and referred to the text under the heading *"Paralysis Agitans."* My six years of Latin in a French *lycée* were more than enough to know immediately that here were two words which I did not like at all.

—"Paralysis!" exclaimed Jim, "Well, you certainly don't have that. You're not paralyzed, as far as I can tell! You're just a bit tired. My God, you never stand still long enough to catch your breath. If you're paralyzed, well, then, 99% of the people on this planet are cast in cement! Doesn't make any sense. Next page, please." He polished off his beer.

"Now, 'agitans,' " I was processing in my head, "agitans, agitate, agitation, nervousness, shaking, palsy...oh, no! Parkinson! It fits. Erwin *is* right after all. Holy shit! what am I going to do?" I got up to empty my beer in the kitchen sink. Janice followed me. *She knew*. All of a sudden, rather incongruously, I felt guilty—and sorry—for all the paraplegic jokes I had ever told.

—"Let's not worry about this right now," encouraged Janice. "Let's wait for the tests you'll be taking next week. Let's not panic. Come back to the living room."

By now, Annalee had turned to the article in question.

—"So, tell us what it says," I barreled. "I'll bet it connects with Parkinson. I am sure of it. Erwin *was* right. OK guys, that's it, I have Parkinson." I started pacing around the sofa.

—"Calm down, Michel," said Annalee. "It says here that 'Parkinson may be induced by trauma or such toxins as manganese, carbon monoxide, and the phenothiasines.' You haven't got any of that, have you? And even if you did," she continued reading, "it says, 'In almost all instances, toxin-induced Parkinsonism is reversible.' "

She read silently for a few more seconds, then lifted her head, and slammed the volume shut.

—"How about some dessert? That's what we invited you over for, not to read out of a medical dictionary."

—"No, no, no, I insist. There's more. Keep on reading." Annalee fidgeted. That made me suspicious.

—"Come oooon, Annaleeee, what did it saaaay?

—"Well, let me find the page again," she said reluctantly, "but as Jim said a minute ago, that description doesn't apply to you. Here's what it says, 'The chronic progressive muscular rigidity, the immobile face, the posture of flexion of neck, trunk and extremities, the poverty of movement and the slow, rhythmic tremor constitute a striking syndrome.' "

—"Here again," said Jim trying his best to sound convincing, you certainly don't fit the bill. Muscular rigidity, immobile face...my foot, you're as agile as a rabbit."

Annalee was reading on ahead to herself, acting furtive, with a touch of embarrassment. It's true, my symptoms were not that visible. How could she know? Naw! I was just being paranoid. Of course not, I didn't have Parkinson disease. I glanced at Janice who sat poker-faced. Our eyes met. No comment, no clue.

But I knew *she knew*!

"Here," said Annalee, "this should comfort you. It says, 'in many cases, there are no mental symptoms.' " She sounded relieved.

—"Yeah? What else?" I asked. Annalee begged off.

—"It's futile, you're obviously not the right person." Janice, comfortably cross-legged would remain non-committal.

—"No, no, please, Annalee, finish it."

—"OK," she agreed softly. But I could read on her face the vow that, never again, would she offer to look up possible diagnoses for anybody. Her voice register lowered.

—"It goes on to say that 'most patients present a good-natured complaisance, but some, in reaction to their disability, are irritable, peevish, and dissatisfied. Depressive reactions…are among the most frequently observed personality responses to this disorder.' " Annalee's voice volume had decreased to a whisper, but she managed to venture to Janice "I still don't see Michel in this description, do you?" To which poker-face replied nothing. *She knew*! Each new word of the description was an added nail in the coffin of the inescapable diagnostic. Only a wife or a husband would know. Janice had suspected. Now *she knew. And I knew*. But I refused to admit it yet. Annalee read the last sentence in a rapid whisper as if afraid to drown us in the despair it forbode. "The fact that the patient finds himself in a continuously contracting environment in which he becomes more and more dependent on other members of the family creates many emotional problems."

A hushed sense of the inappropriateness of playing the amateur diagnostician who conveys the tidings of chronic emotional and physical disability caused Annalee's voice to pale dramatically. She lay the book on the coffee table and looked helplessly on as Janice picked up the sweater she had earlier laid on the back of the sofa and said tonelessly, "The kids were so excited to see Michel. I really think we should get back to them." She grabbed my arm and I knew I should in no way challenge her decision.

Neither of us spoke as we walked home but she squeezed my hand with a gentleness and a tension that told me her unspoken thoughts.

I took some deep breaths to help blink back unwelcome tears as I kissed the children good night and tried to reassure them that everything would indeed be all right. But my heart wasn't in it.

As I opened our bedroom door, the sweet sadness of Pachabel's Canon greeted me. Janice was sitting on the bed just staring at the ceiling. She seemed not to notice as I moved toward her; tears were unabashedly spilling down her cheeks. I sat stunned, at a loss to comfort her, in a chair by the window. She looked blankly at me. I made an attempt to speak. "Jan, you are always so strong, you can't give up now."

—"I'm not giving up," she whispered, "but I have never been so sad. Do you have any idea why?"

—"You're probably worried about how we'll make ends meet. Though you needn't be. I took out disability insurance last year. So if push comes to shove, we'll get some sort of monthly installment."

She cast a long pitying look at me and burst into sobs.

—"My God, Michel, don't you see? I love your hands caressing me, your arms holding me gently as we dance...I can't bear to give up all the warmth and tenderness of our moments together because your muscles tremble and you have become rigid."

A spasm of choking sobs shook her body, and I stood up helplessly. My arms folded round her as tenderly as if she were an infant. My lips encountered hers. And time melted away as we sought the bittersweet and desperate comfort of each other's body. We both drank long and deep at the well we suspected would soon run dry.

What were we in for? The prospect was grim. I wouldn't accept the diagnosis, though, until I had more tests done and had a second, even third, opinion. So I ran to Dr. Halvorson's office to hear what he had to say.

Second And Third Opinions

David Halvorson, M.D., is in my book a very good doctor: he listens. When we moved into town, I went to him and warned him that I was a hypochondriac with cancer phobia, but that I could easily be reassured if he took the time to answer my questions or direct me to appropriate readings. He has always complied with my requests, some of which may aptly be described, by the way, as pretty bizarre.

Dr. Halvorson also demonstrates the courage not to be pretentious. He knows his limitations. That makes him human. He also combines caution with thoroughness. The minute I mentioned to him that Erwin Kabam had suggested Parkinson disease, he brushed aside even the French EEG printout I offered him in order to begin more testing.

—"No, look, Michel, this is serious and I am not going to waste time and delay getting answers for you. I am going to make an appointment for you with Dr. T. in Minneapolis. He is a good neurologist and will know how to proceed. I am sure you'll like him. He's about your age. Great sense of humor, too."

He swivels in his chair, takes the phone, dials and after a brief dialogue, he repeats, "Tomorrow 4:00?" turning his head toward me with a raised eyebrow for approval. I nod back OK.

So I met with Dr. T. He was affable, courteous, but wasted no time in small talk. He had me going through a battery of tests and exercises almost immediately. That resembled greatly Dr. Jones's procedure in Pau. It was the second—and alas not the last—of a series of similar tests that I was asked to perform many times over by doctors and quacks alike all over the world, from Minneapolis to Basel to Budapest, via Pau, Paris and Pomona. After a thorough examination which included a series of rigorous questions on my antecedents and past history, Dr. T. agreed that my ailment could be due to Parkinson disease all right, but that it could also be due to a host of other causes.

—"Well, I have looked and relooked at your French EEG— incidentally, their printout reads the reverse of ours. But that's all right, it's just a matter of getting used to it. Your EEG is good." I sighed, long enough for the image evoked by the thought "brain tumor" to disappear. Dr. T. glanced at me, caught my relief, then added, "But all the same, I am going to set up an appointment for a CAT scan."

—"What on earth for? You just told me that the EEG was normal."

—"An EEG gives a fairly good picture of what is going on, you see, but it doesn't show everything. It's rather crude, in fact, compared with what you can read from a CAT scan. Then we'll know for sure."

—"We'll know what?" My sigh of relief turned into an aggressive snarl.

—"If the CAT scan reads negative—as I am fairly sure it will, I'll make a reservation for you for a week of tests at Abbott Hospital and one by one, we will check for MS, MD, Wilson disease, Huntington chorea, Lou Gehrig's, myasthenia gravis. Is next Wednesday 10:00 AM OK with you for the CAT scan?"

—"Uh-huh."

—"Good, the nurse will tell you how to prepare for the scan. In the meantime, try to relax, and I'll see you Wednesday morning."

Relax.... He must be joking. I was hardly out of the woods yet. That week of waiting was an eternity during which I al-

ternated between horrible visions of brain tumors, and uncontrollable fits of prayer. Although a fervent mystic, I am
not the religious type—as in church-going type—but while
trying to kill this immensity of time, I often found my steps
leading me to the chapels of Carleton and St. Olaf College.
Kneeling in the pews, I spent hours childishly plea-bargain-
ing: "Dear God, dear Jesus, please make it so that it is not a
brain tumor. And I'll do anything to please you."

By the end of the week, I was such an emotional mess that
it was a true relief to lie down into the cavernous, softly purring CAT machine. Throughout the test, I kept one of those
insipid confirmation card images of Jesus in my mind. So intense was the concentration that I felt Jesus was verily next
to me, in the same room, watching over me.

The technician, the nurses and the intern seemed
satisfied, but I had to wait two more hellish days before Dr.
T. got back to me on the phone with the results.

—"Your CAT scan is perfect."

—"Oh! thank you dear God, and you too, Doc."

So off we went for a week of tests at Abbott Northwestern
Hospital in Minneapolis. What I remember most vividly is
the doctor jabbing me two times unsuccessfully before finding the right place to perform a spinal tap. The nurse who
was helping me keep quiet remarked that I was shaking profusely. Bless her heart! When all the poking and scratching,
probing and pricking was finally over, all the results came up
negative. It therefore had to be Parkinson.

Now a new stage of agony was to begin. Dr. T. suggested
three things, "First, go to Mayo with all the test results; second, see a psychiatrist for shock and grief therapy, alone and
with your wife; third, come back and see me whenever you
feel like it, whenever you are ready to start treatment."

I pursued all three. What else could I do? I was too much in
shock to think of anything better, so I followed the spiral of
events as they were planned out by less troubled minds.

Mayo agreed with Dr. T.: it was indeed Parkinson. I agreed
with the psychiatrist: help was needed. Dr. T. agreed with
me: we'd trade green bills for multi-colored pills.

The First Casualty

By the time Mayo pronounced its concurrent diagnosis, I
had accustomed myself to the idea that indeed it was Parkinson and that I'd better do something about it. There had been
no improvement produced by Erwin's scrupulously applied
recommendations and faithfully performed exercises.

School had resumed at Carleton, and with it the growing
nightmare of facing the working world as a handicapped professional. I had never been so ill-prepared for anything in my
life. It began under the protective wisdom of one Harriet
Sheridan, but quickly melted into the pressure-cooker of a
changing administrative environment.

Howard Swearer had been replaced at the helm of the college by Harriet Sheridan, Professor of English, chairman of
the department and Dean. Harriet was a tall, gaunt woman
in her early 50s, graying hair tied in a bun for efficiency, thin-
lipped and angular-faced. In a supermarket line, nothing
would distinguish her from the average American
homemaker. Nothing in her demeanor led one to guess that
underneath that unassuming appearance, there lived the
nimblest, sharpest mind I have ever encountered—nothing
indeed. Until she started to speak. Wit and erudition then
poured out in a mellifluous stream of well-balanced sentences, of infinitely nuanced thoughts and impeccable argu-
ments. Beware, would-be contending jousters!

Harriet, like Howard, had been impressed by what I had
been able to contribute to the college and on several occasions
had communicated her appreciation. It was therefore

without too much trepidation that a week before resumption of classes, I went to see her to ask for some relief time.

First, would she fund a replacement for me during the first two weeks of the term while I was going to be in the hospital? And would she consider, as suggested by another colleague, granting me half a teaching load for the term on the grounds of personal hardship? She did not hesitate one minute. Gracious Fairie Queen that she was, with one stroke of her telephone-turned-magic-wand, she had everything arranged. As simple as that, courtesy of Carleton College. Whatever case may be made against expensive private liberal arts colleges being elitist, they cannot be faulted—at least Carleton cannot be faulted—for succumbing under the weight of bureaucratic red tape. Harriet then showed her concern by inquiring at length about the disease and sharing her well-kept secret: she too, had recently been diagnosed with a degenerative affliction. So I was not alone in my need to adjust to a new phase of life.

Two years after the diagnosis, I felt as though my teaching days were numbered. As I mulled over what I could possibly do, the inspiring example of a Carleton biology professor and his wife began to obsess me. Professor Epstein was a diabetic who had suffered the consequences of his disease by becoming blind. Courageously he had refused to be conquered and had enlisted the help of his wife to be his eyes in and out of the classroom. They had been very successful and much admired by faculty and students alike.

Suddenly, I had my strategy all worked out. Janice would have to be persuaded to quit her job at the high school.

Every year, after registration week, the Carleton French department was always looking for part-time staff to teach the new sections which had been opened due to unexpectedly high enrollment. Janice being eminently qualified to teach those elementary sections, could easily tackle two such sections in addition to being present in my own two classes where she would serve as moral support and pinch-hitter in case I would fumble. We calculated that in the long run this strategy would be financially beneficial because it ensured and preserved my higher paying tenured professorship. And Harriet also agreed to that. While giving Janice a dependable position, Carleton did not lose in the trade: they were getting a full time slot for half the price.

Thus started auspiciously a seven year period of my professorial career which, unfortunately, degenerated as it unfolded. It was marred in the main by a factor which was later instrumental in my decision to organize the Road to Dignity Walk, namely, the devastating ignorance of the public in regard to Parkinson disease.

Harriet resigned soon after. She had accepted Howard's invitation to serve as Provost at Brown University. And Carleton, recently outfitted with a new president, was now searching for a fitting new dean. New, they found. Fitting, they did not. In my opinion, anyway, Dean Livingstone was no gem but he did fit beautifully in the pattern of military-like chain of command which the new president had instituted soon upon his arrival. He had the necessary attributes: brain power, education, stylish arrogance, pervading callousness. In this respect, the title of his book, The Weak at Heart Capitalists, is revealing. Even more so is the remark he made to me once as an excuse for having made me wait more than half an hour in his antechamber, "I was talking with President Edwards," he said, "and that's the one person around here that I can't hang up on..." implying, of course, that "all of you peons, I can pee on."

I am the first one to admit that during those years, my performance in the classroom, although still satisfactory, was going downhill, and that my administrative acumen for the Pau programs had noticeably diminished. In order to prevent a catastrophe—if this is what the Dean feared would happen—he could have called me into his office, he could have tried to learn and understand what the nature of my illness was, he could have inquired why I had gone from an asset to a liability, he could have helped me to ease out gradually and gracefully, we could have hammered out an arrangement whereby I would have employed more student workers. There were a number of ways a crisis could have been averted.

Instead, Dean Livingstone—more like a dead boulder, really—chose to cut me down most ruthlessly and inelegantly. First, he came down on the side of three students who had given Janice and me untold amount of troubles during the program in Pau. One was a female student who regularly closed up the bars of the town; the other two were male sophomores, who, through a series of disobedient actions ended up in a Spanish jail. And the Dean had the gall to accuse me of making *ad hominem* accusations.... Then he summarily relieved me of my functions as Coordinator of the Pau programs. Adding insult to injury, he intimated in a letter that my qualifications to belong on the Carleton faculty were being questioned.

Teaching At Carleton _____

Total frenzy, since 1971. From daybreak to bedtime, students' appointments here; committee meetings there; breakfast with the Dean; lunch in the cafeteria with a visiting fireman; a birthday party at French House.

—"Yes, come along, be my guest. We may finish the day at the Rueb-'n-Stein restaurant. I've told some students to come to discuss the results of the French legislative elections. As a matter of fact, just this afternoon I picked up a copy of the Canard Enchaîné[1] at the Hotel Sofitel in Minneapolis. We had a meeting of the AATF (American Association of Teachers of French, Minnesota Chapter). OK, why don't you meet us at the Rueb around 9:30? Oh, you can't? Then why don't

---

1   A satirical French newspaper.

you stop by the office tomorrow morning around 7:30? I'll be there early; I have some phone calls to make to France to set up this year's Pau program. So, sure, come on up tomorrow morning before 8:00, and if you can follow me or run along with me while I dash off to my first-hour class, I'll tell you as much as I can about the comparative quality of various French universities. But you should really consider going on our own Pau programs."

Such was life for six, seven years, not to mention the development of the Northfield public schools' soccer program (over 100 students, both boys and girls) nor the writing of my Ph.D. dissertation. And on top of that, half a dozen articles in professional journals thrown in for good measure. The Assistant Dean wondered aloud about my never climbing stairs less than two steps at a time; some friends mused that my incessant activities made them literally dizzy; the exhilaration was such that I never once thought that I was running head on towards a precipice.

*   *   *   *   *

—"Five minutes left before I pick up your papers. Remember, I don't want a page of translated-from-English French. You might as well stay in bed for that trivia. What I want is a demonstration on your part that you have assimilated the grammar, the vocabulary, the idiomatic expressions we've been studying for the last three weeks."

There's a hand raised. "Yes, John."

—"Do you want us to use all the new words we've learned?"

—"Of course not, just a selection well wrapped into a ten to 12 line paragraph. Short, but in GOOD French."

I have finished correcting the other section's exam, so I walk through the aisles, point out to Sharon a mistake on her paper which I know she can correct. (She can indeed. She erases, rewrites, then looks up and smiles, grateful for the tip.) I give a brief check over their shoulders at everybody's papers, a tap on Jim's back to encourage him.

—"I know you've been sick. I see quite a few mistakes right here. Why don't you stop at the office after class? We'll go over the exam and the two classes you missed, OK? Stop—time's up. David, please collect the papers for me." And the show is on.

They have signed up for my first-hour class, which meets every day, Monday through Friday, and where three unexcused absences during the term results in an automatic grade down—because I follow the old Horatian principle of combining instruction with pleasure. They willingly get up earlier than they could because they know they will be entertained and, in the process, will master the new material without being ridiculed if they make a mistake. I am extremely sensitive to their needs and I am a good listener. I will always respond to a quizzical look on a student's face. And I conduct the class as a family unit where positive teasing among siblings is a welcome encouragement towards self-improvement.

We laugh a lot. I spend lots of time each day preparing peripheral material, usually jokes in French, which I have to edit and bring to their level of comprehension, always using newly-acquired vocabulary for reinforcement. Some tricks are cheap but one has to be good at acting the clown without losing the students' respect—making them laugh by adopting a comical attitude, then laughing with them at the precise moment that the laughter could degenerate into laughter at you. A piece of chalk deftly thrown at a bothersome whisperer in the back row will do marvels for at least the next three classes. Blithely finishing a sentence that is too long for the blackboard by allowing my writing to spill over onto the wall will insure their benign approval and reset their attention span for another five minutes.

Speed and timing are also essential, throwing a question at the student who was just about to talk to his neighbor, pivoting from the blackboard to face the class again, switching questions from front right to back left, asking a follow-up question to the student who thinks she is off the hook for at least the next ten minutes, imitating, eliciting, cajoling.

—"Oh, come on Mary, you can't do that to me, I know you know the answer...No, it's not coming? Well, listen carefully to Jim. He is frothing at the mouth to tell us the answer. Now, Mary, your turn. You repeat the answer...that's right, good, and you ask Karen the same question...good. Karen, sorry, I didn't hear your answer. Please repeat it. Come on, once more, louder so that I can hear if you are saying 'le' or 'la'....Oh, come on, everybody, what's wrong this morning? You didn't sleep last night? Come on, stand up, quick, stand up. Everybody take six deep breaths; now everybody run in place, come on, dix-sept, dix-huit, dix-neuf, vingt (17, 18, 19, 20). Good. Now the counting game, two by two. Christopher, you start. Good, now Elise, ten by ten starting with 11. Bien. Everybody feeling better? Good, now I'm going to teach you a poem. It's very short and I want you to know it by heart for Friday. It's a poem by Prévert, Jacques Prévert. I'll write it on the board; you copy it down.

> Une orange sur la table
> Ta robe sur le tapis
> Et toi dans mon lit.
> Doux présent du présent
> Fraîcheur de la nuit
> Chaleur de ma vie.[2]

There is a pun in there. Find it by tomorrow and also, those of you who are applying for the Pau program, don't forget,

---

2   An orange on the table
     your dress on the carpet
     and you in my bed.
     Sweet present from the present
     coolness of the night
     warmth of my life.

Friday is the deadline for turning in your application. Only
26 places in the program."

Classes in Pau were even more fun for me. Surrounded by
a dozen bright Carleton students who gaped at their French
guru, I was at the pinnacle of my professional life, doing what
I like best: combining my native background with my love for
teaching the language—that is, teaching French in a totally
French environment.

Of course, many of my colleagues back at Carleton raised
an academic eyebrow at this somewhat unorthodox method
of mine. As one of them said, "Experiential learning does not
deserve credit for it is not backed up by scholarly reading."
Hah! scholarly reading, my eye. That may be a valid statement for certain disciplines, true, but to learn how to speak a
foreign language, by all means get out of that library and go
rub noses with the natives, make mistakes—social, linguistic, or otherwise—but for Babel's sake, go out and mix. This
tower of Babel is not an ivory tower. All the same, in spite of
spiteful criticism by possibly envious colleagues, this was
professional life as I had dreamed it.

And yet, I knew something was wrong. What was that nagging thought that surfaced time and again? Was I just a hypochondriac?

One memorable evening while directing the Pau programs,
in a little country restaurant where the warmth of fellowship
matched the *garbure's*[3] rich aroma, somewhere between the
pungent ewe's milk cheese and the sweetly fragrant Izzara,[4]
the conversation turned to nutrition and health. I was describing some of the sensations that triggered that nasty, episodic thought when Matt Piucci, one of my star students,
said, "What you describe could be Parkinson's disease, multiple sclerosis, you know, or a brain tumor. Instead of worrying

---

3   A French peasant soup.

4   A local liqueur.

about it, I would go see a doctor, a neurologist even. I wouldn't wait if I were you."

So Matt had noticed my slowness as I reached for my glass, and my awkwardness with my fork. Big deal!, I thought at the time.

The Decision _____

During those last five years of teaching, Janice's help became more and more necessary as I became less and less capable of performing my duties. The handwriting was on the wall of the classroom, spilling over from the blackboard, and it was not pretty.

Sometimes I could not sustain the pace required of me to retain students' attention; sometimes I was just too weak to finish the hour, so I'd leave the room, with Janice in full control; other times I would count on facial expressions as I used to do in the past, to carry a meaning across to a student, only to realize too late, by the student's frustration and even anger, that my intended facial expression had fallen short of the mark. Unbeknownst to me, it had been blocked by a mask of rigidity. The Parkinson mask.

To keep a class alive, sitting down is deadly; an absolute no-no. For a long time, I combatted almost daily the urge to sit down. Before, I would wind my way through the individual desks, reach across the room with loud questions, I could run back to the blackboard to graph a quick explanation, then jump back to the front row, do a couple of verbal pirouettes keeping one eye on my irretrievable, hopeless D minus case in the back row, while the other eye kept an accurate check on the clock. In fewer words, I was all over the place. The kids loved it.

Now all that was coming to a standstill. For a while I countered by spending part of the hour immobile, leaning the back of my head and shoulders against the blackboard, one leg bent with my foot against the wall for balance, book open on the lectern in front of me. It was far from perfect, but at least I was not sitting. If I had to die, it would have to be standing on my feet.

However, I gradually gave in to comfort. First I asked the Carleton shop for a high stool. Then I needed a wider surface to spread my books and papers around more conveniently because shuffling papers and turning pages had become a nightmare, so I asked Heinz Lobitz, the Carleton cabinet maker, to build me a removable inclined platform that would fit snugly over the desk top. Vanity could not afford 18 pairs of eyes scrutinizing my hands' febrility. But since this contraption was about one-third the height of the old lectern, the stool had suddenly become too high for comfort. I would have to settle for a chair.

I went on long-term disability instead. The exterior manifestations of Parkinson were debilitating enough. The inner humiliation, in spite of all the coping tricks and devices, was intolerable. Two events occurring three years apart, stand out in my mind as mile posts in my downhill journey.

Fourth day into the quarter, I am in a class of freshmen at the French II level. The newness of the situation, the awkward arrangement of the chairs, the poor acoustics of the room have made me ill at ease. The ripple effect on my forehead again; a sensation of lightheadedness, of aloofness; the impression that someone is gently pulling my hair back; I feel sort of floating, not quite focused. But, by sheer force of habit, the routine starts rolling; the questions start tumbling out with seeming ease. The answers, supplied somewhat haltingly, lag behind.

—"Bien, David, bonne réponse. Maintenant, toi, Carole, demande à Kevin s'il peut acheter une baguette avec quatre-vingts centimes."

—"Kevin, est-ce que vous pouvez…"

—"Non, the 'tu' form. Kevin, est-ce que tu peux…répéter."

—"Kevin, est-ce que tu peux…"[5]

—"I forgot, what *is* the question?" asks Carole, her steely blue eyes riveted on my suddenly expanding void. I knew it! I knew she was going to do that. I knew she was going to turn around and ask me to repeat the question! And from that split second of awareness onward, I panicked.

What WAS the question? Blank, blank. By the time Carole has turned to me and asked me to repeat, a total debacle has gone on in my head. Quick, what WAS that question? Disconcerted neurones are racing like mad, trying to establish meaningful connection with other equally disarrayed neurones, who in turn seek the solution from their retreating neighbors in a classic case of nuclear chain reaction that threatens to unravel or at least incapacitate my whole brain.

All that has taken place in no more than two seconds. The steely blue eyes do nothing to open the impasse. Three seconds. Panic! Then, the thought, "Boy, they all must think I am dumb." Four seconds—before the appropriate neurone fires up at the propitious moment, and jumps to the fore. Five seconds, and I hear myself say as if nothing happened, "Kevin, help Carole out. What was the question?" (Please, Kevin, please come through for me. Yes? Merci, Kevin.)

But when three such events took place that day in the same class period, I decided to investigate. What was I doing different from the other days that could produce such a difference in behavior? What about those Akinetone™ pills that the osteopath in Northfield had prescribed two weeks

---

5   —"Good answer, David. Now you, Carole, ask Kevin if he can buy a
     loaf of bread for 80¢…Re…peat after me…Kevin, can…you buy a
     loaf of bread for 80¢?"

ago? But if they were the cause, why wouldn't such a strong side effect have manifested itself sooner? Dr. Johnson, the prescribing osteopathic doctor to whom I put those questions over the phone, recognized that yes, they could be the cause of such a reaction, and that the reaction had waited until now to manifest itself because it took time for the drug to build up in my body and because I was now under mental pressure—the term had started three days ago—and that I'd better forget an Akinetone™ treatment.

* * * * *

The other event, somewhat similar, was banal enough. It took place in the winter of 1984.

Ten minutes into the class, it became obvious I had forgotten what assignment I had given the students for homework: I proposed to correct an exercise that had not been assigned, while brushing past one that had been. Some confusion resulted, with several students talking all at once. Nothing terribly unusual or irreparable. What struck me to the core, however, was that in the midst of the brouhaha, I overhead Kathy Bauer, my star student, say to her neighbor, "My God! He's become completely senile." That was it. I cancelled the rest of the class, packed up my papers and books from my inclined podium-desk, stepped across the hall to my office, and told Janice, who was preparing to come to class as she did daily to help.

—"That's it, Jan. I've had it. I don't know when yet, but not too far down the road, I think I'm going to have to quit." I plopped myself heavily down into my swivel armchair, and proceeded to tell her what had happened.

She got up from her desk, came around behind mine and putting her arms around my neck and shoulders, she said, "Michel, love, please don't despair! You've fought valiantly and you've worked hard. You're just feeling a little depressed, that's nothing to be alarmed about. You know, I forget just as many things as you might. But I understand why you feel you want to quit. Hang on though. Remember, I am in this with you. Don't you think we make a good team? We can go on a little bit more. This is just a bad day, but in general you hold yourself very well. For someone who doesn't know you, you don't look as if there's anything wrong. You keep yourself in shape, you run your mile three times a week. I wish I could say the same. So cheer up! You have your phonetics class in 20 minutes. Do you need me to write transcriptions on the board?"

—"Yes, for about 15 minutes. But if you don't mind, could you stay the rest of the period? Just for moral support. Or in case my mind goes blank if someone asks a question and I start stammering. You see, as I have told you before, it's not necessarily the physical symptoms that bother me, but rather a sort of psychological phobia I perceive so intensely that I am diminished. It becomes a vicious circle. But anyway, I feel a little bit better now. Thank you, love, for cheering me up. But really, I am wondering if I can go on teaching much beyond the end of this school year."

—"Don't panic. We'll see. Let's play it by ear."

I did feel as if I had been rescued from the well. This breather gave me time to put things in perspective. I played and replayed the scene in my mind. It was stupid of me to bear a grudge against Kathy. She could have been a little more discreet, a little more sensitive, a little more compassionate. But, I asked myself, had I shown any of these qualities myself toward Professor Reese of St. Cloud State 20 years ago? So, what was I expecting? Kathy's remark was maybe not the ultimate humiliation but it was nevertheless the indication I had reached a threshold opening on a new era for me: I was no longer protected by the kindness and goodwill of my students. I had reached the point where my behavior had become in itself the tacit authorization for others to take over for me, and, in a closely related second phase, to step over me if I did not get out of the way. I suddenly realized that I had become expendable. I had but one grace left: to remove myself gracefully.

Among my colleagues in the department, I heard varied comments. Yodi Campbell's in particular had that unmistakable ring of a double edged sword slithering along a granite slab, "Oh, Michel, it's amazing how much you can still accomplish," or "You know, I wanted to sit in on your phonetics class this trimester, but there are so few students registered for the class that I would feel self-conscious." Under the smiling, face value meaning of the sentence was a meaningful sentence pronounced to my unsmiling face. In the first case, the other meaning to be read was: there's so much you can no longer do.... In the second case, the substitution implied was: it's clear that you no longer attract students into your classes; why don't you pack up? "Besides," she said one day, "I told my husband that you had mentioned quitting—*en passant*—and he said you should not quit, but instead go on disability. Apparently, Carleton has a good compensation program; why don't you?..."

—"I already have. But what I was not aware of was the extent of your solicitude in helping me clear out! I am most honored and touched by the confidence, Yodi. But don't worry, I have seen the Dean this afternoon and it is all arranged. I am going on disability at the end of fall trimester."

I don't think she caught my irony! The Dean was most thankful for my initiative as it saved him the awkward task of having to ask me sooner or later to consider stepping down. In contrast with his predecessor, Dean Elveton was humane and receptive. He inquired at length about what I was going to do, what was in store for me, and when he asked where my next steps would be taking me, I answered deadpan, "To Los Angeles."

Stepping Up _____

The decision to quit had been relatively easy. I was taking a cut in salary, but there were other benefits which, everything considered, made the prospect not as bleak as it could have been. The real question to address had been: "How will I fill the vacuum?" The answer which had been latent and germinating in my head for as long as I can remember, came into focus all of a sudden like a Polaroid picture coming alive in my hand.

It was a beautiful day late in August 1984, coming home from a trip to Alaska. The northern Montana sky was full of smoke, the dry prairie burning wild over thousands of square miles. As I read the headlines of the local ragsheet while the car was being serviced in a little Montana gas station, I stumbled upon a title in small type: "Man Walking For MS Mugged in the Suburbs of Pittsburgh."

Whoever were those pimping and pimply hoods, I was going to show them that they meant nothing in the accomplishment of a just cause, and that where one man fell, another was ready to pick up. Other memories sprouted, noblest among them, that of Terry Fox, the one-legged Canadian athlete whose left leg had been lost to bone cancer, but who, nevertheless raised $24,000,000 for the Canadian Cancer Society by hobbling across Canada, mile after killing mile, bleeding from the friction of open blister wounds upon his wooden stump, grimacing from the pain, emaciated from his battle against the killer. Yes, if he had had the guts to make it on one leg, there was no reason I could not finish on two. The decision was irrevocable. I was going to walk to raise consciousness about Parkinson disease and to raise funds for research into it.

Part Two

...To Courage

*I have a hard time with people who
fold up and accept the inevitable.*

—*Myrna Merken*
Psychotherapist

6

Journey To Utopia

Mental Set

I wonder how many Parkinsonians have been in the same boat, victims of derision, bullying, and criminal arrogance; how many lost their sense of self-worth and dignity at the hands of dwarfish minds and mutilating arrogance. Too many, no doubt, for as long as the dignity of even one person remains assaulted, the answer will be "too many."

In such flagrant cases, it is difficult to resist the temptation of vindictiveness and not to wish the transfer of our lot upon the head of our tormentors. However, when common sense prevails over anger, when rage turns into courage, it becomes plain to see that vengeance is a futile sentiment. There are better things to do.

There is the business of coping to be dealt with, to be worked at; there is a positive attitude to be developed, a whole new way of life to be discovered, a world where all the Waterloos can be turned into Austerlitzes, a world where small victories can be as rewarding as winning the New York state lottery. Not the smallest item on this agenda is to face the truth. And so I decided that if I did have a debilitating disease, it was time to accept the fact.

I needed to admit that, in spite of all my attempts, I could not hide the fact that my hands were shaking, my walking steps were shorter, and my smile was strained.

—"So," I asked myself, "why waste time in pretending, in trying to invent artifices to cover up the uncoverable when precious time could be spent productively and positively, fighting the dragon, inventing strategies and stratagems, sharpening our understanding of the beast's habits to better trap him, organizing all fellow Parkinsonians. For my motto

I plagiarized Karl Marx and I shouted to whomever cared to listen: "Parkinsonians of the whole world, unite! You have nothing to lose but your shakes."

In a parallel effort, as soon as I became convinced that what ailed me was Parkinson disease, that it was a correct diagnosis, I faced my parents with the news in the following letter:

> Chère Maman, cher Papa,
>
> I just came back from Mayo. The doctors are agreed. It cannot be anything else but Parkinson. It is a shock all right, perhaps even greater to you than to me at this point.
>
> However, I am young, I can take the blow, I'll roll with this punch. I know how back at home, this kind of setback is hush-hushed as if it were shameful to be sick.
>
> Well, I want you to be assured that I have no shame in the face of this new development and that not only should you not hide the fact, but you should announce it to other people who might be afflicted so that, all together we can find a solution to our predicament. Only our mental flexibility will prevail over our physical rigidity.
>
> From my readings these past few months, I have discovered that research is going on all over the world and that within ten years, there may be a cure. I will live with this hope and your love.
>
> —Michel

Thus I became aware that to survive this inclemency, I had to count on myself, supported as I could by my fellow sufferers on one hand, and by what medical establishments had to offer. And for that I searched high and low, the process took me to all sorts of doctors and researchers, quacks and crooks, narrow-minded degenerates, saviors of mankind. So began my doctors' round, and I took to the road once again.

At Syng-Yu

One of the stops on my journey toward truth was *chez* Syng-Yu. The breeze blowing from the nearby harbor has chased away the morning mist. Only a remnant of moisture in the air betrays the proximity of the ocean. Clicky "plocks" of tennis balls splattering against the training wall of the court reach the guest's bungalow with unexpected delay.

Janice and I have gotten up early, we have taken our morning tour of the property and helped ourselves—as we have been congenially invited to do—to all the fresh fruit begging to be picked from the loaded branches. The orchard numbers 210 fruit trees insuring a year-round supply of rich vitamins. As I wander in this garden in search of a cure, I cannot help thinking of Papa's own orchard.

There are, of course, differences dictated by the climate. Even Papa's best labors could not induce a persimmon tree or a Japanese pear tree or a mulberry bush to come to fruition. But this mid-June weekend in a sun-soaked Los Angeles suburb, the peach trees are bending over forward pleading to be delivered of their ripened pregnancy. In a couple of days the apricots—already juicy even though still green—will turn golden and succulent. Then the plums! Ah!...the plums! I remember the joy I felt as a healthy child, still able to run and play and nimbly pick the fruits of my father's carefully tended garden.

—"So what do you say I pick a couple of oranges for you and I squeeze you a glassful of fresh juice?" says Syng-Yu. "Then you can give me a tennis lesson."

—"Hen Hoa," I reply in honor of our host.

I thought Syng-Yu was Taiwanese at first. He does speak
Mandarin. Actually, he is a leading figure in the local Korean
community, as well as one of the very few acupressurists
settled and practicing in the Western world. At least west of
the Rockies. Yes, acupressurist. He does not puncture. He
simply presses. With both thumbs and all fingers. God, how
he presses! Actually, you could almost say he is all thumbs, if
it weren't for the fact that he is very accurate at locating the
exact spots on your body that need that revitalizing jolt of the
circulatory, neural and hormonal systems. I have come to his
garden seeking a cure.

Syng-Yu and I met in a classic way, another bonus of the
Road to Dignity Walk. As I approached Palm Springs, I was
met by Lynn Simross whose interview and subsequent story
in the Los Angeles Times was one of the most thorough and
sensitive in all the press coverage that we received. Being a
medicine man, Syng-Yu could not miss the Times' health section where Lynn's article appeared early in January. To protect my privacy, she had only divulged the fact that my wife
was a teacher at the high school in Northfield, Minnesota.
But this was sufficient information for Syng-Yu to write to
Janice at the high school telling her that he had read my
story; that he was admiring the feat; that he thought he could
do something for me and my condition; and that he was inviting me to his home for a free treatment of acupressure
whenever that would be convenient for me.

I kept that thought for future reference and tucked it in a
remote cortical circumvolution. First I needed to attend to
the double header ceremonies in Los Angeles to celebrate the
successful completion of the walk. But my quest did not start
here at Syng-Yu's. I only prayed it might be the end.

My search for a betterment at least, and for a cure at best,
started long ago. I read what researchers had to say, ordered
copies of hard-to-find articles from inter-library loan services, wrote to authors to ask for clarifications, even had a student at Carleton, Thorston Kjelstrand, translate an article
from Swedish for me. And by one of those strokes of luck that

have been following me even in my misfortune, it turned out that Thorston's father was a Swedish nephrologist in residence at the University of Minnesota Medical School and what's more, he had been a classmate in Stockholm of the doctor whose team made history by performing the world's first brain implants on humans back in 1981.

I corresponded with Dr. Backlund who took time to describe at length his on-going research and offered sincere words of encouragement. And since in this saga, which is not just Scandinavian, I learned that we the patients make a team with researchers and practitioners, whose encouragement must be returned under the form of financial donations and contributions, no one in this fight can afford to be stingy. I am no longer afraid to tell even my friends that the plight they contribute to with intent to avoid may be their very own. No one is safe until we know the causes of Parkinson, and by extension, the ways to avert them. It is up to all of us!

My three-week visit with Syng-Yu, while it did not seem to affect my Parkinsonism, nevertheless, did me a world of good, one of the most salient aspects being the restitution of my olfactory nerve. I was able to smell again, to enjoy once more the inviting scent of an orange grove.

The Swedish/Kuwaiti Connection _____

In our helter-skelter pattern of zig-zagging through Europe and America, in our rage to race about the planet, Janice and I have met many wonderful and wonderfully different people, from all lands and all ethnic groups. Of particular importance in my search is the Swedish/Kuwaiti connection, which, as geography would have it, landed me in Basel, Switzerland via, of all places, Chicago.

—"Michel?" came over the telephone one day of October 1978, "I've just talked to Mother in Stockholm,"...by now I had recognized the melodic iambic modulations of Christina's Swedish accent. Christina is one of our dearest friends in Northfield.

—"...and she says that through her Anthroposophic Society acquaintances, she has found two homeopathic doctors for you. One in Evanston, Illinois, Dr. Page, who is highly recommended. The other, Dr. Gudrune Hoffmann, at the Ita Wegman clinic in Arlesheim, Switzerland. By the way, have you ever heard of Rudolf Steiner?"

In due time I would learn of Rudolf Steiner, this great modern mystic, latter day Renaissance man, philosopher, sculptor, literary critic, poet, architect, physician and visionary, founder of the Anthroposophic Society.

—"No? Well, for the time being," added Christina, "you should take one thing at a time and contact Dr. Page. Later in the spring you can contact Dr. Hoffmann, make an appointment with her and eventually reserve a room if you want to be a patient at the clinic in Arlesheim during the summer."

So the journey continued, and the following weekend Janice and I set out for Evanston, in search of homeopathic treatment of Parkinson disease.

Dr. Page was indeed a homeopathic doctor. She showed a great deal of concern for my well-being. She made it very clear from the beginning that her approach to Parkinson could not rid me of the affliction, but that a comprehensive program of vitamins, phytotherapeutical teas and baths, would do me a world of good. It would bring my body and mind to a state of well-being from where I could keep in check the otherwise unavoidable encroachments of the disease.

She could explain and prescribe her program theoretically, she said; she would demonstrate the eurhythmy exercises. And she did. Dr. Page showed me the "L" and the "O" and the "M" positions. But who would show me the rest of the alphabet? Who would determine the exact dosage of arnica, lead, zinc and *arsenicum* that my body needed at any one given time? Who would prescribe the appropriate nature and quantity of the medicinal teas I was to drink in any one day? Who would administer the daily shots of diluted *argentum* and *aurum* and brain cell extracts? Janice. However reluctantly, Janice was ready and willing to give me daily shots in the abdomen. The needle was small enough and the procedure was safe enough. But where would we get these miraculous medicines? There seemed to be one answer to all those legitimate questions: Dr. Gudrune Hoffmann at the Ita Wegman clinic in Arlesheim near Basel, Switzerland. By the way, had I ever heard of Rudolf Steiner?

No matter! So both roads converged on this little village on the outskirts of Basel in the Jura Mountains. Perched on the next hill is the village of Dornach, where the Goetheanum stands, that marvelously elephantesque structure designed by Rudolf Steiner himself in the purest tradition of Bauhaus crossed with romantic Gothic.

Some people have also seen it as a cross between a Hobbit House and a Buckminster Fuller geodesic dome. Its library is the headquarters and intellectual center of the Anthroposophic Society. There, I would be able to read and learn about my unknown benefactor, guru before the fact, that giant of modern thought, Rudolf Steiner. I would be able to take long walks in the beech tree forests, dream of past glorious days in front of the *schlosse*[1] in ruins, and indulge in a bit of eccentric romanticism: I would pretend to be Jean-Jacques Rousseau's forgotten ghost! So enthralled was I with the fantasy that I forgot for a minute that I was going to be there to treat—perchance to cure—an incurable disease.

—"Then you *are* going there?" asked Janice, a slight note of defiance in her voice. "And for how long and how much?"

Adieu, mythical heroes of my youth, castles too soon built in the air, glimpses of Merlin playing hide-and-seek with jacks-in-the-pulpit! Adieu J.J. *rêveries*.

---

1   Castle.

Once again, as I am wont to, I had not bothered to check with Janice on the practical side of things. Did I realize that a minimum requested stay of three weeks at the clinic cost $3,000 and that we didn't have $3,000? Where would I get that sum? I didn't know. What I did know was that my cause was good enough and just enough for someone or something to come to the rescue. Even if worse came to worst we could borrow from the bank, or from my parents, I don't know. Besides, you know very well that I would go all out, too, if something happened to you or any of the kids. Right? Right!...so don't worry.

It was winter by now. Christmas vacation. All the revellers we had invited for our annual sledding party on Evans Hill at Carleton were now crowding the house, first converging toward a huge pot of chili, then retreating and diverging to renew their spirits in the verve of the nearest conversation or in the warmth of the mulled wine ladled out at various locations in the house.

It was the moment Janice's student Abdulla chose to introduce his mother. Ten years later and with a memory largely singed by too much dopaminergic drugs, I cannot bring back to mind the actual picture of Badrya. But I know she was beautiful. Modern day queen of Sheba, equally at ease in Persian Gulf Arabic, English, Spanish and French, she was enchantment personified, seductive incarnation of the heroine of the Thousand and One Nights.

Badrya, however, was much more than her appearance wrapped in all that jewelry. Heiress to the largest fortune of Kuwait's landed gentry, her family traced its roots back to the cradle of civilization, that fertile crescent of Mesopotamia, at the crossroads of the Gulf shipping lanes and transcontinental caravan routes. Her eyes sparkled with the light of age-old wisdom. Her whole demeanor exuded radiance and warmth.

All the same, sadness was only an eye blink away, for this woman's past was as filled with grief and sorrow as it was graced by felicitous blessings. Married to the heir of the largest fortune of Kuwait's new oil money, who had raised himself to the position of that country's Secretary of State, Badrya and her life had been shattered by her husband's death from cancer at age 33. Abdulla was her only child. She then made it her business to protect his gigantic inherited interests and holdings from family predators and self-serving would-be investors. Indeed, the pressure was so great on both of them that she had enrolled Abdulla in a private American school, as far as possible from the champing and preying crowds.

Thus, via the intermediary of one of Minnesota's largest grain and flour fortune families, Abdulla was enrolled in a nationally reputed school for adolescents in Faribault, Minnesota, 12 miles from Northfield. But it was not long before Abdulla wearied of the geographic confinements of Faribault and sought refuge in the smaller but culturally more diverse offerings of Northfield. He gravitated to the high school, matriculated and ended up in Janice's French class. With her Labrador Retriever instinct, it took Janice about two class sessions to realize that here was a disturbed young man who was totally alone and who needed love and attention. We took him in until the Swensons were able to offer more permanent quarters.

Badrya never forgot our gesture. She stayed with her friends in Minneapolis for a month, coming down to Northfield for frequent visits. Neighbors never quite understood what the black limousine and attendant chauffeur were doing outside our house. Natalie, Patrick and Gigi, occasionally driven to school and back in the limo, never did quite know how to explain it to their curious and envious classmates.

Badrya and Janice became fast friends while I took succor in her genuine concern for my health. In February, with Abdulla in better spirits, she left to tend to business at home. When she returned for a short visit in May, she discreetly left me a fat envelope on the sofa. Inside was a card wishing me luck. It also contained in its fold crisp hundred dollar bills,

enough to cover half the cost of my proposed stay at the Swiss
clinic.

Thus backed by my Swedish/Kuwaiti connection, I spent
three weeks in August 1979 at the Ita Wegman Clinic, intensely devoted to nurturing my poor degenerating body—
and mind—back to health. Parkinson symptoms had
increased markedly, and were more noticeable now from the
outside.

I remember having to make a conscious effort by now to
swing my arms while walking on level ground. They still
swung freely and widely on uphills and downhills. I also remember bumping my shoulders against door jams and
against other shoulders in a crowd. Shaking was not a problem yet, except for aesthetics. However, I did become scared
by previews of coming attractions when Dr. Hoffmann asked
me if I had had problems controlling my bladder. Did I not
know that this was one of the symptoms? I guess I had read
about it—how could I have missed it—but I must have subconsciously repressed it, so undignified and embarrassing
such a failure seemed to me.

But by the time Dr. Hoffmann's questionnaire had ended,
I was immensely proud of myself and my condition, and I had
a better idea of what to expect. For the time being, my handwriting was good, in spite of occasional stiffness of the fingers, but the homeopathic drugs prescribed by Dr. Page that
I had been able to obtain at Weleda, New York, seemed quite
helpless in relieving my limbs' rigidity and heaviness. Two
other things stand out: I now needed to use an electric
toothbrush; and I experienced feelings of lightness just under
the scalp.

On my second morning at the clinic Dr. Hoffmann brought
with her my daily routine that she monitored. Every morning
I would have muesli for breakfast followed by a bath of *equi-
situm* (horse tail grass). After that came the long, luxurious
massages, soft, in-depth massages administered with fragrant arnica lotion. The morning was completed by a

eurhythmy lesson, which, once devoid of its physical jargon was no more nor less than deep-stretching exercises.

The theory behind this therapy is that each letter of the alphabet symbolizes a cosmological truth. The possession of all 26, both in their choreographic realization and their innate meaning, is supposed to bring control and understanding of one's being, short of catapulting one's ego closer to the inner spheres of Nirvana.

The afternoons were to be spent on rest and relaxation, except for a painting class where we were forever chasing the pastel shades of an elusive sunset. Dr. Hoffmann confiscated all the pills I had brought along with me, giving me a replacement set that seemed very similar to mine. In addition, there were ampules administered as shots in the abdomen. The rest of the time I was to take a nap. I read avidly. I could also do all the walking I wanted, provided I was back for the doctors' evening rounds.

Dinner was served in the room, which I preferred to the table for four setting of lunch. This marked preference illustrated for me, I believe for the first time, the emotionally crippling aspect of Parkinson, the irrational shame to be seen shaking in public, the erosion of self-confidence, the gradual loss of self-assertion, the furtive looks to see if anybody sitting at the next table had noticed an abnormality in my movements. When I think of that rationally, even today when my symptoms are inescapable, I am sure that I was and still am making too much of it. But I have also learned by now not to look at strangers in public places, avoiding the reflection of their perceived image of me. It makes me much less paranoid and that much happier.

The Cat And Mouse Game _____

Some of those lessons are not so easy to learn. Parkinson
does not erode our faculties brutally. He is much too clever
for that. He comes and goes. He first comes to recognize his
domain. You catch him strolling by for the first time. So, you
make a passing reference to him in your journal:

> Today, I felt a new intrusion of Parkinson. He vis-
> ited what seemed to be the very busy crossroads of
> bones, nerves, tendons, muscles located in my
> knees. It was not painful, just a little bit stiffer; not
> even; just a tip of the hat, a soft, friendly reminder,
> a caress *en passant*. You almost want to go out of
> your way to greet him, "Hi! We've met before,
> haven't we?" to shake his hand, before ruefully re-
> marking that he has already shaken yours.

And you forget the encounter. Because a few days later
there are no traces left of his transgressing. But six months
later, while shopping at the supermarket, a friend will surprise you with, "Say, Michel, did you hurt your foot? You're
limping a little bit."

—"Oh! really? I was not aware of it." And you suddenly
blush. Your cheeks cannot lie, even if the subconscious denial
has already taken place. And you add in your journal a paranoid: "What else will John notice next?"

From that day on, if you're astute, honest and observing
enough, you will notice that you invent all sorts of subter-
fuges and excuses to avoid John. But chances are good that
you have just lost another friend. Indeed, now that it has
been openly mentioned, you no longer attempt to minimize
the limpness. You will let it run its course for a week or

whatever length of time it takes Parkinson to vacate the premises. And that will be when he has found a new abode or decided to revisit an old one, on which he now has a greater hold.

The cat and mouse game will continue like an unending game of chess. He'll snatch a rook while you capture a pawn, and reach your queen while you're still groping in the dark for the entrance to the fortress. It was months before I noticed his next hold on my limbs again, but one day I recorded in my journal that I could run only six laps that morning before the stiffness forced me to quit—whereas I could run eight laps before. And that was when I was running with old, heavy, worn-out French tennis shoes, and also without the benefit of Sinemet,™ a drug I later discovered.

All the same, I'll give old Parkinson a run for his money. See if I can beat him at his game tomorrow, same time, same place. But the next day, like the coward that he is, he didn't show up for the duel. Of course, that was the day when I ran my eight laps in an almost record-breaking eight minutes! Could he have disappeared? Wait a minute; what was that stiffness in my wrist as I reached for my pen to record the event?

Bizarre!

The First Drugs

And so my journey continued. In the spring of 1979, I went to my neurologist, Dr. T., to seek some relief from the advancing symptoms. I felt that I needed some help for the very bad days when my arms hurt from being so heavy and seemed to be pulling my shoulders downward and forward. On those occasions it took a conscious effort to say, "Come on, my boy, straighten up those shoulders of yours. Stand tall. You're about to teach a class. Fire yourself up. Get that adrenaline pumping, get that dopamine flowing!"

So Dr. T. started me on the blue pills. Half a pill twice a day. They were Sinemet™ low dosage 10/100.

Two weeks later, having noticed no improvement, I went back to the office.

—"Well?"...

—"Well, it doesn't work. I still feel tired and a little bit out of focus, and I still had trouble pulling down my sweater from the head to the waist."

—"So why don't we double the dose?"

I had no experience in drug dosage, but a 100% increase seemed a bit excessive. Was the increment worth the excrement, I asked myself?

—"Look," I told Dr. T., "I read the description of Sinemet™ in Dr. Halvorson's Drug Handbook. I don't like the caution regarding melanoma. I have a hunch that substantia nigra and melanoma on the one hand, and melanoma and skin problems caused by Parkinson on the other, are all somehow related, interconnected. So, even though the bad days are getting to be pretty bad, I can still function, albeit below par. So I think I'll tough it out, Doc."

I was really counting on Dr. Page's drugs to tide me over until I got to the clinic in Arlesheim, and indeed, they worked according to plan. Then Dr. Hoffmann's drugs—which were basically of the same nature, but perhaps more specific, more potent and certainly administered more regularly to the inpatient that I was—took over until February 1981, when I finally gave in and embarked on a dual tract drug program: continuation of the homeopathic drugs with the addition of two tablets of Sinemet™ 10/100.

I do not have any scientific proof that this home-brewed program was effective, but it kept me going and I suspect it is the reason for my somewhat dyskinesia-free condition six years later. Of course, during these years, changes have occurred. I have increased the Sinemet™ to three tablets of

10/100; have added intermittently Symmetrel,™ Parlodel™ and Deprenyl™ (JUMEX), and stopped the homeopathic drugs.

Basically, I function in my environment. At this point, I am unable to resume teaching, but I have managed to keep my days full, almost for a year: first with the walk and its preparation; and most recently for another year with the writing of this book and the preparation of two others.

I stopped the homeopathic treatment about two years ago, for a number of reasons, but I still go to Arlesheim once every summer for a maintenance shot, an evaluation and a faith boosting pilgrimage and meditation in the shadow of the Goetheanum.

Back in the summer of 1981, I came across a French bestseller entitled Tous les espoirs de guerir.[2] It was a compendium (in two fat volumes) of all parallel medicines, from the most esoteric to the least probable, with a good deal of horse sense therapies sprinkled in between. Incidentally, my offer to translate it for a big health press was turned down. I wonder why, since it had lots of good tips—along with some goofy ones, too—which would make it a hot bookstore item. The yuppie culture would go wild over it.

Among its more credible bits of advice was a way to treat Parkinson. It accomplished miracles in old folks homes, where suddenly octogenarians forgot their age and cavorted gallantly about. "The drug" was apparently a fairly common compound with a few extra ingredients and was made and sold in Germany as KH3 under license of the world renowned Romanian geriatrist, Dr. Ana Aslan. Her version, the original elixir, was called Gerovital and could be administered orally, or, under a doctor's supervision, intravenously. "But, of course," added the brochure we had sent for, "nothing equals the one month cure that we offer in various towns throughout Romania, in the choicest hotels reserved for foreign visitors and at the most reasonable prices. For further

2 All Hopes of Healing Allowed.

information, please contact the Romanian Embassy in Paris, charters available from Romanian Airlines, etc."

Papa, who was experiencing the first attacks of arthritis and sciatica, was also interested, but the more we researched, the more we became convinced that all this hype was aimed more at filling the coffers of the Romanian treasury than at healing people.

Nevertheless, I did smuggle into France enough tablets for a three month treatment which seemed to help. To what degree, exactly, it is very difficult to assess due to the multiplicity of the parameters involved. There simply is not enough stability in my life—what with trips to France twice a year—to make valid observations based on changing one parameter at a time, and long enough to study its effect. At any rate, I would put the KH3 treatment in the plus column. It certainly presented no negative aspect.

Hello, Sucker!...Four Times _____

It is truly amazing to see what people will do when, for whatever reason, they reach a state of desperation. To cope with their spiritual needs and physical impairments, they have been known to take to the road and travel thousands of miles. Many examples come to mind.

Malcolm Miller, the official guide at the Chartres cathedral, theorizes that cathedrals were built on the sites of already well-known privileged, telluric spots. Thus Chartres is built, he says, on the site of an old fountain which was known for its medicinal properties, and received the devotions of our ancestors the Gauls and quite probably of their ancestors the Ligures. Nothing has changed today. Millions of French people still converge every summer on the spa towns of Vittel, Vichy, Evian and Thonon, to drink the water and thereby undo the evils of the wine that they have drunk all year.

Nothing is new under the sun. The Greeks went to Delphi to consult their oracles, we go to our local palm reader or spiritual advisor. Every day bus loads, train loads, and plane loads of people from Ireland, Spain and Italy pour out their contents—and malcontents—onto the streets of Lourdes, Fatima and Paray-le-Monial. Our human condition is yearning for perfection. And that yearning can become so imperative and relentless a drive that we entertain the wildest dreams at the hands of the weirdest charlatans. We are so afraid of losing our parochial Nirvanas that we grovel on our knees at the slightest hint of hope for betterment. And I found myself no different.

If I allow myself to report on the irony of our Faustian condition and tribulations, it is for the pertinent reason that I am no different from anyone else, and that I, too, submitted to the humiliations of the desperate. I struck so many deals with the devil that he'll have to be mightily organized to remember which contract to honor. So, I too, I'll admit, went to Lourdes to drink the water and took to the road on four occasions to seek four faith healers' deliveries of their aberrant promises and pretensions.

In spite of that apparent crust of cynicism, I consider myself a true mystic at heart: I ardently believe in the power of faith and prayer, and yes, even in miracles. But somehow I don't think they should happen with regularity every Sunday morning, for the benefit of those who can afford a television set. Besides, the media's treatment of the message is not refined or convincing enough to make me swallow on faith that Christ appeared to Oral Roberts under the guise of an $8,000,000 ultimatum! Talk about transactions with the devil!...Yes, I do believe in miracles, but I do have my limitations.

The following episodes may better illustrate what I mean. The first experience occurred early on. My good friend Tom Dandelet, of the younger and charismatic sort, took all kinds of precautions and beatings around the bush one day to announce that the following week, in the Faribault Catholic high school, some reputed lady would be passing through to pray, preach and project her gifts of laying on of the hands upon the afflicted. For my sake, wouldn't I go to the service with him?

Sure! Why not. I had never taken that tack before.

The service was held in the cafeteria. The public address system was bad. I could not hear what was being said, and I was feeling more self-conscious than ever. I was miserable. I knew a miracle could not happen to me in this state of grace-lessness. And when I saw two Paul Bunyan size volunteers get up and come forward to catch in their arms the swooning healed ones, I knew I was a sure bet for the heaping pile of those destined to the roaring pyre. Tom was disappointed and visibly felt sorry for me. I was sorry he felt sorry and we spent the return trip to Northfield justifying our feeling sorry for each other.

Story number two has to do with laying on of the hands also, this time by an amateur, a retired teacher, ex-colleague of my father's. He explained that he had become aware of his gifts just a few years back. His nephew had broken an ankle and it was healing with difficulty when, perchance, the toddler happened to climb on his uncle's lap and remarked that his uncle's hands felt warm around his ankle and made his wound feel better. By coincidence, the very next week, similar remarks were addressed to him—I've forgotten the details—so he began investigating, asking family and friends to let him practice on them. He started with minor sore throats, soon graduating to strep throats.

At this point he was slowly enlarging his sphere of action, he said, specializing in curing tobacco addiction. He would gladly give me a whirl—as he told my father—if I was not turned off, that is, by the incongruity of the prospect. But for the desperate who seek relief, there is no pride left, no dignity saved. Neither is there any left, it seems, to the purported provider of such relief. This last statement, however, does not apply to Papa's colleague who triggered no more than a heating sensation on my back, but who never said he could achieve any more; nor did he ask for a centime from us.

This statement does apply, however, to Chardin, hero of story number three. Paris, the fall of 1981. The epitome of Mr. Charlatan. The fake, the quack *par excellence*. Warned by my highly recommended—and otherwise trustworthy— source, that this Chardin phenomenon was an extraordinary sourpuss, who charged an outrageous 350 francs (about $85) a visit, I nevertheless wittingly decided that I would be, once again, the desperate sucker.

Chardin would not let me stand on ceremony or otherwise.

—"Sit down!" he ordered, pointing his chin to the chair by his desk.

—"How long have you had whatever it is you have?"

—"About three years. It is Parkinson...."

—"*I* will tell you what you have."

I was too stunned to do anything but drop my jaw, swallow my saliva, and venture a very tentative, "Well, er...I just thought that you m...might, er...." He curtly interrupted my stammering by handing me a piece of sandalwood, thrusting it in my palm.

—"Hold this in your left hand, like a tennis racquet handle and grab the edge of my desk with your right thumb and index finger."

He then opened a smart-looking wooden box full of multi-colored vials, gave a swing to his pendulum rotating over my left hand, then brought the detector either to rest or to agitate over one of the vials. He repeated the operation about ten times, each time pulling out of the box the target vial. Once the selection process was over, without looking at me, he took the time to put his tools away neatly, and still standing up, he muttered, "Give me your pills."

Once again, the surprise was too great. Before I could think, I was handing him my combined treasure of Sinemet,™ Symetrel™ and homeopathic pills. I was not yet on Parlodel.™ He glanced at them and with all the scorn he could seemingly muster, he dropped, "You have Parkinson disease."

I was finally able to squeeze in a sarcastic, "You don't say!"

It was now his turn to register a jolt. He looked at me for the first time, and as the French expression goes, "If his eyes had been pistols I wouldn't be here to tell the story." Short of that civility, he handed my pills back to me with a leer and the distinctly disdainful pout of one who does not want to be contaminated by the proximity of a dangerous and stinky product. And sat down. Then he proceeded to write an illegible prescription. Eyes cast down again, the turned up nose and the pointed chin aimed at my pills again, he said, "Stop taking those!"

Then he handed me the scribbled-on half sheet, saying, "And three times a day, take six drops of these on a washcloth held for ten minutes on the nape of the neck."

—"And that's it?"

—"That's it."

—"But don't you think that my dopaminergic agent will soon be depleted in my brain, and that...."

—"Did any of those drugs you have taken until now ever cure you of Parkinson?"

I had to confess, "No, but...."

—"You see!...That will be 400 francs." (About $100.)

—"Four hund...but the lady who recommended you said 350 francs a visit."

—"She was wrong."

Six days later I was flat on my back in our small apartment in Paris, stiff as a board, begging Janice to give me back my pills. So much for this Chardin the Charlatan character.

My fourth episode of such encounters is somewhat similar to the last one, except that in addition, it involved a ring of "legitimate" French doctors. My cousin Jean-Pierre, a well-known figure in the sports scene of the Dauphiné/Savoy provinces, had come across a real "guérisseur"— a psychic whose uncanny intuitions he could swear by. Wouldn't I come out of my Burgundian seclusion, make an appointment with Mr.

Gross in the suburbs of Grenoble? It would be a good excuse to see each other again. My! how long had it been? Twenty years? No! Twenty-two! Let's see, yes it was in 1959. Yes, 22 years. OK. Why didn't he, Jean-Pierre, make the appointment, and I would plan to spend a couple of nights with him and his family. Great!

Mr. Gross was not as astute as Chardin. He asked first thing what drugs I was taking. Then, the classic, "Oh yes, I could tell as you entered the room that you were Parkinsonian."

I thought, "My foot, you could buddy. I have been in Parkinson circles long enough to know that when one hears Sinemet™ or Madopar™ (and Parlodel™ nowadays) one immediately thinks: Parkinson. You don't need to be psychic to come to such deductions."

On his desk was the *de rigueur* pendulum, but instead of little vials, he assayed his detector over big, scientific-looking, laminated maps of the human body. He checked over the circulatory system: clear; over the respiratory system: clear. But when he turned to the central nervous system map, the pendulum started to gyrate as if out of control. He switched to a larger scale map of the brain. Same thing. Then to two more maps, the nature of which, from my inverted position, I could not make out.

—"I see," he said as he replaced his pendulum in its holster. "I see what it is. You are having a 'fausse' Parkinson," peering over his glasses as if to see how the news registered with me.

—"And what is a 'false' Parkinson, pray tell?"

—"I could go into details, but let's just say for the moment that it is a condition which is not Parkinson, but exhibits many of the symptoms...." Profound! He was nodding his head, up and down, up and down as if he needed to convince himself and was looking at me as if to ask, "What do you think of that?"

After a few seconds of this reflection, I broke the silence and asked, "Well, where do we go from here?"

—"I don't know." And he looked at me weirdly again. Gathering from my reaction that this would not do, he embarked on a long-winded treatise of how nefarious my pills could be to my liver. He was in the middle of a sentence, groping for new words to an old song, when all of a sudden he hit his forehead with the palm of his hand, jumped up and yelled, "Hallelujah! I've got it!"

—"Well, what is it?"

—"Hanaberg's serum, that's what. Yes, it may sound a bit bizarre; it's a wide spectrum serum made from turtle blood." (It was difficult to hold back a snicker.) "It has great antibacterial properties; it has been used effectively in many cases of tuberculosis. I think it can be applicable to your case: as a matter of fact, I am certain it will help...."

—"How fast acting is it?" I asked eagerly.

—"You should start to see some improvement in about six months."

—"How and where do I get it?"

—"That is the problem. It is not approved by the French FDA. I can prescribe it, but only as a referral, and very few doctors registered with the Official Order of Physicians will touch it. Let me call Dr. Michel. He practices in a private clinic in downtown Grenoble and since you're only passing through, he might oblige." Mr. Gross' stubby index finger dialed the number.

—"...not in his office now? I see.... Regardless, please be advised that I am sending a patient, named Michel Monnot, for a heavy dose of Hanaberg serum. Yes, he'll be by your office, let's say within half an hour. Merci." And off I was to the Quai Voltaire address in downtown Grenoble on the Isère river banks, to be greeted by a smiling secretary who handed me a small package saying, "Here's the serum. Dr. Michel isn't in, but you can probably find someone to give you the shot. That will be 180 francs."

The collusion gimmick was crude, but who gives a damn when cornered into desperation? Too many crooks, unfortunately, know that answer.

Credo

Fortunately, I think I have learned my lesson, even if it is at my expense and expenses. I have come to understand that there is no panacea. There is not one method that possesses the whole truth; it is only a combination of positive aspects taken from all schools and methodologies which can hope to bring any sign of relief. A good, balanced diet will provide a healthy terrain (body soil) upon which some diseases won't latch, but will not counterbalance the deficiencies produced by hereditary causes or the evils caused by an inescapable fallout from a radioactive cloud.

Nor can exercises bring back the fountain of youth to a quinquagenerian body. And the advanced miracle drugs of recent years cannot be expected to work without producing deleterious side effects. But some of the toxins released by these drugs can be annihilated through a comprehensive program of diet, exercises or acupressure therapy. Still, it would be utopic to think that acupressure alone, or dieting alone, or stretching exercises alone can deliver a 70 old man suffering from Parkinson for 15 years and on heavy dosage of a combination of drugs, from the throes of the disease. He can be made to improve, to feel better, but one should not expect to see him climb the stairs three steps at a time. Even with new techniques of brain implants, either of autologous adrenal glands or of borrowed fetal cells, a well thought out program of eclectic components is bound to bring better results than the operation alone. No single truth can boast of offering the whole TRUTH.

That is why I do not reject any idea *a priori* and wish that practitioners of all ilks and medical confessions would do the same: keep an open mind *vis-à-vis* their colleagues' endeavors. I want to shout that it's the well-being of your brothers that is at stake here. So won't you be civil to each other, bury the political hatchet, and work together for the greater good of your starved egos and of mankind? Who knows? There may be a Nobel prize at the end of the rope for the individual or the organization who will make hands shake from brotherly accord rather than from irate discord.

That is why I have simultaneously put my name on the waiting list for a brain implant and am seeking relief from Syng-Yu finger pressure therapy, to say nothing of the fruit diet provided by his loaded peach, apricot, plum and fig trees. And I am also faithful to my walking/jogging program.

So, I put it to the experts, the researchers, those who have pledged allegiance to the Hippocratic oath, to the nurses who see so much suffering and tend to so much pain; I put it to the chiropractors, the acupuncturists, the acupressurists; I put it to the deans of medical schools, the ubiquitous paramedics, members of the boards of Parkinsonian organizations, officials of the cancer societies, to all the fund raisers, editors of newsletters and health related magazines, to the Ralph Edwards and, of course, also to you, Jerry, and yes, to you Muhammad Ali: Let us together put our partisans' heads aside, let us have the COURAGE to be different, let us join hands for the eradication of unacceptable evils from this planet. Yes, it's quite a program, but man has put man on the moon. Man can put ills and evils out of this world. Suffice it to be willed.

7

No Man Is An Island

Gigi's Ordeal

During all this time, while I was following the road of the homeopathic cure to my own greatest comfort and promise of salvation, my family were lost on different paths, each leading slowly but inescapably to their private hells. While I was home between clinic visits and Parkinson consultations, I awakened to a new stage of awareness— probably my most costly discovery.

One sunny spring morning, with the gravity of a gavel falling down to finalize the verdict, the heavy double door slammed shut and locked behind Gigi without a prayer of an appeal. With the best of intentions, we had just committed our daughter. Put her away. Locked her up.

—"Mr. and Mrs. Monnot," the world expert on anorexia had said a few days earlier at the Mayo clinic, "this may seem barbaric and medieval but it is the best way we know to take care of your daughter's problem. St. Mary's hospital has just completed a wing of its new psychiatry unit entirely devoted to the treatment of anorexia. Gigi will be closely observed around the clock. She will not be allowed to leave the table before she has eaten everything served to her. She will be followed by her private case worker even when she goes to the bathroom to ensure that she does not make herself throw up. And for the first month of her confinement, you will not be able to see her nor to talk to her."

The armored sash locked us out. With our gazes unable to pierce through the mute wall into Gigi's new quarters, Janice and I turned to each other for a big question mark hug. Were we doing the right thing? Would she ever crawl out of this self-induced nightmare? How long would it take for the first healing thread to appear?

The doctor tried to lighten our load by saying that Gigi's prognosis was relatively good. He based his opinion on the fact that Gigi seemed more amenable to behavioral changes than most anorexics and she was not vehemently opposed to being treated. She needed help, and via the medium of starving her body, she was subconsciously seeking that help. In effect, she was—and had been—screaming a warning, which I was too deaf to the world around me to hear and too selfish to heed. Also too myopic to see that she had already lost enough body weight to inflict permanent damage to herself.

It was high time for a change of optics on my part. Gigi was bleeding while I frivolously focused on how long I could get by on my homeopathic drugs only, how long I could go without submitting to the poisoning of my inner sanctum by the likes of l-dopa and amantadine. That change of optics came fast and forcefully.

Dejected as we were by the radical manner in which Gigi was treated, and powerless to do anything about it, Janice and I needed a change of scene for a bit. So we packed a few things in the car and headed straight north to Park Rapids to visit Dr. and Mrs. Vernon E. Shuckhart, my American AFS hosts back in 1957-1958. To them I owe my Americanization of which I am so proud. To this day, they have offered golden advice. That was particularly true that weekend.

It did not take Vernon very long to assess the changes which the illness had wrought upon me, but which I pretended not to see or did not want to accept. After all, I could walk, I could talk, I was still teaching my classes. Why should I contaminate my body with artificial compounds?

—"But don't you realize," said Vernon, who had taken me aside, "that in the first place, these new drugs are not the poisons you make them out to be. They're safe. They have been thoroughly tested. They may have a few unpleasant side effects, but look at it this way, Michel, you are denying yourself a greater and richer wellness today by trying to save the sanctity of your body for a day in the future that may never come. If you love life so much, live it to the fullest. Don't idle when you can go full throttle. Enjoy life today. I noticed at dinner the difficulty you had with your salad and with your steak. Right now, you're staring at me fixedly with big round eyes instead of your normally intelligent twinkle. What about your kids? They are growing fast. Tomorrow may be too late to enjoy them. Spend as much time as you can with them. It's a real luxury you cannot skip or gamble away on the flimsy excuse that you may live a few years longer if you hold out on the drugs that will provide relief for you and your family."

That was a piece of advice I needed to hear. So selfishly engrossed was I in my predicament, that I had not sensed my flower child wilting and withering away. What would it be next? So I started gobbling down my triune patriotic redemption: red Symmetrel,™ white Parlodel™ and blue Sinemet.™ Whenever I come to a therapeutic crossroad nowadays, I apply this advice as a measuring stick: Is the increment supposedly gained in longevity worth the excrement generated by the greater encroachment of the symptom?

Indeed Parkinson is not an individual battle. It is a social disease; it affects the whole clan.

While some members of the family needed more love and caring, others were able to fight the communal battle in a way that I learned only too late.

Avuncular Love

Uncle Robert, Tante Edith's husband is one who went all agog in that respect. He sifted through all the traditional and parallel medicines' literature, sending for articles here, making international telephone calls there, to try and unearth the well-kept secret which, by some miracle, would be lying dormant somewhere in a faraway land's lab or in some ghostly alchemist's sunken cove. He checked on the homeopathic clinic in Arlesheim and gave it the good medicine chest seal of approval which it so richly deserves.

He checked with nutritionists and herbalists, he talked to iridologists and phytotherapists, and he is the one who first heard about Deprenyl,™ researched it, thought I should try it and has become the chief supplier of said drug: since the French authorities are as slow as our own FDA in approving the drug, Robert goes faithfully to Italy three times a year to smuggle it for my close friends' and my personal benefit.

Salient among the more ludicrous things that the family has done or is doing to chase Satan away are Robert's and Maman's weekly attempts at winning the jackpot in the nationally televised French horse races every Sunday, and in the nationally televised Loto (bingo) game every Wednesday. The pledge is of course directly meaningful: should they hit that jackpot, a substantial donation will be bequeathed to research for Parkinson.

Natalie's Dummy

This willingness to help, however, can take some fairly circuitous approaches and involve subconscious subtleties. Daughter Natalie quietly brought her stone to the edifice, when, on the day of her high school graduation, I asked her, "Well, Nats, have you thought ahead? Do you have any idea as to what you'll be doing in the fall?"

She gave me a long look, half mocking, half patronizing, and replied, "I have registered at the vo-tech in Mankato, in their nurses' aide program. I figured that some day, these skills might come in handy." She smiled. "Don't you?"

Coming so unexpectedly from Natalie who does not usually display her feelings, such a revelation could not but pierce me to the core. But I knew that for this declaration to take hold, the trick was to register it, but not to acknowledge it. So I went nonchalantly about, simply adding, "Good idea." Could this be the point of departure of a new understanding between Natalie and myself? I certainly was, in a sense, flattered by the *attention* and the *intention*. Could Parkinson be the missing link in our chain of paternal/filial love? And Natalie would have picked it up? Hallelujah!

My yearly summer trip to France prevented testing those premises. But it was not long before one evening in September Natalie called home in a state of panic.

—"Mom and Dad, I was wondering if Dad would come to Mankato to be my dummy."

—"What?"

—"Well, see, the facilities at school are kind of cramped, and I can never get time to practice long enough with the dummy...and we're having a test at the end of the week..."

—"So you want me to drive 60 miles to Mankato to be your dummy? Hmm! I guess in either case I lose, right? So I'd better come."

Parkinson cements the bonds.

So the next afternoon, I was in Mankato, in Natalie's apartment, lying on her bed, playing dummy while she busied herself, glancing at her book to follow the right procedure, taking off all the covers and sheets, manhandling me, the dumb lump, tugging at my leg to free the bottom sheet, scooping under my knees and neck to lift my dead weight from place to place while trying to make the bed from scratch. We spent a good 15 minutes trying to figure out the simple moves necessary, which were so badly described in the book. At one point I slid through her arms, bouncing off the bed and quickly regaining via reflex action—which does not disappear with Parkinson—a believed to be long gone life-saving agility. I landed on my feet; we had a good laugh and it was only after Natalie rearranged the sheets around me, more mummy fashion than boot camp model, that we decided to quit and go out for a pizza.

—"After that, there still will be time to call Mom." She would be able to shed some light on this clinical gibberish.

—"I was about to suggest the same thing. You call her, OK?"

Efficient bed making practice had been a fiasco, our father/daughter re-bonding an unmitigated success. Parkinson after all was *bearable*—if not *bed-able*. We still laugh reminiscing about that scene.

Patrick's Surprise

My son Patrick's ability to cope with a disabled father was at once rational and loving, sensitively researched with both my growth and protection in mind.

In the fall of 1981, I had a National Endowment for the Humanities fellowship to do research in Paris. Gigi came with us while Natalie kept the house and Patrick stayed with our good friends Phil and Lila Miller. Lila was in the English department at St. Olaf College, across the tracks and the Cannon river from Carleton. Phil was a first rate woodworker. He had shown me his workshop in the basement. The room was small but impeccable; all the tools neatly arranged, each one in its own place; shiny adjustable spotlights ready to turn their attention on the merciless biting bit or on the smooth piece of walnut, rich grained and warm colored. With it, Phil was making a new butt for that double barrel rifle over there in the corner. With his palm, he wiped off any unlikely dust particle, blew on it, sniffed it, examined it close to the light and gently put it back on the workbench. Delicately, almost reverently. Yes! The way Pépé Monnot used to court his wines. A genuine love affair. Phil and Lila. Craftsmen. Nothing phony about those guys. Patrick would be in loving hands.

He certainly was. Yet, he had doubts. "Patrick is troubled about something," Phil wrote in a letter, "but I haven't been able to put my finger on what it is, yet. I am sure it's nothing very serious. He's simply preoccupied by something—otherwise, he seems happy, he's a delight to have around. He reads a lot, he seems to study adequately, loves his biology class, comes home punctually on his bike at 10:30 every night. At any rate, we'll keep you informed immediately of any development."

When we got home, in the second week of December, Pat had grown, and grown up into a man. His voice had changed, he towered above his mother, he had filled out into a solid chunk, topped with curlier and darker hair and underlined by a becoming mustache. Right away, he wanted to talk to Mom, he had something important to impart, which had been gnawing at him for a long time.

—"You see, ever since this summer when we were on the bike trip," he confided to his mother, "I have been thinking about Dad's progressing handicap, and your reaction to him. Sure, he's got motion problems, but he is not paralyzed. He's become a real slow poke (do you think his stay at the Swiss clinic did him any good?). But what I want to say is that I have observed you again for the past two days; you should not help him so much. He's gotta do things he can do, by himself and for himself. You see, I was in this neat biology class taught by Mr. Johnson, our neighbor. We had to choose a research topic for a ten page paper, and I picked Parkinson disease—got an A by the way, it'll be $10, thank you, ma'am—I'll show it to you. But I wanted to tell you right away for Dad's benefit: don't do things for him. What if something happened to you? He would have to accommodate and fend for himself. But I learned that if you do things for them, then they come to rely on that help and they turn into vegetables. That's true of their brains too. Thank God he can still pun."

—"And if he can pun," jumped in Janice, "there's nothing degenerating about his mind."

—"So promise me that you won't help him."

—"I promise I'll do my best to refrain and combat the reflex, but there are situations when he's so helpless that I decide to lend a hand."

—"That's precisely the problem. You pity him, so you baby him and the vicious circle continues."

Patrick's stance and theory were thoroughly tested within a few days. Janice had gone Christmas shopping with Natalie and Gigi, so Patrick and I were fending for ourselves.

—"I'll tell you what we'll do," I said to Patrick, "we'll go to the Northfield Bakery and Deli for lunch and I'll treat you and me to a Bayou Boy."

—"A Bayou...what? Ish! Sounds like catfish to me."

—"Come on, Pat, put a little adventure in your life. All it is, is a small, but good submarine sandwich. I discovered them last spring one day for lunch. I just remembered them."

In the well stocked glass-doored refrigerator lay the Bayou Boys. I reached for two. The frosted chill came tumbling down. A black veil fell over me: I had forgotten that all the sandwiches at the Deli were wrapped in two or three layers of the most staticky sticky plastic wrap. But stoically, knowing what I was in for, I decided to hang in there. So I paid at the counter and we sat at a table.

Janice had relayed to me her conversation with Patrick, so the challenge became a matter of pride. Never mind the hunger. The problem of removing the wrap was enough of a battle.

First, I looked at the thing, sitting there, inert on its paper plate. Then, I ventured a flick of the finger to see if it would turn upside down: maybe it would develop a hole in its armor. But no such luck. I recoiled. Patrick was eyeing me sideways. I sat up straight in my chair, hands on my lap, plotting the next strategy. Let's see...I studied its position on the plate. I'll move in with a determined left hand for the hefty grab, twist it bottom up and I'll use the right hand for the more precise finger movements. Hopefully, I'll get an edge of the wrap, from which I'll be able to go on to stage two: pulling the two membranes apart. One is reduced to leap-frogging, proceeding from one meager move gained to the next, like building space stations on the way to the conquest of Mars.

Plastic wrap is not serendipitous, for Parkinsonians at least. Patrick was a quarter finished with his Bayou Boy, already.

—"Not bad," he said behind a mouthful. "Good submarine." By now, I had managed to put both hands on the sandwich. But neither one was doing much good. I couldn't even see where the damned wrapper started. It dawned on me that I would have a better grab if the sandwich was oriented at a 2:40 position on the plate rather than at the 10:20 position where it now rested. Seemed that way, anyway! My hands were starting to shake and stiffen. Knowing that Patrick was observing while pretending a casual aloofness, increased my self-consciousness. He went on munching. I was still salivating. I had to attempt something. So, with a surge of will power (or whatever it is that triggers dopamine pumping) I grabbed my plate with both hands, lifted it, and jerkily rotated it 120 degrees to the right. It was indeed easier for my right hand to operate and after a good 30 seconds, miracle, I succeeded in prying open the two layers of the wrap. Rolling gently at the edge by rubbing with the thumb and index finger, was the clue.

The third stage was to undress the submarine. All I had so far was a precarious grasp of its hemmed skirt. I pulled the two layers about an inch apart. Stopped to catch my breath—one gets winded doing all those exhausting exercises—but soon I realized the futility of the task: the wrap had been done on a heating unit and the two layers were hopelessly welded together. Patrick had two bites left of his. I had to start from scratch. Had to imagine a totally new approach. I got up, went to the counter and asked for a plastic fork. The tines are very sharp on those little plastic forks. With it, it was fairly easy to poke and rip through the wrap on the flank of the sandwich rather than on the bottom. Small victory. I had made an opening about four inches long, but the goodies

remained snugly inside the wrap. The opening had to be en-
larged. With both thumbs and index fingers I clumsily
tugged at the two lips of the opening. Patrick fidgeted.

—"You all right, Dad?"

—"I thought you'd never notice!"

And almost absent-mindedly he threw out, "Well, tell me
about France."

—"Sorry, man, it'll have to wait. I am concentrating on the
preliminaries of eating my lunch. Can't do more than one
task at a time. As it is, I am not quite sure if I'll get to my
sandwich or not."

Shreds of lettuce were falling out. A slice of tomato came
out next, gliding on a combination of house dressing and
mayonnaise. I thrust my tongue out just in time to catch a
self-liberating cold cut. Juice and dressing ran between my
fingers, past the back of my hand, toward my wrist.

—"Pat, unwrap this thing for me and rearrange it so I can
eat it, will you?"

Patrick sighed heavily as he reached for the sandwich.
"You do need help, don't you?"

Janice's Load

Parkinson was indeed playing havoc with our individual
plans, and those of the family as a whole. And as usual, it was
Janice who carried the brunt of the inconvenience on her
shoulders.

One summer in particular, after we had lead a bicycle tour
throughout France, her share of the burden consisted of accompanying Patrick and Gigi back to Northfield, touching
base with Natalie and the family she had spent the summer
with, and packing her off to Holden Village where she attended school in the state of Washington. She would also
have to find a host family for Gigi and Patrick for the fall

term, get them ready for school—clothes, shoes, supplies, allowances—make out the checks that had not been written all summer, fill out questionnaires at school, sign releases, prepare the house for the three Carleton students who were renting it for the fall. All that in the two short weeks allowed by the cheapest round trip airline ticket.

To this was added the emotional turmoil and physical exhaustion brought on by circumstances beyond our control. After a long, hot and cramped trip from Digoin across Burgundy, Franche-Comté and the Black Forest with six of us in my father's Citroën (Papa, Janice, Gigi, myself, Patrick with the mumps diagnosed the day before, and Alex, Patrick's friend who had spent the summer as our guest), we arrived at the airport in Frankfurt the next morning to be greeted by the news that the charter airline pilots were on strike. Our tickets were no good.

For an additional $250 per person we could take a train from Frankfurt to Copenhagen, then fly Northwest to Minneapolis. However, a rapid calculation of our monies at hand versus expenses still to meet, and we were off to Copenhagen in Papa's Citroën—bless his soul—hot, tired and cramped. I called Maman to let her know that Papa and I wouldn't be back for a couple of days.

And that's when all hell broke loose at the Copenhagen airport. Alex, who had been put in charge of watching over the luggage, tugged at a small bag in the middle of the pile to retrieve God knows what. In so doing he upset the gingerly balanced mountain of luggage and the top bag on the cart came crashing down, spreading all over the rest of the bags and filling the airport with its fragrance, the sweetest, most indelible purpleness of a bottle of Dijon cassis. Adieu, Kirs! Hello, stains!

Two weeks later, Janice came back to France. We had decided to trade plans of Hawaii for Greece, macadamia nuts for olive branches. I went to Luxembourg to pick her up, and a few hours later we were in Donremy visiting Joan of Arc's birthplace. Janice fainted and a few minutes later, threw up. She had just contracted a very bad case of mumps.

So there she lay for the first two of the ten weeks we were planning to spend in Europe, sick as a dog, wasting away in a darkened room during the most brilliant French Indian summer I have ever seen. Even my brightest childhood memories are no match for this intensity of blue skies.

Janice's fever did not relent for most of the two weeks. The doctor, a friend of my parents, came to the house every other day on his regular house call rounds. She was in good hands, and Maman saw to it that each meal was the quintessence of taste and of garden freshness. I just had to be patient, reluctantly enjoying the beauty of each day. I casually helped in the garden, read listlessly, painted over some old pieces of furniture to be taken and used in St.Denis, our own little farm house located eight kilometers (about five miles) from Digoin.

I first fell in love with the little farmhouse four years before the diagnosis. I was on the train between Lyon and Digoin on my way back from Pau. I had been supervising the end of the Carleton Pau I and Pau II programs and was thoroughly tired. The railroad tracks followed the steep and luxuriant valley of the Azergues. Between intermittent cat-naps I was catching sight of bucolic scenes: a farmer, gadfly in hand, was poking his oxen to pull the hay cart which his family was loading. Scenes out of a Millet painting; lyrical vales worthy of a Lamartine poem.... When all of a sudden, I was wide awake: 200 yards downstream, neatly sitting on the deep green field, its toes dipping into the brook, was a small renovated sheep shack.

It was obviously a weekend/vacation residence, I decided. And sure enough, reading while gently swinging in a hammock was a young-looking man. Probably a yuppie Lyonnais unwinding for the weekend. Right then and there, I knew that I had to own a similar setup: a little farm house where we could and would spend the summers without imposing on my parents. That is how, for a song and a dance we acquired the little farmhouse in St. Denis. The dream of every French teacher in America! What more could anyone want?

No wonder that I smiled cryptically and repressed a possibly bitter, certainly sarcastic, laugh when one day, two years into my diagnosis, a chance visitor was casting an endless string of praise over our luck, our taste, our *savoir-vivre*.[1] Little did he know!... To my ear, his tribute sounded more like a eulogy. Luckily, a flash of an Aragon poem blotted the blues away: "Nothing can ever be claimed as one's own..."

Thank God for small miracles.

As soon as Janice felt better we moved up to St. Denis, an anachronistic cultural pocket with geese, chickens and ducks, with green water ponds in barnyards and the castrator's wife always yelling after her dog; with little old men in wooden shoes going to work in their vineyards up the hill exposed to the south; with little old ladies without tennis shoes, but forever buttoning and unbuttoning their black wool cardigans; and the local minstrel sharing with "the Americans," his latest crop of mushrooms, wild blackberries or fish he caught by hand in the nearby Loire.

There, up on the St. Denis hill, Janice convalesced nicely, beefing up her stamina and building up her endurance by taking progressively longer bike rides. We picked chestnuts and we roasted them in the fireplace alongside Papa's garden-grown potatoes. We made blackberry jam; the neighbor farmer invited us for the grape harvest. For two to three weeks we lived in a time warp that unwrapped itself when we'd go to Digoin and would recoil and recover its shape as soon as we started up the St. Denis hill, right after the railroad underpass.

Then off we were to Greece with $200 in our pocket and the car loaded with victuals and camping gear. That was to last us for at least two weeks; we'd come back when it was spent.

---

1   Lifestyle.

We started our trip with a detour. Dr. Hoffmann had insisted that I come by in the fall for another series of fresh cell
and mineral shot therapies. So, our first camping stop was in
a lush Jura mountain prairie near Arlesheim, in the outskirts of Basel. That's when I felt one of the first handicap-
ping influences of Parkinson, the subsequent rage and
powerlessness, and the inevitable take-over of my domain by
Janice—albeit for the sake of efficiency.

—"So, honey, you can't pull the canvas over the metal tube
frame? That's OK, I'll do it. Just get me a folding chair from
the trunk."

Her reactions were much less lenient when, a week later,
in Epidaurus, our hastily pitched five-man tent became the
toy of a violent storm. In the proximity of the great am-
phitheater, we fought like demons to get out and re-anchor
the tent amidst flailing canvas and clanking poles, tripping
floor cover and recalcitrant zippers. The stuff epics are made
of! Slowed down almost to a standstill by the tension of the
situation, unable to find my glasses, I could sense Janice
seething under the raging rain, cursing those damn spikes
that would not sink into the rocky ground.

I was worse than no help: I had become an obstacle. I became increasingly aware of the limitations imposed by
Parkinson. From the fall of 1978, when Erwin Kabam said,
"You have Parkinson disease," until December 31, 1984,
when I went on disability, many things changed.

The accuracy of my memory is one of them. I suffer from
cortical time warps. I do believe Parkinson—or perhaps it is
the drugs that are to blame—has affected my short term
memory as well as my present perception of events on the
time vector. For instance, just a week after the fact, I cannot
remember for the life of me, whether I sent a thank you note
to the Carleton College Mortar Board Society officers for the
honors they bestowed upon me: they made me the recipient of
their annual award, and one of the Society's honorary members. But were I asked to describe that September afternoon

of 1978, when I was waiting for Dr. T. to phone me the results of my CAT scan, I could go on forever.

Depending on the vantage point, this five year period can seem to me like a blink or an eternity. It is filled with the fear of ignorance, with the trauma of uncertainty, with the vicissitudes of adapting to a new reality, but also it is replete with the elations of discovery and the sweet rewards of daring. But the time must have passed slowly enough for my family. Certainly my wife continued to suffer quietly in a hundred different ways.

Especially in the beginning, Janice and I had to make rapid decisions; we had to take risks, and there were no paved roads and no maps. In essence, we opted for the road less travelled and that implied downshifting. On all fronts. It is here, in part, that Janice shares the credit for Courage. One thing we knew: I had Parkinson, and it wasn't going to get better.

We therefore had to make the appropriate changes, the propitious choices, the smart moves, on instinct, without real guidance. Slowing down on work, trimming down on related activities seemed compulsory for the maintenance of our sanity, and our solvency at the bank.

The first casualty of this reshuffling was Janice's job. After long considerations and weighing the pros and cons of the two French teaching positions (at Carleton versus the high school) and throwing in the estimated time I had left at bat, we came up with the educated guess that it would be better in the long term if Janice quit her job at the high school and came in as a helper in my classes at Carleton. This meant increased longevity in my tenured position. So, two years after founding the French program of the Northfield school district, Janice reluctantly resigned her position.

It was a difficult and brave decision. Janice had worked like a slave; she had managed to land her own position, she had established her own program, she had practically become her own boss, she had been named chairman of the languages department, she had her own set of fringe benefits, and figures for enrollment in her classes had been playing leapfrog. With the same gutsy determination, she threw all that away, principally to save my skin, or rather the empty shell I would become two or three years later when I could no longer teach without her presence in the classroom and her secretarial skills in the office.

I came to learn how to skirt many of the limitations of Parkinson, though. I tried to be as independent from her help as possible, and learned how to plan ahead. What my life lost in spontaneity, it gained in efficiency. Breaking down small tasks into their components became a model for unraveling the structure of larger tasks. For example:

—"Janice, I'm going to the post office to mail some letters and buy stamps. Need anything?"

—"No, just be careful! Have you got everything you need?" Once more, I replay the scenario in my head: have I taken my pills? Because should I hit a "low" while standing in line at the counter, my legs will start shaking. Have I got money for the stamps? Yes! Where? Let's see once more: yes, the bills— there were five ones at last count—in the right pants pocket. I can feel them under the material, no need to entangle my hand in the pocket to verify. On the left side, I shake the pocket. Jingling. Good! I've got some change. Remember, it's always the same, bills on the right, change on the left. I should know that by now, but I just want to make sure. I hate to sense people getting impatient behind me. You give the money with the right hand from the right pocket, and you get the change back into your extended left hand, to go into the left pocket. Yeah, and don't forget to extend your hand for the change, otherwise the employee at the window will put the coins on the flat polished marble sill and you'll have a deuce of a time picking them up.

Unless of course I have the right combination of coins. On my way to the post office, a rapid calculation tells me that the stamps will come to about $2. I park the car, get out and put on the final touches. First, retrieve the $5 wad and peel off two bills which I fold in fours and keep in the left palm while

I put the three bills back in my right pocket: neatly folded in fours if I feel sure of myself, crumpled up if I feel someone is watching. Transfer the two bills from the left palm to the right palm.

Now, to the coins. How much have I? In my freed left palm I count 56¢, two quarters, a nickle and a penny. If the stamps come to less than $2, I'll turn my wrist downward, open my fist and plop the two greenbacks on the marble slab, and for the change I'll extend my right hand since it is now free and since my left palm is occupied by the four coins. I'll do the rearrangement transfer later.

If the stamps are more than $2 I'll plop both handfuls on the marble and I'll slide the adequate number of coins from my collection towards the employee. Shoot! But suppose the stamps come to more than $2.56? Then Monnot, you're up "merde" creek with a sieve for a paddle. You're gonna have to tangle with the wad of three singles and start all over again.

Is there a (good) flip side to the Parkinson coin? Yes. It is called humor!

And so we plodded along the road with as much humor as we could carry along. It has saved us many times from skidding off onto the shoulder and finding ourselves stuck for assistance that we could not provide each other. In fact, in one of our darkest hours, our sense of humor held us together.

For some time I had noticed that Janice had lost her usual Zorba-like zest for the nitty-gritty of routine existence. But that was understandable: she was overworked.

She seemed to shun crowds, but this corresponded so beautifully to my own needs that I accepted it as a necessary adaptation that she had made on my behalf. Her fatigue was visibly great to me, although she always managed to appear full of vigor to everyone else. I knew, however, that she had begun to require many more hours of sleep than ever before.

Who would not understand? My disturbed sleeping pattern had caused her years of fitfully interrupted rest which she once jokingly described as sleeping with a jackhammer in motion. I noticed that her patience had worn thin too.

Whereas before she was slow to anger, now a cloud of irritability hung threateningly over her head.

When Christmas vacation rolled around she disappeared under a down quilt and didn't surface until Christmas Eve itself. This was so contrary to her usual Christmas beehive behavior that we were all somewhat stunned.

I really wanted to give her something that would make her chimelike laugh resound joyfully again. So I had all our prints and photos framed by a local artist. This was something we had often intended to do but had always put off until a more propitious financial moment.

As the family was gathered around the Christmas tree, I told the children I needed their help to set up while Janice was requested to play possum until we had strung out at least 20 newly framed masterpieces throughout the living and dining rooms.

Janice disappeared dutifully into the bedroom but did not reappear when I called her. She had fallen asleep. This both hurt and annoyed me. But the thought that something was not quite right gnawed away at my consciousness.

So I was not surprised, one January afternoon, to find her literally convulsed with sobbing as she stared out the bedroom window. The sky was a pregnant grey and school had been let out at noon because a blizzard was rampaging across the plains. The snow was already piling high in white drifts outside as we heard the shriek of the wind whipping through the lilac bushes and elm trees in the backyard.

I could not get one coherent word out of her. She sobbed uncontrollably as if she were involuntarily ridding herself of all her vital organs.

I knew there was only one thing to do. Within moments I had Dr. Mellstrom on the line. "You'd better bring her right in, Michel," was all he said.

She offered only passive resistance saying that she felt foolish to visit the doctor when there was nothing wrong. However Dr. Mellstrom thought there was plenty wrong and informed me that she needed medical attention right away.

—"Unfortunately," he sighed, "we don't have the facilities to help her in Northfield. She really needs to go to Abbott Northwestern Hospital in Minneapolis where they have a psychiatric ward...Look, do you have a friend who would be willing to drive her? We've got to get her there tonight!"

There was a sense of urgency in his voice and I racked my brains to think of what compassionate and foolhardy soul would be willing to venture out on a night like this.

No, I couldn't ask Joni and Ted. They would not refuse, but their family required their presence. I needed a friend without those obligations. Then it occurred to me that the perfect choice was Virginia. Virginia whose natural verve was matched only by Janice's usual reckless buoyancy.

A quick phone call assured us that Virginia was up to the challenge and would pick us up at the doctor's office.

When she arrived she had assembled a host of Minnesota blizzard paraphernalia: blankets, candles, matches, road flares, two shovels, salt, chocolate bars and a jug of water.

Dr. Mellstrom had already made the necessary arrangements with Abbott Northwestern and Dr. Keller, a psychiatrist whose reputation was already known in the Carleton community. He and his team would all be expecting us.

So with the visibility virtually disappearing by the minute, we inched our way toward Interstate 35W. Icy patches whose slipperiness was magnified by the drifting snow caused the car to skid dangerously on a road we could only guess at.

Virginia valiantly navigated, but there was no guiding polar star or even the outline of a trail. The Volvo made one final skid from the edge of the shoulder into the median. Virginia and I looked resignedly at each other; Janice sat inert in the back seat either oblivious to any danger or cognizant of the fact that here was where it all ended.

There was nothing to do but get out and push. I told Janice she'd have to help and she complied by taking the wheel while Virginia and I pushed the car with all our might and main. We only succeeded in getting the wheels rutted deeper into the snow. We started to shovel, poured out a whole bag of salt and ended up more successfully stuck than before.

While we were contemplating the thus incapacitated Volvo, two trucks stopped on the highway. Both drivers sympathetically invited us to accompany them. The hitch was there wasn't room for all three of us in either truck.

Not willing to be separated, Virginia and Janice climbed into one truck and I jumped into the other while shouting that I would meet them at the 98th Street exit at the first establishment open on the right side. About as clear as the visibility on the already dark and invisible landscape.... And so we sped away into the night!

My driver informed me that he would have to make a stop to pick up a delivery of chickens. Of course, there was no problem with that because the order would be ready and waiting for him with no chance of thawing. He chuckled here.

I assured him that that was not an inconvenience and just relaxed, dozing as we drove.

Virginia meanwhile found herself seated in the middle trying to maintain an upbeat conversation with the driver on one hand and ascertain what could be done for Janice who was trying to disappear by slouching as far down in the seat as she could.

—"Have you been driving long?" the driver ventured.

—"Well, actually not," she truthfully replied. "You see, I'm taking my friend here to the hospital and we're only coming from Northfield."

—"Oh, well fancy that! I'm from Northfield myself. They called me to get up to the Metrodome in Minneapolis to shovel off the snow from the roof because they're worried it'll cave in. Wouldn't be the first time, you know! What do you all do in Northfield?"

Janice slouched lower. She'd become a round ball and was no doubt envisioning that the next interchange would reveal that this man was the father of one of her students.

Virginia, alerted to Janice's sensitivity, began to play with the radio and answered that she taught at Carleton and that

Janice too was associated with the college. In no time some great country western music was blaring loudly so that she didn't have to risk any more conversation.

At the 98th Street exit the driver kindly offered to take them to Abbott Northwestern. But they got out at the first establishment on the right side. Appropriately it was a gas station. But no Michel!

Indeed! I was waiting for the chickens which hadn't yet been delivered.

Thoroughly chilled, Virginia thought that something hot would help pass the time until I showed up, so she inquired if coffee or hot chocolate were available.

—"Oh no, ma'am," came the reply, "but there is a Perkins just up the way."

—"Great!" exclaimed Virginia. "Say, could you tell our friend who should be along any minute now that we've just walked over to get some hot chocolate. You won't have any trouble recognizing him because he's pretty short, dark, and speaks with a French accent."

—"Well, ma'am, I'd be happy to do that, but I can't assure you of anything because I close here in an hour."

—"He'll be right along any minute now. I'd really appreciate it because my friend here is on her way to the hospital and really needs a place to just relax."

—"Well, sure, ma'am, from your description I shouldn't have much difficulty picking out your friend. But don't forget that I close in an hour or maybe a little sooner if business doesn't pick up."

Virginia gave Janice a nudge toward the door and she obediently followed. .

The snow swirled in all directions and the wind blew head on as they trudged through a foot of snow that had already fallen on the road they couldn't discern.

As they approached the Perkins restaurant, they saw the manager preparing to lock up.

—"Hold on!" shouted Virginia. "We'd like to get something to eat and drink while we wait for our friend. He'll be along any minute and will be having dinner too."

—"OK! It's not exactly an evening to shut you out! But we'll be closing soon."

The waitress brought them hot chocolate, a hamburger-to-go which they had kindly ordered for me and a telephone. Virginia called the number of the nearest AAA agent.

—"Yes, ma'am, our car is stranded on 35W going north, milepost 42...No, ma'am, we're not north of Minneapolis. We're south...No, ma'am, we're not going south, we're going north...We're just south of Minneapolis...Yes, ma'am, we're south of Minneapolis, going north on 35W...Yes, ma'am, 35W north, near the Elko-New Market exit...But we're not with the car...Well, you see, ma'am, we're not with the car. We're at the 98th Street exit. ...No, we're not at the Elko-New Market exit, the car is...Well, ma'am we couldn't call you if we stayed with the car. So we left the car to come and call for assistance...You mean if we're not with the car we can't get any help...But, ma'am, how would we get help if we stayed with the car...Ma'am, why do people buy your insurance?...Well, ma'am, couldn't you just tow the car in?...Look, I'm not trying to make a joke out of this...And that's your final answer?"

Virginia hung up the phone and burst out laughing at the absurdity of the conversation. But the seriousness of her plight soon dawned on her and she decided to risk getting another employee.

So she tried again only to be identified as the "New Yorker who had called before and couldn't decide where she was."

—"Well, isn't there someone else I can talk to?"

—"She's put me on hold, Janice, she's put me on hold and they're playing Rachmaninoff. Listen...This is absurd..."

Even Janice began to giggle.

The employee finally gave Virginia the name of three garages who could help them. Hastily made phone calls revealed that the first was no longer associated with AAA, the second had no tow truck and the third would pick up the car with no problem between 2:00 AM and 3:00 AM.

An hour passed. The restaurant personnel had all left. Only the manager remained. He called the gas station to see if I had arrived. The gas station had closed for the night. He tried every establishment that was likely to be open in the immediate vicinity. No luck!

—"I really have to get home and I can't leave you out on the street either on such a night. How about my driving you to the Denny's on the other side of the freeway? Just maybe your friend went there. You know, it's open 24 hours a day."

So they piled into the manager's pickup truck, got stuck before they got out of the parking lot, shoveled themselves free and with great difficulty made it to Denny's with the Perkins hamburger-to-go in hand.

No, I wasn't there either!

So they ordered hot tea, and Virginia spoke with the manager who gallantly ordered a taxi for them.

An hour later it still hadn't arrived. Virginia began to get nervous. Why hadn't she thought of it before. Of course, she'd call Natalie who would no doubt have all the answers to the puzzle of the whereabouts of everyone.

Natalie, levelheaded, told her that I was safely at Abbott Northwestern and awaiting their arrival.

(The chickens never did arrive that night. And after having missed the closing of the gas station, the truck driver had graciously proposed to drive me to Abbott Northwestern. I, of course, had not refused.)

—"But," cautioned Natalie,"the hospital has called several times and would like to know where you are, and poor Dr. Mellstrom is very nervous about your being out in this storm, and I've alerted the police."

As Virginia looked up she saw a taxi approaching. The cab driver stumbled in and shook himself at the entrance. A cloud of snow enveloped him, as Virginia rushed up and told him that they were ready to go.

—"No way, lady! I've had it! I'm not going back out there. With the windchill factor it's about 95 below! And you can't see three feet in front of you."

—"But I've got to get my friend here to the hospital..."

—"Look, call the police, but I'm not budging."

—"I don't understand it. If you didn't want to give us a ride, why did you come all this way?"

—"Whatja talking about, lady? I ain't come to pick you up."

The puzzle was quickly solved when the manager called the taxi service who informed him that the driver was indeed on his way, but he had slid off a ramp and had to be towed.

—"Just tell 'em to hang in there. He's on his way."

More cups of hot tea! Virginia succeeded in not only keeping Janice awake but in actually making her laugh with one funny story after another. At 1:00 AM the taxi driver arrived, flustered but courteous.

With no further delays and at the speed of ten miles per hour they pulled up, an hour later, in front of Abbott Northwestern, hamburger-to-go still in hand, but stone cold.

I was sacked out on one of the lounge sofas, but woke immediately as a nurse came to inform me of their arrival.

—"They even brought you a hamburger," she informed me.

—"Well, do you have a microwave," I countered.

—"You betcha!" she replied.

And so it was that I came to be eating a hamburger at 2:00 AM at Abbott Northwestern on the morning of January 20th.

Janice has no recollection of what happened after her arrival until about three days later, but she has often chuckled about the road that led her to the hospital that night. Indeed it was an adventure for Virginia and me as well. One that once more centered around humorous and heartwarming touches of people.

Janice did not return to teaching that year. She needed peace and quiet. I know that the extra burden that Parkinson had placed upon her was at the very core of the depression she suffered. Parkinson disease does invade and pervade every aspect of a spouse's life. Parkinson is a family disease.

8

If You Can Humor It, Go For It!

Examples

This encouragement can be applied, first and foremost, to the neural connections in the brain. As vital as the paycheck to the checkbook, as necessary as the drug to the relief of the symptom, as basic as the exercise to the well-being; so is humor essential to the mind's agility. Yes, of all the ingredients that I bring to bear in my struggle to cope I am convinced that there is none quite so important as humor. "If you can humor it, go for it."

It does not make any difference what kind of humor you indulge in, whether you wallow and revel in the coarsest forms of puns; whether you complacently dwell on nihilistic black humor, or whether you cogitate a lot and hatch the funniest witticisms. As long as you engage in this type of activity you keep your mind working, sharp, nimble. The exercise irrigates your cortical cells with fun and happy thoughts. It is a prevention against depression, a truly therapeutic agent of positive self-healing.

On this score we are all indebted to Norman Cousins' Anatomy of an Illness. Lacking subtlety in taste personally, I favor the scabrous, the unwonted, the shocking value of black humor. I claim Tom Lehrer as standard bearer and his uproarious song "National Brotherhood Week" as touch stone. The old adage "Let's laugh at it, lest we cry about it" takes on all its meaning in our case. Laughter, whatever its origin, allows us to perceive our dark world in a positive manner. Laughter is a light bulb burning in the shroud of evil. Laughter is a sunshine explosion in the darkness of night. Laughter is our last rampart and our last chance to thumb our nose at the Reaper as she prepares to knock and lead us into final oblivion. So find all possible excuses to laugh and be merry while you can, and if you do not find any by simply casting a benevolent look at your surroundings, then take a candid look inward. And you cannot help but laugh at the monstrosities of human nature.

But we need not reach or go so far. The Parkinsonian condition is blatant enough. For instance, before it lost its novelty for me, I used to end my fund-raising speeches on the Road to Dignity Walk by the exhortation: "Get off your derrières and shake a leg." Milking the tremor infirmity further, a natural complement offered itself: "Thou shalt not judge a man by his hand shake." My friend Ken Mills from Tucson also used to illustrate his condition ruefully.

—"Having Parkinson," he would say, "is like having *rigor mortis* set in without the benefit of dying." A prime Catch 22 situation since we know that "old Parkinsonians never die, never die, they just shake away!" While indulging in the vein of parody, I used to finish my unity theme speeches with a take off on Karl Marx: "Parkinsonians of the world, unite! You have nothing to lose, but your shakes."

Similarly, Morris Udall, Parkinsonian Arizona Congressman, and one-time presidential candidate, has howlingly humorous stories to tell of his experiences with Parkinson. Ralph Edwards (of TV's This is Your Life, Truth or Consequences and People's Court fame) and his lovely wife Barbara also bank on off-black humor to keep their sanity and cope gracefully with Barbara's Parkinsonism. Ralph loves to tell his audiences how one never quite understands Parkinson disease, until one has had to help sack his wife into her pantyhose.

What about my dear old friend Milton Krims, director of Confessions of a Nazi Spy and many other films? From the bleakest confines of the dingy locked room of the Los Angeles Veterans Administration hospital were I saw him, Milton was waxing sardonic on his condition and on doctors' ignorance. He was busy at work, in his dwindling productive moments, on a play by and for Parkinsonians, a tragi-comedy filled with verve and black humor in which the hero, through a series of quid pro quos, ends up killing his doctor. The way he kept laughing sustained him and made him an inspired inspiration for all of us.

Still in the world of the Arts, talent agent Joyce Aimée delights in describing the scene when, coming home late one night with Parkinsonian husband Bill, they went into an un-rehearsed dyskinetic love dance, trying to find the light switch, but tripping the alarm system instead, and finally falling into the pool, all under the eyes of their watchful and incredulous French poodle.

Stool Pigeon

In retrospect, some of the funniest experiences come from the silliest situations which seemed really hopeless at the time they took place. In the summer of 1984, we decided to visit our son Patrick who was fishing in Alaska. We drove to Seattle, parked the car and boarded the ferry for the three-day voyage.

I was wearing new jeans for the trip, and had not realized how tight they were until some time into the second day when I abruptly had to use the toilet. In my rush to undress one of my legs—for a Parkinsonian's increased comfort on the stool—I pulled down my right pant leg over my shoe, the way one skins a rabbit. But I was wearing new sneakers which sported a sharp-edged heel made of a thick layer of the most gripping material. The shoe got caught in my pant leg.

Thinking I could clear the obstacle by pulling a little harder, I tugged at the stubborn jeans some more. It moved another inch and squeezed the heel that much more tightly into the inside-out pant leg. I tried again. This time, it wouldn't budge. "OK! Remember Parkinson rule number one: One step at a time; break down your movements; analyze carefully each new motion; fire only one command at a time. Think, then concentrate, then move." But the only progress I made was to jam the shoe a little tighter into the pant leg. "No use. Why not take care of nature's call which brought you here in the first place? Maybe by then some more dopamine will have found its way to your brain."

Five minutes later, not a fraction of an inch gained. "All right, there's another tack. Why don't you stand up, redress, pull your pant leg up and then disengage the shoe by grabbing at the hem and pulling straight out?" Easier said than done. The shoe was stuck. There was not even enough room for me to slip my fingers in and grab. The stall next to mine had already changed tenants three times, and by now some impatient would-be user was banging at my door. In retrospect, a funny quote cited by Peter Stern in his Parkinson's Challenge came back to my mind: "If they try and rush me, I always say, 'I've only got two speeds, and the other one is slower.'"

I told myself "don't panic." But exacerbated by the physical effort I had just furnished, a violent wave of shaking overtook me. I stood up from the stool to examine the situation. And here I was with a pair of jeans that I couldn't slip up past my buttocks because my foot and shoe were stuck at the bottom of the pant leg. A good 20 minutes had elapsed by now. Janice, I thought, would surely start looking for me. I sat down again and reread the scribbled walls for the third time. One piece of graffiti in particular caught my pun-seeking eye with its crispness and its hardly irreverent tone: "Ronald Reagan," it said, "has presidential aids." I chuckled for the third time. Thank God for small favors. But what am I going to do? I certainly will not face a bunch of strangers on deck with my pants all askew, zipper wide open and stepping on my recalcitrant cuff. Where was Janice? I was learning my lessons. Fast.

- Always remove shoe before attempting to remove pants.
- Always warn traveling companion of your whereabouts, so help can be swiftly dispatched.

- Keep searching for excuses to laugh, from conjuring up happy memories all the way to picturing yourself in that ridiculous position you have reached and looking back as a spectator!
- Do not panic. Straighten up and take deep breaths.
- Tell yourself that people stop looking after the initial surprise is gone.

My impatient caller had given up and left. And in the next stall over, I could hear preparations for an imminent exit. Good, I was going to be alone in the room. Water splashed into the sink followed by the high pitched purr of the electric hand dryer. I would now be able to think unhurriedly and collect my wits without the paralyzing thought that somebody out there was prying into my predicament. After all, I had been in that bathroom stall for almost half an hour. But what was Janice up to...lightening struck. Eureka. In a flash I had the answer. It was going to be a bit drastic, but the solution was at hand. Attached to the end of a small chain tucked away in oblivion in the deep of my handbag, was my faithful but underworked pocket knife, a gift from my 1978 Pau program group. Why didn't I think of it before? Except for details, my problem was now solved. I had thought at first that I would deploy the very sharp little scissors on the knife and rip the pants at the bottom of the right leg, but then realized that it would be much more elegant and less wasteful to simply rip the seam. Still, not all that easy. But after another ten to 15 minutes of cutting and tugging in back wrecking positions, I finally met with victory, having accomplished the as yet unclaimed first in the Guinness Book of World Records, namely, that of a pregnant pant leg delivered of a shoe by Caesarian section!

I found Janice two decks up, seated at a booth table, playing Trivial Pursuit with two just-met fellow passengers. "Eh, Michel!" her face lit up, "Come and play this game. But where have you been?"

—"Oh, just here and there" I mused, "doing my own trivial pursuits...."

Yes, it seems to me that a sense of humor is essential; a certain smile of the mind whose by-product is *joie de vivre.*[1] And we have so much to live for! Sure, we are slowed down; sure, we look funny; sure we all have our moments of abandon, of self-pity. And that is normal. What is abnormal is to be beaten by despair; we must be vigilant never to lose our activities, be they physical or mental.

---

1   Zest for life.

Cachet Frères

Michel's hometown, Digoin, France, 1960.

Monette (Michel's cousin and childhood companion), Michel's parents and Michel (age 11) on vacation in Cannes, France, 1951.

Cachet Frères

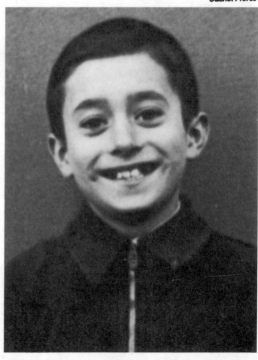

Michel as a 10 year-old French schoolboy, 1950.

Michel and Janice
on their wedding
day, June 3, 1961,
Staples, Minnesota.

Janice and Michel
on their honey-
moon in Uxeau,
France, 1961.

Janice, 1963.

Michel on a rooftop in Pau, France, 1973.

Monnot family at home in Northfield, Minnesota in 1976 (left to right) Michel, Patrick, Gigi, Janice and Natalie.

Daughter Gigi, 1984.

Son Patrick, 1987.

Daughter Natalie, 1986.

Grandson Eric, 1987.

Michel with Dr. Abraham Lieberman in Minneapolis, September 14, 1985, the day before Michel started off on his Road to Dignity Walk.

Along the Road to Dignity Walk, Michel and Jack Perry walking in Iowa, September 1985.

Russ Ahlstrom and Michel entering Mankato, Minnesota on the fourth day of the Road to Dignity Walk, September 18, 1985.

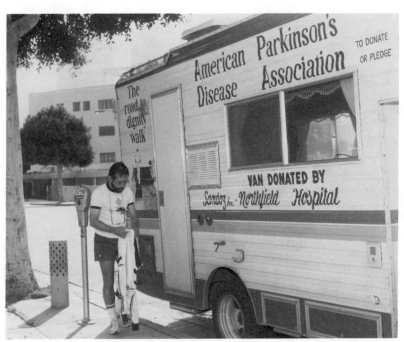

Getting ready to walk.

Michel chatting with U.S. Congressman Morris Udall along the Road to Dignity Walk in Tucson, Arizona, January 1986.

*Near the end of the walk, Michel flanked by Road to Dignity
Walk supporters Ellen Moscinski and Mary Mowry in San
Diego, January 1986.*

Los Angeles reception at the end of the Road to Dignity Walk, February 1986. Left to right: Olympic gymnastics champion Tim Daggett , unidentified supporter, TV personality Barbara Valentine, Olympic decathelon champion Rafer Johnson (in back), Shirley Krims, Michel Monnot, Frank Williams (National Director, APDA), unidentified supporter, Marguerite Sandor (driver of the van that accompanied Michel along the walk), unidentified supporter.

At the end of the Road to Dignity Walk (left to right) Dr. Leo Treciokas, Michel Monnot, Janice Monnot, Richard Simmons, Barbara Edwards, Ralph Edwards in Los Angeles, February 1986.

MELODY SAUNDERS

Frank Williams (National Director, APDA) presenting certificates to Sara Cox and Partick Monnot (Michel's advance team along the Road to Dignity Walk) in Los Angeles, February 1986, at the end of the five month walk.

THE APDA • MICHEL MONNOT

WALK-A-THON

FOR PARKINSON'S DISEASE RESEARCH

SAT., APRIL 16th • REID PARK • 10am-2pm

Info. and Referral: 626-4019 • Walkathon Info. 886-9095

Posters Compliments of: S Sandoz Pharmaceuticals Corporation

Johnny Kamenchuk

Billboard in Tucson, Arizona, 1987, advertising what has become an annual event in many cities throughout the U.S.

Part Three

The Road To Dignity Walk

*The only way I can enter
the social structure is
as a vagabond.*

— J. Joyce

9

In The Beginning Was...The Road

Pre-Ordained Mystic

In the beginning was...the Road. Thus the scholar Joseph Bédier, by this scriptural parody, summarizes and explains the birth of French literature. The road he talks about is the medieval freeway of Europe that pilgrims follow on foot and in horse-drawn carts from the northernmost outposts of western civilization to Santiago de Compostella, in the most remote corner of Galician Spain. They come from Ireland and Scotland, from Saxony, Bavaria and Frisia, Burgundy and Prussia, stumbling along the way, determined in their quest for St. James' intercession in their domestic and personal affairs. They have left family and friends and all worldly possessions to embark on a journey of faith from which the greater part never return. They are not the crusaders, they are St. James' pilgrims.

The crusaders have a nobler cause: they go to the Holy Land to deliver the tomb of Christ from the hands of the infidels, they are warriors, noblemen in search of exotic—not to say quixotic—adventure. But in my young student mind their quest was foreign to me. I could not relate to their plight and tribulations as they crossed lands which did not really belong to my world. Surely Palestine, Transylvania, Tunisia, and Turkey had a certain evocative power over my 11 year-old budding imagination. But I could not warm up to them. How much more at ease was I with the epic tales of Charlemagne and his faithful companions, of Roland and his sword Durandal which were being sung nightly to my pilgrims, my poor ancestors. What happened on the road; why was I so enthralled by their strange Odyssey; how did I ever become "condemned to the road" myself?

First of all, there was a definite romantic element that accompanied the pilgrims. Clad in the simplest of garb, shoeless, girded with St. James' belt of symbolic shells, they trudge mile after mile under all climatic inclemencies. No blacktop roads for them, but muddy paths strewn with rocks, no waterproof Goretex coats on their backs, but rain-soaked pelts and frocks. The luckiest are riding on horseback, most walk all the way, some go on their knees for a while, and all pray fervently, namelessly.

For myself, finding no encouragement at home and very little from the aging parish priest, I soon developed a religious vacuum. The absence of encouragement followed by a subsequent craving for mysticism opened into a huge void, a kind of emotional black hole which needed to be fed, to be filled, imperatively. I don't know if my parents have ever understood this need or whether they think I have succumbed or sunk to irretrievable levels of softheadedness. Whatever may be the case is irrelevant here, but I must say that I was lucky enough to meet, early in my probing career, the woman who put it all in perspective for me, my mysterious, my mystical, my beloved, my intensely Catholic Janice. From my parents I learned determination and the prowess of willpower; from Janice I learned the power of faith. The first is of this world, the second a window on the world to come. One is human, the other divine.

So my poor parents who wanted to make a freethinker out of me were quite surprised to discover that I was engrossed in the study of the birth of French literature, and that this study was inexorably leading me to the baptism and confirmation I was to receive in my 20th year.

The road! The road! Why did I get addicted to the road? Why did I always picture myself on the way to Santiago to light a candle? A romantic notion? An antidote to our modern day rationalism? A covert rebellion against my parents? Was it a premonition of things to come in my life and health? Or a means to an end? As my readings and studies continued to head me toward the road, I realized that from the beginning in the history of Western civilization, the road, symbol of adventure, was the leading thread, the emancipating factor in the social evolution of modern man. Prehistoric men's endeavors were turned toward their integration into the tribe, the gregarious instinct and hunger pains combining to their daily congregating. On the contrary, it is the appanage of modern man to seek a way out of the nest—even if it is to come back, prodigal sons that we all are, head bowed and repentant—in order to explore our surroundings. Yesterday, Columbus and Magellan and the New World; today Armstrong, the moon and the stars, whether it is a conscious act as in Columbus's case or a fatalistic act as in Ulysses' case, or a combination of both in Don Quixote's case. The road is the answer to questions, or at least a window allowing us to ask questions. The road is the stretching exercise which removes the cramps contracted in the confinement of the nest. The road is azure, the road is freedom, the road is wanderlust satisfied, the road is the dream, the dreamer and the dreamed combined.

The only difference that seems to reside between the pilgrims' road and mine is the fact that theirs was host to a religious quest with the Heavenly Jerusalem as backdrop, while mine is host to a medical quest with a much more immediate gratification, we pray. However, in both cases their seekers show and share an attitude of fulfillment and humility, an unmistakable fragrance of faith which pervades all participants, the shedding of a soft light—an amber glow reflected on people and nature, in the deep vesperal blue of the sky, a winsome amber glow which proclaims we are all human, sinners and cripples alike, bent on leaving this earth like our pilgrims with faith in the strength of our silent anonymity.

The story of the Road to Dignity, therefore, is not just the description of a walk from Minneapolis to Los Angeles, but rather the uncovering, the unraveling of an attitude which I was bent on transmitting. The message I preached was twofold: the first was a message of hope and faith directed at the afflicted, a message that said that research was advancing at a demential pace, that finding a cure for Parkinson was a race against the clock, but I also warned that that hope had to be mitigated by faith. Faith that time was working with us, that researchers were working for us, faith that the combined courage of all the afflicted would propel all of us a giant step forward on the road to dignity. But for that—*a la* Jim Bakker—I pleaded also the third cardinal virtue: charity, and addressed it primarily to non-Parkinsonians. Yes, we need money, lots of money to sponsor and support research.

I believe we succeeded in getting both our messages across as the RV became a traveling focus point, closely monitored by Frank Williams and eagerly expected in most communities we visited.

Why we took to the road—be it for private or obvious reasons—is fairly simple to ascertain. Suffice it to say: "I will walk." But getting to the road and taking that first step was another Odyssey in itself.

The Preparation

—"Allô! APDA?... My name is Michel Monnot, I am a French prof at Carleton College in Minnesota, and I have Parkinson."

—"Who do you want to talk to?" The Brooklyn accent is unmistakable; the friendliness of tone, on the other hand, genuine Newyorkese: snarly.

—"I don't know! I don't care! Just let me speak to someone I can tell about my project."

—"What's your project about?"

—"I want to walk across America for Parkinson."

—"Juuust a min...you want to what?"

—"Yes, I want to walk across America for Parkinson. Is there anyone in the office I can talk to? I'm calling long distance."

—"OK! Just a minute please." I sense the snarl has degenerated into a patronizing smile with eyes turned up to the ceiling, asking, good Lord another nut, what is this guy up to? Walking across America, what will it be next? And he is calling from somewhere west like Montana, and he has this weird foreign accent. Says he teaches German or some foreign language.

—"Hello. This is Paul Moontab, can I help you?" I repeat my spiel: my name is...etc. There's a strange silence.

—"Allô, can you hear me?"

—"Yes, yes, I am taking some notes."

—"Notes? What on earth for? Can't we just talk about my project for now? I'll write a more formal letter later." What are those guys doing anyway? Here I am, full of enthusiasm, proposing to help them help people who have Parkinson, donating my time to the cause and all I hear at the other end is a fearful bureaucrat countering me at every turn with "yes-but-have-you-thought-abouts."

—"Have you thought about the danger involved? Have you thought about your health? What about your family? Have you discussed the project with them? Have you thought about insurance, have you thought about expenses? And have you considered walking with another person?" I was fed up. I hadn't been talked down to like that for a long time.

—"And you," I lashed, "have you ever thought of ever having Parkinson yourself? Have you ever thought that there are other groups I can propose my services to? And if they're all like this outfit, pity the poor people who need help. I'll walk alone, if need be. I'll be my own sponsor. Without financial resources, maybe, but free." How I wish that I knew at that time the little motto: "let the experts be on tap, not on top."

—"I'm sorry you feel that way, but we must protect ourselves, I am sure you understand. I'll tell you what. Why

don't you write up a proposal to the board, for discussion. But
I can't promise you anything."

—"When is the next board meeting?"

—"The last Wednesday of each month. Let's see, our next
meeting is three weeks from tomorrow."

I sent in my proposal a few days later. I was aware that
this was the beginning of a huge operation, and that if I were
to leave within a reasonable amount of time—by, say, February 15th—I could not dilly-dally waiting around for month-
long answers. And I figured, "Who needs a sponsor anyway?"

Well, I was inexperienced.... For it became rapidly evident
that if my purpose, or one of my purposes, for this walk was
to raise money, that I soon needed some seed money.
However, as an individual, one cannot collect tax-exempt
contributions. How could I resolve the impasse? That's when
I had a lucky strike. On a fluke I went to see Maxine Lamm,
head nurse at the hospital in Northfield. She was involved, I
had heard, with the local Parkinson group. Would she have
any idea? Indeed, she did.

—"Come back this afternoon at 3:00. I'll call a meeting
with Cliff Christiansen, the Head Administrator, and with
Cynnie Buchwald, the Public Relations Officer. You explain
your project and your problem to them. Say, by the way, Michael, it is Michael, right?"

—"By the way, how come we've never seen you at our
monthly support group meetings? We could use some new
blood, you know...."

—"Tell me when the next meeting is, send me a reminder,
and I'll be there."

—"Great! Then you can tell us about your walk project.
They're going to love that. Well, see you at 3:00."

Maxine, Cynnie and Cliff listened attentively—my voice
was not too shaky and I ran out of breath only two times
during my speech. I showed them my APDA proposal and by
the manner in which they were all nodding their heads, I
knew that I had cleared my first major hurdle.

Cliff asked THE question, "Well, Michel, how much do you think you need as seed money to start your program? I think—and I am sure Maxine and Cynnie feel the same way, right—that this would be an ideal endeavor for us to support."

—"I'm delighted you feel that way, because I was starting to despair—don't you think it's dumb of the APDA not to jump on the occasion? Anyway, I've made a rough calculation and I would be comfortable, I feel I really could start working, with $1,500."

—"Oh! I think we can go with that, don't you? Maxine?"

—"Sure."

—"Cynnie?"

—"Sure."

—"Oh! I think it's absolutely marvelous and would make great publicity for the hospital, don't you? I can already see the motor home Michel suggests, following him across country and on it, it says in big letters: 'All this started at the Northfield Hospital.'" Cliff got up.

—"I've got to run now, but let's meet again in four or five days to work up more details and get moving. Michel, see you then. It was a pleasure."

—"Thanks for everything. You made my day!"

The APDA board meeting was going to be in a week. In the meantime, according to plan, I selected my local committee:

- Cynnie Buchwald, Cliff Christiansen and Maxine Lamm from the hospital, with Cynnie as Treasurer
- Jeff Reichel, Director of Major Gifts and Planned Giving at Carleton College, as Chairman
- Dori Tuomi, Carleton College Modern Languages Department Secretary, as Secretary
- My doctor, David Halvorson, as Medical Advisor
- Curt Swenson, businessman and trusted friend
- Jim Larson, architect and friend whose judgment I respect
- William Goldstein, Carleton College student whose grandmother has Parkinson disease.

It struck me funny that, so far, in all the conversations I had had regarding the march, no one had asked me whether I had ever walked 15 miles in one day, let alone for four days in a row as I was suggesting to do in my original proposal. I even surprised myself when that question popped into my mind. I had no doubt that I could, but just in case…. So, one Thursday morning in October, since we did not have classes that day, I gently woke Janice, whispering in her ear, "Love, I am going to test how far and how fast I can walk." Approving grunt from Janice. "I'll be walking on the road to Cannon Falls. Why don't you come and pick me up around 10:00?"

—"OK."

—"Don't forget." Negative grunt.

—"Bye! Sleep well! It's only 6:00."

I left at 6:30 AM with a couple of granola bars in my pocket, met a few joggers on the way, and proceeded to enjoy each step. It is such a rare treat to witness the rising of the sun, and most of all on a glorious Minnesota Indian summer morning.

I walk well, my arms loose, shoulders back, excellent morale. It's one of those "good" days that Parkinsonians both love and fear. We love them because they are our link to the "good old days" when you didn't have to think and study how you were going to grab the spoon for the breakfast cereal before actually grabbing it; days when you could comb your hair, smoothly sliding the comb all the way to the nape of the neck; days when you could dip into the bowl for a full handful of popcorn, instead of coming back to the rim with two kernels gingerly held between the tip of the index and the middle fingers, and between the tip of the middle finger and the pinky. On the other hand, we fear those days because of the nostalgia they create and because we know that tomorrow will be devastatingly different.

All of a sudden, however, my left leg started to stiffen. It was not the first time it happened and I have learned to best treat it by ignoring it and walking on it. It disappears within a few minutes. Is it another sign of Parkinson? Will it spread?

And how fast? For the moment I choose to disregard it. It's time for my pills, washing them down with half a bar of granola.

Walking is such a luxury. It offers time to think and time to feel, time to imagine and time to dream. In my shoulder bag I packed a little tape recorder for the long moments of uninterrupted thought. Picturing myself already on the proposed walk, I recorded a list of articles I'd have to take with me:

- tape recorder
- recorder (musical)
- granola bars
- whistle (against possible stray dogs)
- a set of weights for arm exercises
- and definitely my soccer ball
- a radio-phone would be a good idea, too and let's not forget to take songs along, vibrant marching songs that Father used to teach us and oh, yes, a French poetry anthology. That'll be ideal to rememorize my favorites and maybe learn a few new ones.

A few miles later, it had become very hot and I was not unhappy to see Janice coming on the horizon. A fast calculation showed that I had covered 11 miles in three hours and seven minutes for a walking speed of 17 minutes to the mile. Just under four miles an hour. And I was not tired! I could well have walked for another hour to reach my 15 mile goal.

The first meeting of our committee was a brainstorming session. While almost everyone espoused the general outlines of my proposal, they did not want to undertake any action before hearing from the APDA board meeting.

And they made one thing clear to me, unanimously, "Michel, you're not going to leave on February 15th. In the first place, you would freeze to death, and we want no part of that; secondly, it's going to take a while, several months at least, to organize this whole operation. So, sit tight, your project is in good hands."

I should have known! Even my hand-picked committee already smacked of paternalism.

The third Wednesday of the month came. I sat all day in front of that persistently dumb phone. All day and all evening. Not one ring. What could have happened? "I'll bet the proposal was turned down and Paul doesn't feel like giving me the bad news."

By 10:00 Thursday morning, I was fit to be tied. I called the APDA, my emotions playing havoc with my voice and speech.

—"Sorry; Paul Moontag is no longer with us, but Frank Williams would like to speak to you."

—"Yeah, Dr. Monnot," the tone was jovial, the accent still hard-core Brooklynese. "I've quickly glanced at your proposal, and I think there are some good things in there. But before I present it to the board...."

—"You mean the board did not discuss it yesterday? It was the third Wed...."

—"No, no, the meeting was cancelled. What I would like to know, though, is how you're going to fund such an ambitious venture."

I told him about the Northfield hospital pledge and commitment; the proposed plan to contact all the Carleton alumni/ae who had been my students (over 1,000); plans for a dance; for a raffle. There was an attentive silence at the other end. (Was he taking notes, too?) There were plans to contact all the hospital administrators; all the high school principals and all the newspaper editors along the proposed route; not to mention all the support groups presidents.

—"By the way, we will need the APDA roster of chapter presidents and also...."

—"Listen, listen to me, Professor. When are you people meeting next?"

—"We were waiting to hear the decision of the APDA board to schedule the next official meeting, but we have established that, during the beginning phase anyway, we would meet every other Tuesday afternoon."

—"OK, look Professor, get your people together for a 2:00 meeting next Tuesday. I'll take a late morning flight, rent a car to drive to Northfield, meet with you for a couple of hours and take a late afternoon flight back home. We may be able to work something out. Where do we meet?"

—"It will be at the hospital unless you hear differently."

Great Scott, we had his ear and maybe more. It was getting serious and Janice was afraid I had embroiled myself in another one of my harebrained schemes.

—"And when will you leave?" she asked defiantly. "Remember, you're going on disability at the end of this trimester. But I still need you around here to help me. So don't think you're going to fold up shop and go do your thing."

Ahh! There was the rub. But it soon became clear that there was no way I could set out on the road before the end of summer. Frank, who had made a good impression on the committee, confirmed that the APDA would step in after we showed a substantial commitment.

—"You raise $10,000 locally by May 1st, and we go national, full blast behind you."

Apparently, I had passed the test. Frank had carefully looked me over as cattle farmers judge a head of Charolais. I guess I was credible enough, my argument cogent and convincing enough to embark on the big time adventure of preaching and fund raising. I made a special point to emphasize that the walk should be dignified all right, but that it should focus on joy and hope rather than on sadness and mope. A traveling Ninth Symphony Hymn to Joy on wheels.

Winter term was busy. A constant stream of volunteer students ebbed and flowed through the office, typing, photocopying, making telephone calls, addressing and stuffing envelopes. A letter was sent to thousands of people. A dance was organized, raffle tickets for a week for two in Hawaii were sold. By May 1st, we had over $7,000. It was not the $10,000 Frank had set as our goal, but it was proof enough that we were "for real" and that I could be counted on as a somewhat nutty but reliable character.

And so the APDA took us under its giant wing. Frank was going to firm up the tentative itinerary I had initially outlined; he was going to take care of production and distribution of press kits to all the radio and TV stations and newspapers along the route (see Appendix A). The task at hand was so awesome I became jittery.

—"Michel," said Frank, "You are in good hands. Go to France for the summer, like you had planned, and don't worry about a thing. Just go on training."

I WAS being swallowed up all right, but as long as they let me walk, as long as they let me carry on with my self-assigned business which was spreading the word about Parkinson; soliciting funds for research; and mixing with my fellow Parkinsonians—giving courage to and taking courage from them—as long as I could do that, my ego could take any blow, and the experts could stay on tap AND on top all they wanted. I felt more useful than I had for a long time. If somebody, Frank or anyone else, had the desire, the know-how, the manpower, and the means to provide a better itinerary and wider publicity toward the goal that I had designated, then more power to that person. I was willing to sacrifice that much usurpation of "my" domain for some greater good. So Frank thought it would be better for the cause that I spend a carefree summer in France so that I would be in top shape come the date of departure. I had to have faith; I had to trust Frank. I did, and I was never sorry.

* * * * *

—"Janice, my love, I've been pondering for a while now who would be a good person to accompany me during the walk."

—"You know Patrick would love to do it, don't you?"

—"Yes, I know, but I'm not sure it's the best idea."

The thought of a possible father-son authority struggle frightened me. "Besides, I'm going to dictate lots of things while I walk, and a good part of it is going to be in French. I need someone who can spell French. And what about his own studies?"

I knew that Patrick was eager to come, and I wanted him along, too, but in a different capacity. When I reflected on his strengths, I realized that Patrick would be the perfect advance man. I tried to imagine a typical scene, a realistic scenario of how it would be when I entered a town. In most cases, the local Parkinsonian support group would have arranged for a reception, but who was going to tell me the name of the person who was in charge, where to go at what time, or which room of which building, what to look for, what to expect? While walking on the road, I certainly would not have time to coordinate all that ahead of time. To obtain the maximum exposure in each town or city, we needed someone to refresh the news media's memory (they had received a press kit during the summer) about the man walking across the country for Parkinson. He would be coming through town in a couple of days and the media should be prepared to cover the event. Would the mayor, also, want to welcome the walker with a little reception on the steps of city hall? Giving him the keys to the city WOULD be a nice gesture. And would the chief of police protect this man's safety by giving him a police escort from the city limits to downtown?

That was indeed a whole program that no one had thought of before. Creating that position for Patrick turned out to be one of the most significant factors in the success of the Road to Dignity Walk.

Who else, then, would we ask to drive the van? We agreed that Marguerite, a young French woman who had served as French House Director at Carleton, was a great choice. She wasn't keen on returning to France yet, but she didn't have any job prospects either. And besides, she was lovely, lively, bright and very efficient. Happily, she accepted.

Throughout the summer, Mary Strandness, a self-appointed scout for an adequate accompanying RV had scouted high and low for that rare bird. Thanks to donations from the Northfield Hospital and Sandoz Inc., I took possession of a van on August 15th. In four weeks, we would be on the road. There was no time to waste.

Way to Go, Monnot! _____

On the morning of September 15, 1985, with Janice's public benediction, I set out on my 3,801,600-step journey—the Road to Dignity Walk, with balloons and fanfare, speeches and champagne, old friends and new friends, all of them well-wishers, with TV cameras, mayors, majorettes, and congressmen, and finally, proudly closing the procession, the RV, freshly painted with slogans and toll-free phone numbers, slowly moving like a pachyderm, with Marguerite beaming at the wheel.

She was triumphant, and with good reason: the day was glorious. In St. Louis Park, a suburb of Minneapolis, the Methodist Hospital had gone all out to publicize the event and the Minnesota Chapter of the APDA had provided the manpower for the realization of my project. Hundreds of celebrities had been invited. Not all had responded, of course, but we were greeted by the U.S. 1st District Representative Bill Frenzel, several Minnesota State legislators and the mayor of St. Louis Park; there was also Janice's sister, Elly, with all her clan: Terry and family, Becky, Tom, Barb and family, and Bob, plus a wide assortment of friends from Brooklyn Center; there were my dear, devoted friends and colleagues from St. Catherine's College, Sister Marie Philip and Sister Mary Henry taking pictures that they would send to my parents; Milan and Vera Kovacovic, our old friends from the University of Minnesota, Duluth (UMD); our new colleague Joe Krause whom we lured to Carleton College from UMD; friends from Northfield; people from local support groups; some of whom I had never met who introduced themselves to wish me well.

All had come to encourage me and lend moral support. I was particularly pleased by the presence of Ron Sellnow, an old friend from Staples, Minnesota who had been my accomplice and message transmitter when I was courting Janice 28 years ago. And standing in for themselves and *in loco parentis*, as they had so generously done 29 years ago, were my American parents, Dr. Vernon and Linda Shuckhart. It was in their home in Park Rapids, Minnesota that I learned to become an American; my debt to them is eternal. I have tried to reduce it throughout the years in various small ways: I tried by dedicating my first book, the product of much loving attention, to Vernon and his sense of humor, but the debt can never be totally repaid.

Under the huge canopy tent that has been pitched to shelter the snackers from an eventual shower, a warm feeling of camaraderie is taking root between the well-wishers and the walkers, those who are staying and those who are going, and for the first time I feel that there is something tangible to this crazy idea: that the gestation period is over; that a living entity has been born which is going to require all my attention and vigilance. And euphoria overtakes me.

While a huge APDA banner is being mounted on the van, dozens of candy stripers are filling a thousand yellow balloons with helium. In the background the St. Louis Park High School band is rehearsing; loud thumps of the tuba prepare to accompany the waddling steps of a carefree crowd. In front of the upright microphone people are starting to fill the benches. More people are coming from all sides and it becomes difficult to speak to anyone as more and more newcomers offer their hands as their hearts' extension. But, parallel to the swelling feeling of elation, another sensation is starting to take hold.

It started gnawing at me yesterday when I was unexpectedly presented with a beautiful scrapbook at the APDA Symposium. All of a sudden I had to face a room full of people to say "thank you." That was not too demanding and besides, since it came as a total surprise, I had no time to worry about it. Today, however, I've had time to think about preparing the little speech I will have to give and the jitters are slowly starting. Marguerite, already in full command of her functions and duties, has picked up my vacillation on her most sensitive antennae.

—"Michel, isn't it time for your pill?"

This question she will ask hundreds, thousands, of times during the trip, reaching an incredible degree of accuracy based not on reading her watch but on her keen perception of my changing mood and behavior. And this morning on this first occasion she is already right. It is time indeed to replenish my dopamine-starved *locus niger*.

—"Would you like some water or some pop? I'll get you some at the stand. And maybe you should get ready and look again at your speech."

She knows that emotions are my affliction's worst enemy and that my shaking will be increased if I do not try to relax. But how can I relax?

Mary Strandness, our RV scout, emerges from the crowd. "Oh, Michel. I am so pleased you found the van to your liking. It is probably the best we can ever expect to find this year. And what makes it so attractive a buy is the very low mileage. At 11,000 it's a real steal. Believe me, in the last two months I've seen quite a few RVs and I know you'll love this one."

And she had done a great job. She started looking in mid-May after hearing my plea at a support group meeting in St. Paul, and throughout the summer, while caring for a stricken husband, she kept me posted on her finds and tribulations. Mary is a fighter, a tough-minded Irish teacher of Latin who doesn't take "no" for an answer. The van became such a vital part of the walk that I often wondered what inadequate substitute we would have had to contend with if Mary had not steadfastly looked, shopped and bargained and finally come up with this almost brand new vehicle named FLAIR. As other well-wishers are pushing their way toward me, Mary understands that another time would be more appropriate to talk about the van. I hug her good-bye just long enough for this loving and lovely friend to reach in her bag and pull out an assortment of little gifts, products of the most thoughtful attention.

—"Thank you, thank you so much. And you must know in return, dear Mary, that a day never goes by without my thinking of you and saying, 'thank you,' even if it is silently." Releasing my squeeze in too obvious a hurry, I turn around abruptly and awkwardly:

—"Well, Dr. Zwiebel, I'm so glad you could come. This party wouldn't have been complete without you. After all, this march would never have seen the light of day without your professional approval." Dr. Zwiebel is my neurologist at the PD clinic at Methodist Hospital.

—"No, no," he replies with his usual modesty. "I had nothing to do with it. The credit is all yours. Say, Michel, I would like you to meet Dr. Silverstein, director of our clinic, and here are my wife and children. They wouldn't have missed seeing you off for the world." A quick handshake, a wink to the neat-looking kids with a remark coming from the heart.

—"You kids can be very proud of your dad."

The milling about, the laughter, the warm gusts of an Indian summer breeze, the hustling and bustling activities everywhere on the expanding lawn, the omnipresent yellow balloons yearning to be unleashed, the acrobatics of the pompom girls moving to the marching band staccato, everything suddenly comes to a halt when the loudspeaker shatters the ambient cacophony, "Testing, one, two, three...testing...testing," bringing everyone's attention back to center stage.

Frank Williams is there at the podium dominating the scene, seemingly at ease in front of that crowd which I am soon going to have to face myself. How I envy him. I haven't had to speak publicly since last November when I taught my last class at Carleton College before going on disability. I am scared silly that I won't be able to say more than three sentences without stammering or shaking uncontrollably. To say nothing of the embarrassing silence that will follow, when, in total despair, I will have to signal to Janice to come to the podium and finish my remarks.

Frank is a consummate master of ceremonies and a master fund raiser as he diplomatically plugs for the APDA. He thus introduces several people who each speak in turn, each one waxing more eloquent than the other, extolling the worth and virtues of the walk. When my turn comes, I have had enough time to jot down the headings of the very brief remarks I intend to make, and I have been put in such positive light by my predecessors at the mike that I am somewhat calmed down. It may be the pills, too. Besides, Janice is on the alert should I stumble and freeze and Marguerite has brought me a glass of water. I now feel more confident to address the crowd. I step up to the podium. The very short speech soon becomes only a pleasant memory. Then the event receives the blessings of the hospital chaplain, the last speaker. He gives a quick *urbi et orbi*[1] benediction for which I am thankful.

There is an awkward moment of silence during which Frank winds his way back from the band to the podium. He grabs the mike and shouts, "...This is it, let it mark the official beginning of the Road to Dignity Walk. Let's give Michel a gigantic kickoff. On the count of three I want everyone to repeat after me, 'Way to go, Monnot!' Attention, one..." loud drum beat "...two" ...drum beat and tuba thump..."three, Way to Go, Monnot!" and at that point a thousand yellow balloons released on cue vie for first place in their race toward a tempest of blue sky.

The walk is off and...running. The Road to Dignity is now unfolding before me, created anew at each step, groping for its identity, forged out of its own uniqueness. In spite of the noise, in spite of the general state of elation and mutual congratulation, I cannot help but wonder to what destiny this child is bound. I am ready to wager that not one person in the

---

1   The traditional papal blessing, "To the town and to the world."

crowd isn't asking himself the same questions: what will become of this enthusiasm, of all this hype? Can the pace be sustained? Can this little guy deliver what he so glibly said he could do? Will he raise enough money to make a difference, or is he just going on a lark after having conned all his entourage and benefactors? When looked squarely in the eye, the task at hand is awesome, but deep inside of me the same drive for success, the same realism and solidity, the same arrogant spunk that have guided me throughout life are churning in high gear. I simply know that we are going to make it, that the dread disease is only an unfortunate accident shared by many; and that come the end of the march, we will be ever so much closer to a cure or at least to a significant easing of the burden.

As the crowd slowly empties the hospital grounds and spills onto Excelsior Boulevard to accompany me on a symbolic first mile, my last thought goes to those who haven't been able to make it to so joyous an occasion: my parents and relatives back in Burgundy, Mary Strandness' husband whose Parkinson is too advanced to join us, my daughters Natalie and Gigi who had to work, Patrick and friend Sara who had to forge ahead to Faribault and points beyond in order to rev up the media's idling engines and questionable memory. I think of all the afflicted who have wished me luck while excusing themselves for not being able to take part in that first mile, all those teary-eyed elderly gentlemen who covered me with their trust and confidence that my quest might bring them back a cure. I catch myself drifting into mythical comparisons—I see myself dressed in Theseus's garb psyching himself to slay the Minotaur. No fear though that I will unfold a black sail if I succeed.... A white sail and a green light.... I am walking along the Pireus.... The crowd is roaring.... Yes, I have killed the monster!... But I must have lulled myself into dreaming for a few seconds, here. The light at the curb has turned and Janice is at my side, her eyes reddened with emotion, urging me to move up to the head of the march. The crowd is 200 strong, the light of day could not be more limpid. Jubilation is the password of the hour.

10

The Walk—
I Take To The Open Road

Minneapolis To Northfield

Yes, on the 15th of September 1985, jubilation was indeed the password. We left the grounds of the St. Louis Park Methodist Hospital in grand style, 200 strong, with fanfare blaring and balloons blazing. Our destination on this first leg was Northfield, 50 miles south. Little by little the crowd dwindled along the first three miles. By 11:30 only a handful of hard-core walkers were left as we crossed Edina creek. I gave a last answer to Diane Rossi's (Channel 11) last question, as she promised to come and shoot a progress report when we reached Kansas City. Soon only my niece Barbara and nephews Bob, Tom and Mark remained, along with my colleagues Joe and Lisa Krause, and Ken Fowler.

Ken is a fellow Parkinsonian who had called me two times already to say that he wanted to walk with me to California. His story is a gripping one: six kids, unemployed, he cannot afford to buy all his necessary medication. This is indeed a walk for all Parkinsonians and I welcome everyone who wishes to walk with me on any one designated leg. Yes, but for four and a half months? I don't think that was the plan. At least not mine. And I doubt it was the APDA's, either.

—"Geez, Ken, I'd love to have you on the walk with me, that...that would be great, the more the merrier, you know, and all that, but really, we haven't planned for three people."

—"This van is equipped for six. You have six bunk spaces in this van. There's room for me."

—"Yes, Ken, I know the van sleeps six, but the expenses have been planned for two people, not three."

—"That's OK. I'll eat on my own money. I can be good help to you. I am a mechanic, you know, and my Parkinson is not so bad. I can do a lot of useful things. I want to go to California with you. Come on. Take me along."

I am a real pushover on the verge of succumbing to Ken's plea when Marguerite comes to the rescue, "This van is insured for only two persons and besides I have no more room, not a single inch of cupboard and drawer left for your clothes and belongings. Sorry, we just can't. But if you want to ask Frank Williams, he will be in Northfield this afternoon when Michel arrives. See what he says."

Frank and company left for Northfield a quarter of an hour ago. Bob, Tom, Barb and Mark are about to turn around. Now only Ken, Janice, Marguerite, Joe, Lisa and myself are left.

—"Well, Ken, you want to come to Northfield with us?"

—"No, I'll go home," he says resignedly. "Good-bye. Have a good trip."

—"Good-bye." My misty eyes cannot find the courage to meet his.

On our way to Northfield, Janice unwrapped some hors d'oeuvres and cake that she had doggie-bagged under the canopy tent at Methodist Hospital. Again, we marveled at the organization that the hospital had put in place for this kickoff celebration, from the program planning down to the various press appointments without forgetting the planned police escort on Excelsior Boulevard, the balloon launch, all the food, the band. Terry, the hospital PR man, must be made aware that we appreciate all the efforts. So we lumbered toward Northfield in that wonderful van, our abode for the next five months. Since we had walked about three miles before getting into the van, we have 12 miles left to walk before our arrival in Northfield.

My Northfield committee, through the channel of the Northfield Hospital, must have made it a point not to be up-staged by the kickoff ceremonies in St. Louis Park. I was absolutely dazzled by the grandeur of the reception. Another 200 people gathered at the Dairy Queen on the outskirts of town. Friends, acquaintances, strangers, they had all come to wish me well, to give me a last hug. Such a display of support I never dreamed of. It was truly exhilarating to see this genuinely friendly crowd united for the single purpose of advancing my cause.

When the greetings were over, the marching band, all decked out in the Northfield High School colors, struck up a tune and the parade wound its way downtown to the square in the center of town, where a public address system had been installed on a flatbed. And the whirlwind of speeches continued. I was so moved by my Carleton colleague Paul Wellstone's remarks—both of his parents have Parkinson—that I begged off taking my turn at the mike. I asked to remain seated instead, for I was afraid that my presence at the mike would be most unsightly.

Among the well-wishers was June Bloomberg, reputed in town for her philanthropic undertakings. She approached me, hand outstretched, congratulated me, and opening her purse, deftly pulled out a white envelope. I must confess to a flash of venal thought; curiosity, however, would have to take a back seat. Later on in the day, I was delighted to see that June Bloomberg's contribution more than met her reputation.

When I fell asleep that night, I shamefacedly thought back to the days when I first conceived the walk, imagining myself crossing the country like Walt Whitman, with a backpack, a notebook and a pen.

Faribault

Our next leg took us to Faribault, an old French settlement, now Rice County seat. Because it is so close to Northfield, we slept at home. But we were expected at the Court House at 8:00 AM to meet a group of walkers, Parkinsonian sufferers and supporters. We were punctual that day, and indeed there was a small group of four couples already waiting.

After the heady kickoff celebrations and huge popular turnouts, I must have looked disappointed by the size of the group because they keep apologizing. In fact I was not disappointed at all. Only impatient and anxious. Anxious to be on my own, to get on my own two feet and start walking.

—"Michel," Jack said, "we're going to stop at the next traffic light and turn around. It's been great walking with you this morning. We wish you the best of luck in your efforts. What you are doing is very courageous and we are very proud of you. Keep us posted on your progress," and he slipped me a check.

Finally on my own, the Indian summer was following me or perhaps better: I was chasing it. The blueness of the sky was matched only by the softness of the cumulus. Come noon it would be hot and I would trade my sweatsuit for my French Lacoste shorts and T-shirt. In the meantime I signaled Marguerite to stop. The van was wide, much wider than a passenger car, and Marguerite and I have to learn how to operate and communicate while moving.

—"Be careful, Michel, you're right in front of the mirror and I can't see what's coming behind."

The shoulder was wide enough for Marguerite to drive on the right side, following a few yards behind me, thus sheltering me from passing traffic. We kept the emergency lights on for added security. But we soon discovered that there were all kinds and fashions of road shoulders: some wide, some narrow; some sandy, others shallow; some are foreboding like a naked snake, others welcoming like a bikini strap; there are velvety shoulders, aggressive shoulders that threaten to invade the pavement, but all are long and faithful like the road they skirt.

The weather was beautiful, but hot, as predicted. The Cannon Valley Reservoir provided our first peaceful oasis.

—"Why don't you park the van in a shady spot of the lot? And I'll walk on ahead."

For some reason, that proposition did not suit Marguerite. I saw her driving into the entrance with a frown. "What can be the matter?" And there she stopped, right next to the entrance way; she got out, lit up a cigarette and walked toward shore where she plopped herself down.

—"Now what can the matter be?" I wondered. At any rate, I had to make a statement. There just cannot be any doubt as to who was in charge of this operation. And it had to be done right away. So I slowly walked to the van, deliberately turned the engine on with my own set of keys and brought the van on into the lot in the shade of a tall elm. Now it was just a matter of waiting. So sudden had been Marguerite's change of mood that this episode triggered an old fear. "How are we going to get along? Have I made the right choice? What if we don't get along?"

Marguerite finished her cigarette and walked back to the van. I think she got my message, so I didn't bring it up again. —"It's going to be noon soon," she said. "According to the map, there should be some hamburger joint in the next town. Should I scout ahead while you continue walking?"

—"Great, yeah! But do hurry, it's getting hot. There's no shade along the road and I still did not get myself a cap."

—"OK, what kind of hamburger do you want?"

—"Anything, I don't care. I'm not very hungry." As I trudged on toward Waterville, a van going in the opposite direction slowed down and stopped across the road from me. A man got out and crossed the road in my direction. I seemed to recognize him, but where did I see him, where did I know him from? And just as he extended his hand where I caught sight of some crunched up greenbacks, I called out,

—"Mr. McEathron! What a surprise! What are you doing here? How did you know it was me?" It was Bob McEathron, my electrician in Northfield, and out of context, I had not recognized him sooner.

—"Well, I am on a job here in Waterville, and when I saw your van ahead on the road, I remembered having seen you on last night's News 11. I thought I would meet you on the road. Well, best of luck to you."

—"Thank you very much." Marguerite returned from her scouting, with good news. She found a delightful, out of the way, shore front little restaurant, where the specialty is the catch of the day. The Melody Harbor restaurant is as colorful as its name is lyrical. It looked very European and reminded me of little fishing villages along the Mediterranean. No wonder! The lady who greeted us had a foreign accent—and as she recognized ours, we soon found ourselves in congenial company. She was German, married to a Minnesota boy. As soon as she saw the van, she had us pegged.

—"I saw you on TV last night."

That was the first time that I noticed the importance of the media. All the way down to this remote restaurant in this remote little Minnesota town the news of our arrival had preceded us. Frank Williams, Patrick and Sara were doing their jobs. We were the only clients and the German lady could devote all her attention to her unusual customers, which she did with gusto.

—"You must be starved, so you be my guests, and you tell me all about the walk. But first tell me what you want me to fix you for lunch. I have wonderful fillets of walleye. Do you like walleye?"

—"I love all kinds of fish and walleye is my favorite."

—"Good! and tell me what you want to drink...you sit tight, you rest up a bit and I'll bring you your meal." She headed for the kitchen, fiddled with utensils, then made a phone call.

—"Say, Sally, guess what? The people who are walking across the country to raise funds for Parkinson have just stopped at the restaurant. They're going to be here for another half hour or so. Why don't you bring your pad and camera?"

A few minutes later, in came Sally, the local newspaper lady. A breed facing extinction. She's all at once the editor, publisher, reporter, photographer, manager and, unfortunately, she doesn't have much more than a dozen readers for each hat she wears. But the picture that made the front page of the Waterville Crest is one of the best we ever got.

Soon afterwards entered Mr. Melody Harbor himself. Handsome and good-humored, he would have given us the store, and before we departed he shot a roll of film in the restaurant, outside the restaurant, on the docked pontoon, in front of the van, all with Melody Harbor T-shirts on our chests and sun visors on our heads. For a first day out in uncharted and unadvertised territory, we did not do so badly. We were jubilant. The walk was being well received on its own, and that's what we wanted.

Mankato

Far from the madding crowds, we entered Mankato the next afternoon. Russ Ahlstrom, Director of the local PEP support group had come to meet us on the road to walk the last five miles with us. He was disappointed by the small turnout. A meager crowd indeed had gathered for the occasion on the shopping center parking lot, but the welcoming French songs on the public address system more than made up for the poor turnout. And the fat envelope he turned in from his support group was proof enough that he and his people cared. Already I started to worry about thank you cards. Russ, a Parkinsonian Director, extremely devoted to the group, asked us to stay for dinner and the night as his family's guests. I had walked 15 miles three days in a row. His offer was eagerly accepted. There was a Channel 11 interview the next morning. I went to bed early.

Diane Rossi became, so to speak, the official reporter of the walk. She had answered the Northfield Hospital press call about a month before to do a report on the human touch at the Northfield Hospital, and since I was getting ready for the

walk, she did a little interview with me. My first TV interview! I was scared stiff. I stammered, lost my train of
thought. How demeaning in front of this articulate, efficient,
to-the-point career woman. Beautiful, on top of that. I had really blown it. What I did not know then was that in addition
Diane had been working as a licensed nurse. As such, she
covered several of my pre-departure appearances as well as
the first day reception in Northfield. What I had judged
harsh and brusk upon first meeting her was only a facade to
survive the cutthroat world of the media. Diane and her
cameraman met us at Russ's home.

—"Now Michel, I want you to stop being nervous," she
nudges with her most winning smile. "We're going to take our
time. If you freeze, don't worry. We'll stop the tape and start
over. And I am here," she puts her hand on my shoulder. "You
know me. I'll ask you only the best questions on the topics
you and I have already talked about," and as she lowers her
head as if to scold me, frowning at me from the bottom of her
eyebrow, she waits while I flail about wondering what is
going on, "...and if you trip, I'll pick you up," she bursts out
laughing. "I see a soccer ball. Come on, boy! Let's get out and
kick a little soccer for our cameraman."

—"That's my game all right." I pick up the ball, dribble
past her, do a ball lift with the right toe as I pivot on my left
foot, control the ball on the ground, move away a few steps
with the ball and turn back. "Think fast," and I kick her a left
that hits her right in the leg. "Diane, this is fun. But it's even
more fun without spiked heels on. You ought to try it.
Honest! But don't worry;" I lean toward her, "if you trip, I'll
pick you up."

—"Swell, you're a great guy! Say, who ever said you had a
debilitating disease? You seem in perfect shape to me."

—"Thanks! You're pretty neat yourself." The interview
went well, needless to say, as we bantered around Russ's
backyard. Diane thought she might get her station to cover
our progress as we forged ahead to Kansas City, St. Louis,
Tulsa, Oklahoma City, Albuquerque, Phoenix, Tucson, San

Diego, and Los Angeles. (As it turned out, she hooked up with us in San Juan Capistrano and stayed about a week with cameraman Rusty to cover the last few days of the walk.)

At any rate, Diane is now a good friend who taught me how to conquer one set of fears; and her reports have had a major impact on Parkinson disease in Minnesota. If the Road to Dignity Walk has succeeded, it is in great part due to people like Diane, people who care—for whatever reason—to alleviate the suffering around them. They shall inherit the kingdom. Amen.

The next day was to see us out of Mankato early in the morning, right after an 8:30 AM live radio show. Russ had set it up with seeming difficulties and it was obvious that his honor was at stake to be punctual. When we left him in the evening, he reiterated his recommendation that we be prompt. We would meet at 8:15 at the first traffic light in town. At 8:25 we were there. Russ was waiting in his car.

—"We're going to be late! Tell Marguerite to follow with the van. You come with me, we have to hurry."

And without the reflex even to give Marguerite the address of the station, we sped away. She followed valiantly for a few miles in the lumbering van, but when, after having taken the wrong turn, Russ made a U-turn in the road, the van bit the dust and Marguerite bid us adieu. We were indeed a little late for the beginning of the show, but it had some flexibility built in, and there was no harm done.

What was more frustrating was the fact that Marguerite and I were now revolving in different spheres in a city of 60,000 with no clue as to each other's whereabouts. One would suppose that a big RV would be a cinch to spot. It was not. We checked the major gas stations at the main entrances to town. In one of the breakfast places, we even stumbled on a retinue of cops who did not seem too eager to help. One of them, however, who had just heard the show and was acquainted with Russ, got up and went to his car to make an announcement for all the patrol cruisers to be on the lookout for a van emblazoned with the APDA colors.

After much lucubration and guessing as to what would have been Marguerite's strategy, I decided to call home to Northfield. Her sister Angela had been there since the preceding week, staying with Janice to learn English and help out with French classes at the high school. Sure enough, Marguerite had called her a half hour before to let us know that she was at the pancake house on Highway 52...exactly five blocks from where we were waiting! It was tempting to criticize and we each did intimate that it was the other's fault. It served as a good lesson. We did not lose each other again until Yuma, Arizona.

Lunch at Eagle Lake _____

Noon. It was dark in the room. It took a few moments to get used to the obscurity. A few habitués were drinking silently at the bar perched high on their stools. The silhouette of their heads and backs came off sharply in front of the background glass display of liquor and wine bottles. There didn't seem to be any other customers, and the juke box spun out the popular tunes of the dying summer.

We stood a few moments in the dark, then I turned to Marguerite, wondering, "It did say outside that they serve lunch, right?"

—"Yes, yes, here comes the waitress," as she led the way toward what appeared to be a low barroom table. While the waitress cleaned the ashtray and wiped the table I had this strange feeling that we were being looked at intently from the bar. Marguerite's good looks, probably....

—"Here are the menus," tendered the waitress. "Today's special is a quarter pounder steak with mushroom sauce, and it comes with Vichyssoise soup, and for dessert, we ha...." The accent was very familiar.

—"Did you say Vichyssoise soup?"

—"Yes, and for dessert, we ha...."

—"Excuse me, but are you from Belgium by any chance?"

—"No, actually I am from France—je suis française—je viens de Tourcoing—close to the Belgium border.[1] My mother is Walloon. But tell me, are you really the French couple they've been showing on TV, that's walking from Minneapolis to California? What is it for already? The boss wants to know."

—"For Parkinson disease."

—"Ah! yes, thank you. I'll be back in a minute to take your order." All eyes were now unambiguously trained on us. A big tall fellow appeared from the kitchen and made his way toward our table on the almost unlit floor.

—"Hello! My name is Joe Kelly. I am the owner of this place. I think what you are doing is just fantastic and I am proud you stopped in. Take a look at the menu. Lunch is my treat."

—"Thank you very much, sir. You're too kind."

—"No, no, don't thank me. So they said you have Parkinson?"

—"Yes, I've had it for eight years now, and I am walking to collect funds for research into the problem."

—"I think it's great that there are still people like you, willing to take the bull by the horn."

—"Well, what I would really like to do is to take Reagan by his nose and squeeze all the research money needed out of him." Oops! I struck a raw nerve. My host was a devoted Reagan fan. A spirited discussion ensued, which could have easily turned into an argument had not my host been so genuinely respectful for what I was doing with the walk. We parted good friends. Marguerite and I thanked him profusely, but I learned another lesson. Under the column of no-nos: "Thou shalt not discuss politics." To convince, you must

---

1   "I am French. I come from Tourcoing."

remain dignified; to solicit money, you must be diplomatic. And I do not have a good head start on either count.

Buoyed by this second lucky encounter and the prospect of free lunches from here to California, I took back to the open road, the healing road, the long, smooth asphalt ribbon that meanders through Minnesota marshes and meadows to lead flawlessly, faultlessly to the next destination. Walking is such a luxury!

I took three deep breaths sucking in through all my senses the beauty, the colors, the smells, the tingling in the autumn air, the crows' croaks of ominous portend. I turned my head back to check on the van. Marguerite must have sensed my wonderment. She, too, was smiling as though touched by the same compelling serenity. It was at this instant that I first became fully aware that we were really crossing America. It was one of those rare powerful moments when the beauty of the instant matched in intensity the evocative power of words: "We are crossing America." The dream was real.

Waseca

I had never been to Waseca before, yet I felt a special bond to this little southern Minnesota town. First, it is the birthplace of David Kuntz, the man who walked around the world to raise funds for UNICEF. I first heard of his feat, which he had just completed, when we moved to Northfield in the fall of 1971. Unfortunately, because of misunderstandings and media inflated misquotes, he never received the recognition he deserved. Embittered, he left the state abruptly in a messy confrontation with authorities and family. So, before I entered town, I paused long enough to reflect on the possibilities of a similar fate and what I should do to avoid it.

My other bond to Waseca is the Welna family. The first year I taught at Carleton, I had two Welnas in my classes,

Mary and Chris. Janice and I selected them both for the first Carleton College program held in Pau in the spring of 1973. They were both prototypes of the ideal student that a professor wants to have on a foreign studies program—bright, witty, curious, open, adapting well to the new ambiance, making friends easily among the native population, full of initiative, learning the language at the speed of sound. Because there were to be six more little Welnas plus two cousins to come through Carleton, we came to know and appreciate the family.

I was deeply touched by their concern and support when they heard I had Parkinson disease. When they learned that my walk was going through Waseca, they invited us to sleep over.

Finally, Waseca was the first community where we received a police escort. I was a bit self-conscious, walking and jogging in the midst of all those cars through downtown to the hospital where a reception was planned. But there had been a breach of communications with Patrick. When we arrived, just a few people with remorseful glances at a picked-over spread of varied appetizers were left. We had arrived one hour late, according to the hospital schedule, and neither the police nor I had been advised.

Owatonna

As expected, the road held delightfully rich experiences in store, not the least of them being the infinite gamut of human nature. Who could have guessed that in the heart of rural southern Minnesota, the Owatonna Cultural Center would be home to one of the most colorful and flamboyant persons we were to meet on the whole trip?

The visit at the Center began with a press conference on the lawn, the largest press conference we had held so far: a two-mike press conference, with media reporters from Rochester, Austin, Albert Lea, and of course, Owatonna. It was followed by a reception inside where I met the members of the Parkinson support group, all the while lending a discreet but curious eye at the art on the walls, the architecture of the building, the huge renovated concert hall. One side was a giant wall of stained glass that dwarfed a lonely concert grand piano in one corner. The otherwise bare room invited memories of sumptuous formal dances at former railroad fortune mansions. In such a sober yet elegant decor, the incongruity of my poor fellow Parkinsonians' dyskinesias—as well as my own—our bent-over posture, shaking and drooling, appeared most striking.

I was thus debating between shame—should I feel any— and our right to the better things in life when a timid and young-looking man hesitantly approached me, offering a limp hand, a cup of punch and a smile. There was an amused look in the round eyes when he introduced himself as the curator of the place.

The punch was good, and in spite of the rain in which I had run the last mile and a half, I was very thirsty. My capacity to empty cup after cup must have amazed him, as he contritely begged to be excused for the inadequate quantity of the beverage. Whereupon he retired to the adjacent kitchenette to prepare a whole new bowl. That did not seem necessary as the crowd was departing and I was regaining my metabolic equilibrium.

—"Look," he said when he reappeared—and the soft hand deftly pivoted around a white wrist. "I have brought you a whole new bowl of punch." The round eyes were seeking approbation, the slightly tilted head was cajoling me to stay a bit and partake.

—"You're too kind, really. But it's getting late, and I'm a little tired after those 15 miles. If you could indicate to us where there is a take-out Chinese restaurant, for instance, we'll buy some dinner to eat in the van."

—"Surely. I'll give you the directions. But, before you go—you have five minutes, don't you? I want to show you our collection, in particular the clothes collection that belonged to Mrs. X, the benefactress of this complex." And while he stepped back and we followed the wavy welcoming movement of his arms, he drew us into a huge closet full of dresses, skirts, shawls, hats and shoes, and there he stood in a corner, the reigning queen spider in the midst of all the exotic, slightly gaudy, webs.

The round eyes watched the intruder carefully while two atrophied front legs articulately pointed to this silk garment specially made for Milady by the best artisans in Lyon, or to that pure cashmere bolero that she brought back from her last trip to India. The curator knew his trade indeed, showed us unusual weaving patterns, told us how to care for this incomparable collection, felt the fabrics with emotion, presented them to us as one would a child, and visibly took his life's breath from the coming and going of far away shuttles.

—"Here, Marguerite, come and put on this sari." As he wraps the material around her, he spins her forward, backward, covering this shoulder, crossing between the legs, tugging here, straightening there. The true artist at work, in love with his craft rather than his model. From the bottom of her silken sepulcher, Marguerite threw me a sidelong look. "Please get me out of here, come rescue me."

My return glance told her, "Hang in there, baby; it's not for long; just a little game of deft manipulation between the dresser and the dressed." He realized that our gaze had undressed him. The sari came down with the same dexterity and sensuality that it had gone on; lights out, closet locked, fantasia was over...or almost.

—"Wait here, just a minute," said he, and he ran out in the pouring rain. We watched him go toward the flower bed, walk between a couple of rose bushes, and come back beaming.

—"No take-out Chinese dinner for two in an RV can go without a rose on the table." He handed the rose to Marguerite. "I'll get you a little vase."

—"It's been delightful speaking with you; perhaps you'd like to come have dinner with us?"

—"I would love to, unfortunately I can't. You see my friend is waiting there in the car; we have to go to a gala opening. Good luck on your walk."

—"Thanks! And thank you for the visit...."

Owatonna to Rochester

The itinerary that I had drawn up with the APDA was a bit tortuous. Walking straight East while going from Owatonna to Rochester, home of the famous Mayo Clinic, I felt a bit funny explaining to carloads that stopped to ask me if everything was OK that I was walking to collect funds for Parkinson disease research and that my destination was Los Angeles.

—"You're heading the wrong way!" Some people were genuinely concerned by my apparent lack of orientation, so I explained that I was first going to Rochester, then south, then west.

That day especially, lots of people stopped. And I think I know why. Up to that point, Marguerite had followed right behind me. That day, however, we agreed that I should walk until we lost eye contact; then Marguerite would catch up, see if I needed anything, then speed on ahead until we lost eye contact again. This way, instead of totally wasting her time, Marguerite could read, write and study for her Graduate Record Examination that she was to take on October 12th when we were in St. Louis. The road was a divided highway with ample shoulders. It cut straight across hills and fields like a giant surveyor's ruler, and I could see the van and be seen by Marguerite for more than a mile in each direction. In this manner people seeing a stationary van and a half mile later a lonely hiker, would automatically assume that we had car problems and offer help. I took great pleasure in reassuring them, telling them that I didn't need a ride, that I was walking to California and that I would like them to read this little brochure that explains what I am doing and that contains a self-addressed, detachable envelope....

—"What are you doing this for?"

—"I am walking across the country to raise money for Parkinson disease." The old man flashed a skeptical look.

—"But why, why do you do it?"

—"Well, I've got PD myself, and the sooner we have a cure for the disease, the better off we'll all be."

—"Oh! Really. You don't look it. You're too young for that, but that's really fantastic. You know, my aunt has Parkinson disease too, and she's doing fairly well. Lots of exercises, you know...."

—"You don't say!..."

—"And you're going all the way to California?"

—"Heading straight to Los Angeles, that's my aim. Should be there on January 24th. You watch the papers."

I gave him one of the brochures I carried with me for such encounters. "If you want to help me and your aunt, just tear this detachable envelope off and send in a check. And thanks a lot for stopping." I turned my back and started walking again. But the old man rolled down his window all the way.

—"Eh, wait a minute," and searched through his pockets to bring out a crumpled dollar bill, saying, "I'll send you more in the envelope." A handshake, a thank you and a good-bye. You dear old man! If every car that passed by gave me a dollar, we would have our goal of $1,000,000 reached in no time at all. If...if...if....

A bit further down the road the tenth or eleventh mile let me know that even though I was wearing the best footwear, I did not sport Mercury's shoes. So far it had been a good uplifting day, but 15 miles for the fourth day in a row was taking its toll. Thank God, the itinerary says: Rochester, day of rest. Further in the distance, the Mayo building already towered above the trees. That was incentive enough to pledge renewed determination. "Straighten up, shoulders back, chin high, step forward, walk."

I was slowly catching up to my normal pace when a big blue Buick pulled off the road. Automatically, I reached for a brochure and prepared to give it to the man who had just stepped out, but he was only interested in shaking my hand. Hesitation, right hand, left hand, amusing confusion, shift of the brochure, two right hands finally meeting each other.

—"You must be Michel." I acquiesced with a blink. "I'm Warren Haven. My wife Connie and I are your hosts for the weekend. Nous sommes très heureux de faire votre connaissance."[2] The accent is not bad at all, the demeanor warm and kind. "You've been told, I assume, that there is a reception for you at St. Mary's hospital at 4:00."

—"No, I wasn't sure. Let's see, it's now 3:00...but, good! Yes, I can make it on time."

—"Good! Connie and I will forge on ahead in the car, tell the welcoming committee that you are approaching, and we'll wait for you at St. Mary's entrance, right on 2nd Street."

—"Fine, I know where it is." But during the exchange, a city police car had pulled up and the officer announced: "I'll be your escort to St. Mary's. I'll be ahead of you with flashing lights, then you come behind, then the van with the emergency lights. You walk behind me, but you set the pace and I'll drive accordingly."

—"Great! Let's go." I turned toward the van, walked up to Marguerite for an encouraging smile and told her what the officer had said.

—"Where do I park the van when we get there?"

—"Ah! good question. Officer, where does she park the van when we get there?"

—"Right by the entrance on 2nd Street. I'll give you a special permit."

---

2   "We're very happy to meet you."

I was feeling good. The Friday afternoon traffic was heavy but it boosted my morale. All those people watching gave renewed vigor to my calves and lungs.

—"Sir, sir?" a child's voice urged. I turned my head to see a little boy struggling to open wide the car window. The flow of cars was slow. I had no problem keeping up with it walking at a normal pace.

—"Here you are sir," and he stuck a bunch of greenbacks in the palm of my hand.

—"That's very kind of you, thank you very much." The cars were picking up speed. Almost unconsciously I started jogging.

—"Thank you," and I bent my neck to see who was driving. The woman was dressed in white: probably a nurse. "But do you know what we are all about?"

—"Yes, we saw you on TV last night. Parkinson disease, right?"

—"Right! Here, here's a half a dozen brochures. Can you spread them around you at work?"

—"Of course! Thank you."

—"Thanks to you."

I was really running now. In fact, at the last corner we turned, I saw part of the St. Mary's complex, the largest one-building hospital in the world. My legs were feeling good. I was breathing a little hard, but if I didn't change pace I thought I could make it running all the way to the entrance. Another turn? What in the world was this cop doing? I took a periscopic look. Seemed like another four blocks, about. But it was uphill. All the same, I had to make it. Furthermore, a TV station van had caught up with us and of course they were shooting my shoes. I tried to breathe regularly, one, two, three, step, breathe; one, two three, step, breathe, regularly, easy does it.

—"Can I ask you a few questions?" yelled the reporter from his van.

—"Yes, all you want as long as you don't expect any answers," puff! "Need to rest," puff! "Catch me later," puff! "At the hospital!" A flash through my mind. What time could it be? I slowed down my pace, enough to take a few steps facing backwards and show Marguerite my left wrist with my right index finger. The answer came pointedly, three minutes to four. Good, I think I can make it. Turn back, step forward to resume pace, puff! puff! clear my throat, puff! puff! spit.

I seemed to distinguish a small crowd a couple of blocks away. Could it be the entrance already? Yes, I think so. Sniffle, sniffle, puff, run past two nuns on the sidewalk, puff, puff, concentrate, watch out for the curb; oops, red light; that's OK, you're covered by the cop; atten...tion: hop, step, step, breathe: step, step, breathe; hop! onto boulevard; evergreen bush at corner; good, clear throat, spit. It's not sanitary, I know, but my legs are hurting, my lungs exploding.

What was that? Across the street, a nurse was clapping... Smile, adrenaline pumping, here are the steps, cameras whizzing, people clapping, straighten your knees, crowd cheering, another 30 yards, stretch your legs, straighten your knees. My T-shirt was drenched. Fine shape to meet a welcoming group! A few more steps, and Warren Haven was there with more sisters. Would I recognize Dr. Ahlskog? Yup! the tall Swede in the back; braking down steps, arms up; nurses; 25 to 30 people crowding, congratulating, shaking hands; let me breathe, let me breathe. My whole body was shaking and perspiring.

—"Maguit?" ah! there was the van. She had already parked it. "Maguit," I pulled on my T-shirt with thumb and index finger. She understood right away, brought me a clean T-shirt, my pills, and with a smile, "Quite a run, old boy."

I began breathing easier. As I entered the main hall, several officials introduced themselves and explained that there was a small reception planned, with TV crews; then we would go to the Havens, then to dinner. In the meantime, we had a problem; I was drenched, in total need of washing up (short of taking a shower), especially if I were going to a reception with TV reporters. But I have Parkinson and it'll take me 20 to 30 minutes before I reappear from the washroom! Of course Marguerite was there to help, and ready. But how would it look if she came into the men's room with me? There was an awkward moment when the welcoming sister brought me towel and washcloth. Since situations like this were likely to happen again we might as well resolve it once and for all.

—"To help you," says Marguerite, "was what I was hired for, right; and provided that you don't request favors beyond what my affection for you tolerates, I stand ready to help. So, hurry up and come in, let's hurry and wash you up," as she took the towel and washcloth from the dumbfounded sister, and stepped with me into the men's room.

Ten minutes later the group was still patiently waiting in the reception room where a fabulous spread was served. People were seated around two long tables and the best thing seemed to be to introduce ourselves going around the tables. Of course I knew Dr. Ahlskog. I was one of his patients on a Pergolide™ experiment for the first six months of the year. Turned out I was on the placebo! Not his fault! He's a good, caring doctor.

Then there was a brain surgeon of renown in his early 50s who had just been diagnosed with Parkinson and who, in spite of his gallant and elegant appearance, was no less scared than any one of us. How devastating it must be, for a surgeon (or pianist for that matter) to see his hands starting to shake and his mind going to pot. Come to think of it, I am sure that there is no profession nor any station in life that makes it easier for anyone to accept the unacceptable news.

When all the participants at the tables had identified themselves, a feeling of sadness overcame me that I tried to analyze and place it in context. And only a few seconds later it came to me: those people are lonely, they don't know each other. No wonder! There is no support group. In Rochester, Minnesota, of all places!

The local human service organization had in fact been trying desperately to organize a group of Parkinson support and they had decided to have the first meeting coincide with our Road to Dignity Walk stop in town. So, after having been treated to an excellent dinner, it was our turn, the next morning, to impart to the group whatever advice we might have learned from the walk.

I was sorry that my experience was so limited, but this was the first support group whose birth we were to witness, if not to instigate. The Road to Dignity Walk was the catalyst. Yes, it had been worth it already.

The Little Prince _____

The next morning Warren brought us to the intersection so we would not miss the small highway. It was a little slower, but much more pleasant, especially at that time of the year.

Yes, it was fall all right. The nip in the air wanted to tell us something that sounded like snow. And while Marguerite gave Warren a last hug, I took their picture and climbed back into the van to get my new Goretex raincoat.

I slowly and awkwardly managed to fasten the new zippers...then I stepped out of the van, shoved my hands in the coat's deep pockets, rounded up my shoulders and started walking.

I hardly saw the miles tick off, and it was only a few hours later that the announced and dreaded first snow flurries of the year began to cover the pavement. September 24th. We stopped in a little town for a hot chocolate. There was diagonal parking all along the three blocks of Main Street, U.S.A. and the van, all painted and decorated with the colors of the APDA, the Northfield Hospital and Sandoz Inc., stuck out like a giraffe in a herd of elephants. In the overheated cafe, the looks we got were suspicious for about as brief a moment as it took my glasses to clear up. By then, we were the heroes of the day.

—"Excuse me, Miss," said the waitress, "aren't you the people walking across America?" Marguerite giggled with pleasure while a smug smile of satisfaction invaded my face to the ear lobes.

—"Yes! How do you know? This is our last day in Minnesota and it seems that everywhere we go, people know who we are."

—"No wonder! You've been on the local TV news for the last three days. Last night, we saw you run to St. Mary's entrance. The day before that, you were on the Albert Lea station, and the day before that...I forget...Owatonna, maybe. Well, anyway, no one can miss your RV. Do you sleep in that thing?"

—"It can sleep six, but we haven't used it yet. So far, we've been invited every night to people's homes. But it could well be that tonight will be the first time. Our advance team hasn't been able to set up any news conferences or reception in Austin. Say! Could I have a cheeseburger and a small coke to go?"

—"Make that two, will you?"

—"Oh! I am so sorry, I got so excited I forgot to take your order. I'll be right back."

The cafe was packed with customers, farmers mostly, dressed in Oshkosh blues, b'gosh! and local merchants out for lunch break. It was hard to pick up any conversation or parts thereof in all the din, but I think I overheard several times the names Hormel and Albert Lea. Since the beginning of the trip my interest in news had strictly been narcissistic, so that I didn't know that the meat packers at Hormel had been on a strike attracting national attention. The waitress came back, without our order, but instead with an envelope which she held out for me.

—"My grandfather has Parkinson," she explained, "and when I saw you walking on TV, I decided to collect money for you. This is what I got from all the waitresses in the cafe. I was going to mail it in, but it's so much more exciting to do it this way!"

—"Geez, Miss. I am very touched. I just don't know how to thank you...but I can tell you one thing: with support like yours, our goal of raising $1,000,000 is going to be a cinch, and finding a cure will come so much sooner. So thank you very much." And I got up to shake her hand and kiss this rosy, friendly, bespectacled face. It was the boss himself who brought out our order.

—"We all think you are doing such a great job. This lunch is on me. How about a piece of pie for dessert?" And solicitously, he added, "Are you going to be warm enough? It's cold out there," and with a conniving wink he added, "You never know what Iowa has in store for you." Oh, God, not another Iowa joke, I hope, as the boss prepared to see us to the door. No, he's not the type. A bit patronizing, rather, "I was going to warn you…"

But Maguit interrupted, "Sir, could you stand by the van, I would like to take a picture. And could we get the waitress, too?"

—"Kathy," yelled the boss through the door he had kept ajar, "come on out for a picture," and while she took off her apron, dried her hands and rearranged her coiffure, he started over, "Yeah. I didn't want to tell you inside, but please, don't go to Albert Lea. The strike has turned violent and there's no reason why you of all people should get clobbered." He gallantly kept the door open for Kathy, they posed, Maguerite shot the photos, and it was a cross fire volley of thank yous, take cares and good-byes. Those good old Minnesota folks….

Direction: Iowa border. We had our free take out lunch in the van and I walked for another couple of hours. In that short a time, the weather had reverted from wintery back to Minnesota autumnal. I am walking well today! Funny, that's one thing I forgot to tell the group in Rochester when they were asking me about my illness. One of the first things I noticed about Parkinson, was that its manifestations recur regularly about once every three or four weeks. In a given period when, say, bradykinesia dominates, the slowness will hit the fingers for a few days, then move to the hips or to the shoulders or to the ankles; then the tremors will take over for a week settling in the forearms, or the head, or the knees. Then the symptoms switch again and this time it will be stiffness, striking various parts; then in each cycle a new organ or part will be affected, or an already affected one will be more seriously impaired than in the preceding round.

In the midst of these considerations, all of a sudden, out of nowhere, my very own Little Prince appears at my side. Is this a mirage? He is blond, Minnesota blond, with deep blue eyes. The exact living replica of the illustration from the children's storybook I loved so much as a child.

He's riding his bike effortlessly, even though he has a puppy in his free arm, and in a crystal voice he is asking me, "Tell me, sir, what is Parkinson disease?"

I am not one to be subject to hallucinations—I have no problem with Parlodel,™ or Sinemet,™ or Symmetrel,™ so I looked at him incredulously for a trifle too long, for he repeated, "Tell me, sir, what is Parkinson disease?"

The mirage was somewhat too much for me to sustain, and I was seriously tempted to reply, "Go ask the lady in the van," when he took the lead.

—"Hi! What's your name? See my dog Springer? I am wondering, could you tell me, sir, what Parkinson disease is?" The blow was still too much. He even sounded like the Little Prince I had imagined! I had to regain my aplomb.

—"Hi! What a nice puppy you have here. Can I see him?" and out came the wonderfully wrinkled face of a baby boxer. He had skin folds to spare while waiting to grow into them, but under the extra large size skin, a supple and muscled body could already be guessed at which should certainly develop into a prize-winning animal.

—"I can see why you call him Springer. I'll bet he jumps like mad at everyone who plays with him."

—"How could you guess?" I breathed a deep sigh of relief. My Little Prince was not a mirage.

—"When I was your age, I had a boxer also. I called him Henri Quatre, French for Henry the Fourth. By the way, what's your name again?"

—"Vince, short for Vincent."

—"How old are you?"

—"I'm going to be ten next month. My brother, he's 13 and he's in school until 3:15. Our grade had the day off, so I can ride a little bit longer with you if you don't mind."

—"No, I don't mind at all," and sensing that we were going to be pals, "I'll tell you what I can about Parkinson disease. First, my name is Michel. That's French for Michael. Can you say *Michel*?"

—"Michel."

—"Very good, A+ in French for Vincent. Well, I happen to have PD myself." Fearing a sense of rejection from my young friend, I hastened to add, "But don't worry, it is not contagious and it is not a deadly disease." He rearranged Springer on his arm, tilted his head and winked at me in the sun, "Oh, good."

—"It is, however, a troublesome disease which makes people shake, makes them do things more slowly, more hesitantly because it also makes their muscles stiff. It starts mildly at first, but the symptoms get worse and worse until there is no way to stop it. Up until 20 years ago, people became paralyzed and nothing could be done. Now, fortunately, we have drugs that hide the symptoms more or less adequately. Researchers at big universities are working day and night on the problem. But they need money to carry out their research and that's why I am walking from Minneapolis to Los Angeles: to raise money to give to researchers."

"You see, for instance, if I did not take any drugs, I would not be able to walk. I know that for a fact because about two months ago, I was in France, in my little hometown of Digoin. I ran out of one of my medicines on Friday morning and could not get any more until Monday morning. Well, when I took a bath Sunday night, I could not get myself out of the bathtub and had to yell for help. Monday morning, same thing. I could not extract myself from my bed. Believe me, it's a scary feeling, as you can well imagine."

The way Vincent fidgeted on his bicycle and kept looking behind him made me think that I had used up his attention span. And with a cursory, "Well, I gotta go..., 'bye," he vanished out of my sight as suddenly as he had appeared.

—"Did you see this neat little kid?" I asked Marguerite.

—"Yes, he asked me what we were doing and where we were going, and I told him to go and talk to you. Did you see his puppy?"

—"Yup, a boxer, my favorite!...Say, nurse, how much longer before my pills? This time I would like them served with *tapas y cerveza*."[3]

—"Oui, mon vieux. Et sur plateau d'argent peut-être?"[4] Marguerite is French, from a Spanish background and I love trying my fading Spanish on her. She closed her Graduate Record Exam manual, stopped the Dire Straits tape she had been listening to, verified some notes. "My friend," she said, "your pills are due in 18 minutes. You've walked 11 miles, and it is 2:30 PM. You are approaching Austin, Minnesota, and the world has its eye fixed on you." She fixed her dark eyes on me and, full of irony, the epic tone suddenly turned mock confidential.

—"Say, boy, by the way, what's your name again?" She laughed, and in the epic style again, "but the big question now is: will our hero reach the Iowa state line? Tune in tomorrow for our next episode of the Frank Williams traveling troupe show."

Interrupting the bantering, I yelled, "But hark! What light through yonder van doth shine? 'Tis our Prince, and Springer in his arms. Or maybe, could it be the blinding light of Asteroid B612?"

—"There he goes again," said Marguerite, "our St. Exupéry and Shakespeare quoting bard," as she deftly turned the Dire Straits back on again, full blast.

---

3   Spanish for "snacks and beer."

4   —"Sure, my friend, and served on a silver platter, maybe?"

Vincent had caught up with us.

—"Well, Vincent, you're back. What happened to you?"

—"I went home for a while. I live back there." He looked very serious for his ten years, almost solemn. "And I am bringing this back for you." A hurried handwritten note on the envelope said, "For my friend Michel."

—"What is it? Can I open it now?" I tear the envelope open. "My God! a...check and a bill."

—"The check is from my mother. I was telling her that I met you and she said that she had seen you on TV last night."

—"And the bill?" I inquired. It was a crisp Lincoln face that had never been used.

—"It's from me for you, from my paper route money." I folded the bill carefully and put it in my Goretex deep pocket. I straightened my shoulders, lifted my head and looked at the little boy. The face looked so innocent, the motive so transparently candid.

—"This is wonderful. Thank you, Little Prince."

—"What?"

—"Oh, nothing. I just said, 'thank you, Vince.'"

11

Vagabonds Over The Border

Wuthering Hollow

We arrived at the campground just before the office/convenience store closed. I ran toward it while Marguerite scouted the place for level ground. The manager looked sickly, as if she were just coming out of a long, bleak midwestern winter or else a week in an intensive care unit. With a tired gesture and a string of garbled monosyllabics I think she was trying to tell us where to park the van: next to two other RVs that had already beached themselves there for the night.

—"And how long is the store open?" The lights blinked on and off a couple of times.

—"Closing. Now," she finally articulated. Under her disapproving but helpless look, I rushed to the refrigerator section, slid several glass doors open, reached for some milk and cheese, a six-pack of Squirt and a couple of yogurts. During this time, Marguerite had gone around the campground three times. After a long day at the wheel of this behemoth, driving a boring three miles per hour, she was bushed. Her fatigue and impatience were transparent.

I also was looking forward to eight hours of good, repairing sleep. It was the first time we were sleeping in the van, though, and we had no idea of what to expect.

The campground was located about eight miles from Austin. It was already dark when we reached town, and a freezing rain storm was raging. I was confused as to directions. All I could make out were wooded areas in the middle of fields. Eerie scenery; foreboding elements; desolation! And now that the store was closed, an almost total darkness reigned over the grounds except for one small lonely bulb at the entrance to the washrooms.

We parked the van in what I thought was the proper designated area and prepared to settle in for the night. We were exhausted. I hadn't previously mentioned to Marguerite that ever since I saw the van had an overhanging cabin, I thought it would be fun to sleep in what was actually a little loft. I also thought it more gallant to give Maguit the bed in the main part of the cabin. Would I be able to climb up there, though? I could try.

But before I even had time to orchestrate the sleeping arrangements, a yawning Marguerite ordered, "Michel, the beds are already made. This is yours," and she pointed to the small couch across the rear of the van, "and...."

—"But, Maguit, wait a min...."

—"...mine is made here, on top of the cabin. You see, ever since I was a little girl, I've always imagined...."

—"You persnickety sneak! OK, OK, I've got the point." She laughed.

—"Actually," she explained, "it's Janice and I who made that decision the other day when we prepared the bedding. We decided that you would have a hard time getting in and out of this loft. Nor would you get much headroom in your flailings and attempts at finding a comfortable position. But listen, Michel, before we go to sleep, let's take a look at the gas heater. God knows we're going to need it tonight."

—"Right, my hands and wrists are already getting cold and stiff. It's another one of Parkinson's jolly benefits." I knelt in front of the gas heater door.

—"In fact, you may have to give me a hand. I can't turn this valve open." I knew it was an imposition, for Marguerite looked very tired.

But good humoredly, she said, "Sure, I'll take a look, but I am not sure I remember everything the salesman told us and showed us the other day. Between the gas system and the electrical system and the water system and the toilet system, I am a little confused."

But with her superb mechanical skills, Marguerite had the thing going in no time at all. A good smell of warm air invaded the cabin, and our shivers soon subsided. Our defense against the inhospitable outside so far was successful. Soon, a warm cup of soup and cheese and crackers would enhance this sense of security, while the wind howled ominously.

So, I stretched myself out on this couch-turned-into-a-bed, making sure that my body was positioned just right, my head resting at just the perfect angle on the pillow, my feet with just enough clearance not to get hopelessly tangled up in the sheet later on.

I have often wondered, in moments of insomnia caused precisely by less than perfect conditions, how I could ever impart and explain the ludicrous proposition of being the prisoner of a bed sheet, the hostage of a blanket. And still, this is what millions of us face at some point or other, in the development of the illness, before we learn how to cope, or before we get smart and find an artifice to skirt the difficulty. How indeed explain that although you can walk 15 miles a day and you can still kick a soccer ball to just about the same distance you did when you were 25, the slightest wrinkle in the sheet—especially the top sheet—can send you into a panicking frenzy because you cannot command your big toe to get past that wrinkle. Still, you have the strength, in those powerful legs, to kick the sheets and all the bedding off in three or four wide-sweeping kicks, thus leaving you totally uncovered. Would it not be wiser, though, if not simpler, to learn how to negotiate that wrinkle and not have to remake the bed at 3:30 in the morning?

OK, so easy does it. First you have to bring your right leg up. Command, execution. Nothing; it won't move. By now, however, you've learned that if you wait a few seconds and reiterate the command with more determination, a more "positive" command, your chances to move the leg up are greatly increased. But watch out. It's going to be a jerky motion—the wheel cog motion symptoms—and the tip of the toe may catch in the wrinkle. So you anticipate and send a stronger command. On the third attempt maybe you succeed, but in the process, inadvertently, you've bunched up another part of the sheet under the right hip and this is most uncomfortable. You'll have to move your whole body now, send a new series of commands which may or may not be adequate, but which, in any case, will have pulled you up higher from the depth of your sleep.

My sleep pattern has been blessed with three characteristics that I always considered enviable: first, come bedtime, be it at 10:00 PM or at quarter to 12, I have absolutely no problem falling asleep. In fact, so much so that in social situations I have to be careful not to let myself be lured by the lulling chatter of the company. In these last few years for example, I have lost track of the number of movies for which I bought a ticket but failed to remain awake to witness the denouement.

Second, I must come from a long line of sun-worshippers, for I wake up with the sun. A day without paying my tribute to His Rising Majesty feels like a day half-wasted. Rare are the mornings when in lieu of thanksgiving I do not recite Rimbaud's Aube d'été: "A la cîme argentée, je reconnus la déesse." [1]

Third (and least enviable) is that once awakened, I must get up and do something: go to the bathroom, read, write or contemplate my navel in purely narcissistic delight. Sometimes I fix myself a can of soup, play with the cat or write out checks. Once one of these fancies has been indulged in, sleep's sweet ebbing forces sweep back over me and it is "Forward ho," towards new dreamy seascapes of the mind.

That night, however, since the weather was so contrary, I paced restlessly in the van. The storm had become a monsoon.

—"Putain, merde, Michel. Qu'est-ce que tu fous?"[2]

---

1   "By the silver crest, I welcome the Goddess Dawn."

2   —"For God's sake, Michel! What are you doing?"

Marguerite had been awakened by all the commotion and accompanying noises, and it did not take a Ph.D. in French literature to guess that she was very upset.

—"You've been coming and going in this van for the last half hour. Don't you realize that every step you take makes this cabin sway like the Niña in the trade winds?"

The trade winds it was not, but the wind continued to blow increasingly harder. I tried to sleep again. Maybe sleep would come. I lay flat on my back. Unfortunately, the van must have been parked close to a bush or a hedge: an incessant scratching irritated the teacher in me by its disturbing resemblance to a fingernail ripping on a hard slate blackboard. If this does not stop, I'll have to move the van. But Marguerite has the keys. How would I do it, without incurring her wrath?

With the scratching and the blowing, a third element of discomfort had now penetrated the van. It was getting cold. At the risk of disturbing Marguerite a little more, I decided to see if the heater was working properly. And so another production began.

Not wanting to turn on the ceiling lights, I groped for the flashlight. I was pretty sure Marguerite left it on the sink counter. From my couch I could reach and explore the counter top with my fingers in the dark. My perception through the sense of touch is not altered by Parkinson disease, only the movements of my fingers which are slow and erratic. There, push a little more with the index finger. Right, I feel the rim of the sink. Now, follow that rim a few inches toward the window. Nothing. My arm is not long enough this way. I need to turn on my side.

Situation analysis. OK Monnot, you can do it. Let's see, to move from your back to your left side, put the right knee over the left. Let your hips follow in that leftward motion; now take a good footing with your left foot, push upward; that should liberate the left shoulder as all the weight is now resting on the left forearm. Bring your right shoulder up and rotate your trunk to the left. Fine. But now, your abdomen is

resting on the left forearm which is stuck underneath. I need
to do some jerky motions to liberate the prisoner left elbow.
That would work only if this damn pillow were not stuck
under the elbow. So, first things first. With this useless, dan-
gling right hand over my head, remove the pillow; pull up,
pull up, pull harder, here it comes. Still with the right hand,
I nudge the pillow on my left shoulder, filling the space on my
neck between my left ear and left clavicle. Now all I have to
do is to resume and complete my rotating motion to the left so
that I am totally on my tummy, breathing freely, with an un-
encumbered right arm and hand now reaching a few inches
farther. I locate the rim, push up; yes, that's it! but oops, my
thumb has hit metal. I know by the noise it makes on the for-
mica top. Gentle tactile exploration, more metallic noise;
coins perhaps? Ah! What is that? It feels soft, a piece of plastic the size of a guitar pick. That's Marguerite's keys. Eureka!

The cold was now nipping at my uncovered right side, and
only the flashlight was still to be found. The cold made me
shiver. I heard Marguerite sigh and turn in her loft, and I
wondered if I could make the final discovery without waking
her. I bemoaned how simple it is for most people to turn over
in bed without thinking about it, without waking up. Was I
ever like them? It's been ten years now of such slow deteri-
oration that I have lost track of what is normal and what is
not. Even my shaking has endeared itself to me to such an extent that most of the time I no longer feel it. Parkinson disease and I have established an osmotic relationship, like
mistletoe on an oak tree.

But perhaps not, for as I extended my right hand to probe
the counter top between the keys and the window, I felt the
flashlight all right, but I did not have the agility to grasp it in
my shaking hand. ...Bang, smash, clink, clink, clink, clang,
roll, tilt. Before I could assess the situation, a torrent of
Spanish invectives and expletives tumbled from the loft,
filling all the interstices of the van and asking me to remove
myself from the premises.

It was a maddening night, and the few winks we caught were just the teasing but unsatisfactory hors d'oeuvre to the banquet of peace, dreams, and mental abandon that we had justly merited. Before lying down to that elusive banquet, however, I realized that I still hadn't checked the heater. I sat up on the couch, retrieved the keys, and finally relocated the flashlight, which still worked, luckily. But the heater was breathing out what certainly did not feel like warm air. In fact, it was downright cool. It was 2:00 in the morning, and bound to get much colder throughout the night.

I fiddled with the knobs some more, which made the van rock back and forth. I heard some rumbling inside from Marguerite's quarters. Half frozen by my fruitless foray, I got ready to go back in. A foot in the air to reach the first step of the doorsteps, I met Marguerite in the entrance way. Crossing her arms over her lightweight bathrobe, she stood on the steps towering over me, shivering. No more shouts, no more harsh words. I could not quite make out the features of her face, framed as it was by her luxuriant wheel of hair.

—"Maguit?"

—"What?" came out in a weak, tired voice. She was sobbing, quietly.

—"What is it, Maguit?"

—"The toilet tank is full."

Iowa Patrolman _____

And so the road continued to stretch before us. I was walking on the right side of the highway, van in tow, emergency lights flashing. Road runner speed of three miles per hour! Minnesota was behind us now. The walk was entering its adulthood, Minnesota apron strings cast to the wind. Crossing the state line into Iowa had something scary, symbolic and titillating about it. We were really on our own this time.

It took me back to the first time I left France. Monette, my parents and I had just entered Italy. It was early August and we were going for a two week trip following the Po Valley to Venice. It was difficult to comprehend, at least in my young mind, why, across a border that divides two countries, and separates two nations, there was so much similarity between the people living on either side, in the way they dressed, the way they carried out their business. The language was different certainly, but it was made, just like my "universal" French, of consonants and vowels, of intonations and smiles, of laughter and gestures, of silences and passion. So, if everybody were the same, maybe not absolute replicas of all other people, but similar enough to warrant that we all belong to one indivisible species, why, then, why elevate barriers and borders? I was thoroughly confused. Was it because we are too similar, because other people reminded us too much of ourselves, that we had created a border? If they had been different, I would have understood that, but imposing differentiation between kindred spirits was beyond my grasp. Children sometimes have a way of making the most flagrantly logical associations.

John, our hostess's son in Waterloo, Iowa, nine years old, had been told that Mommy would not come home for supper that evening because she had to greet and introduce Michel Monnot to a group of Parkinsonians. His name, Michel, was French for Michael.

—"So this guy is French?"

—"Yes."

—"Then if he is French, how come he has Parkinson?"

Would all problems be that easy to resolve!

In the middle of my rêverie wherein man is good and all is for the best in the best of all possible worlds, I started whistling Sibelius's Finlandia, recalling the lyrics the United Nations adopted as its anthem: "But other lands have people too," when I hear a car rapidly coming to a stop behind the van. Marguerite had already stopped. She must have seen lights approaching in her rearview mirror. I only noticed them now as I heard a door slam. I turned around. A big, monstrous Iowa highway patrolman was rolling his massive shoulders towards me.

—"Oh! my, now we have the law with us. Good morning, Officer."

—"Morning! What do you think you are doing walking on the right side of the road? Can I see your driver's license?"

—"Sir, I usually walk on the left side, but I switch occasionally to prev..."

—"In the state of Iowa, you have to walk on the left side."

—"I know! I am trying to tell you that I switch occasionally to prevent shin splints. If you walked yourself, you would know that it helps to..."

—"Show me your driver's license."

—"I don't have one." I brashly lied. "I didn't know that Iowans needed a driver's license to walk. I mean, in Minnesota I have heard Iowa jokes, but..."

—"But what? Will you please get back to the other side of the road?"

Sensing that I didn't appreciate being treated this way, but knowing also that I would be splattered if I gave this ape the slightest opportunity to become physical, Marguerite opened her door and tried to come to the rescue.

—"Officer, would you please read this?" as she handed him a brochure, one of the 600,000 that had been printed. Slick brochures for the Road to Dignity Walk designed by the Bill Ford Agency, with a detachable self-addressed envelope, in full color. And the dinosaur had the gall to come up to me, flicking the brochure with a twist of the wrist, his mouth deformed by contempt.

—"You know, that doesn't tell me anything about your identity. Anybody could print this kind of stuff."

My scoff surprised him; he looked at me from top to bottom as if he were going to give my measurements to the tailor or maybe to the stone cutter, and at the very instant that I started worrying about his intentions, he took a step back, pivoted, and headed back towards Marguerite.

—"At any rate, you can tell your friend there that he is not fit for this kind of exercise," and as if he were answering a secret message on a concealed radio, he hopped back into his cruiser and sped off, leaving us totally confused.

Iowa IOUs

As the days on the road started adding up, an expected process of forgetfulness and confusion occurred.

—"Now, Maguit, refresh my memory. When and where was it we were given a $5.00 check by that older couple in a green Volkswagen? Was it before Rochester? Or maybe before Owatonna?" Marguerite could always find the answer in her notes. She kept an impeccable record of all the gifts we collected on the road before mailing them to Frank.

She was busy with the driving, my pill schedule, the thank you notes and her Graduate Record Exam, but she predicted that someday, who knows, I might want to write a book on this Odyssey. There was a real story to tell, and there were some moments I didn't want to forget. In fact, I thought that if I were to write a book, there were two such moments in Iowa that I would not omit.

We were approaching Mason City, Iowa. The van was purring placidly paced at three miles per hour. The weather had been lousy all day; it poured most of the afternoon. The Goretex raincoat had finally come in handy. Nearing the end of the fourteenth mile, my steps became heavy. I walked with shoulders stooped, head down, hands thrust deep inside the raincoat pockets, with fingers clenched in a tight fist. The artist who designed the Road to Dignity logo must have caught me in one of those moments. I was tired but, more than ever, determined. I wanted to make it on time for the mayor's reception at the public library at 4:00. I had to make good on all the trust that had been vested in me. I was driven to show the world that Parkinson may yet be unconquered, but it is not invincible. And I do think there had been some change in attitude. I felt I had matured, in the space of just a very few weeks, from a blasé dilettante verging on the cynical into a credible standard bearer, conscious of the hope I represented.

Up ahead there were lights flashing. The escort I had expected at the city limits was actually the size of a crowd. At the prospect of such commotion, I stepped up my pace to a slow jogging. There was also a journalist—I had not seen him—with camera in hand. I realized I had turned into quite a ham. I fielded questions while the loaded, top-heavy cameraman struggled to keep up. Not to lose a fraction of a second of exposure, I pivoted half a turn as I moved past the camera and finished my answer while jogging backwards. The gathering around the cruiser was composed of the patrons of the bar up ahead on the left, the Ace Bar. They crossed the street, glass of beer in hand, to greet the hero.

As I approached the group, I slowed down my pace. The welcoming whistles and hooplas started bursting from all sides while a spontaneous line-up of raised mugs lifted at arm's length formed a protective canopy, much like swords at Annapolis on graduation day. There was handshaking and encouraging and congratulating.

—"Thank you, thank you people, for this fantastic welcome, but how did you know?"

—"You were on TV last night. Great job! My grandmother has Park...How about a beer?" And all the head fattening clapping! Soon, spanning a wide variety of keys, a tune emerged that I finally recognized: "For he's a jolly-good fellow..." Psyched by the applause and a sense of excitement and glory, I felt as if all fatigue had left me, and I am sure I could have gone another five miles. And it's "thank you," to this well-wisher; showing off my thigh muscles to that other; a cajoling "will you walk with me tomorrow," to a pretty woman; a hug to the local giant who proposed a toast.

—"Friends, as you know, some people would walk a mile for a Camel, and I've been known to cross the state line for a Grain Belt, but this guy is walking across this country— would you believe—to raise money to cure a terrible disease. So I say: More power to him. And God bless." And turning his head down toward me, he added: "And I'll tell you what: we just passed the hat around, and this is what we came up with."

He presented me with a fat envelope, in which, an hour later, I happily counted a total of $116 in cash and checks.

—"And don't forget to come back to Mason City."

* * * * *

Americans are indeed, as they say themselves, "something else." Writing a book trying to explain them and their country to the French public would be a very good idea. Where else does one find this ever-readiness to act, to laugh, to help, to say yes, to accept the untried, to tackle the impossible? And if it fails, to try and try and try once again? Europeans may, after all, have those qualities too—they must—but what sets Americans apart from their old-world cousins is the immediacy of the welcome, the no-questions-asked of the helping hand, the sincerity of the parting hug.

One living example of this congeniality was Jack Perry, the man who orchestrated our passage in Waterloo, Iowa. As president of the local support group, Jack pulled out all stops to make our stay a memorable one. He organized a 12 mile walk and he tenaciously kept up with me in spite of enormous foot blisters. I remember feeling queazy as Marguerite cleaned them, but at the same time filled with respect for the courage of this admirable man. He also prepared the welcoming ceremonies at the hospital.

When we arrived at the main gate, clapping and cheers accompanied Jack and me to the mike-equipped podium. I was visibly agitated by all the pomp; but Jack was looking about him, radiant and confident, remarkably free of the usual dyskinesia[3] that besieges him, day and night. A cortege of red-coated ambassadors, white-clad nurses and pale green-frocked technicians were shaking our hands. I later learned that all of these people had taken time off, unpaid, for this reception. That would be something unheard of in France, where instead, members of vying trade unions are more likely to bicker and fight over who gives them the best representation, and where the whole idea of the walk would be considered *a priori* as pertaining to the looney rather than to the noteworthy.

But as we two men stood there, I could not help but notice the ravages that the disease had wrought in us, even though with different manifestations. Jack stood impeccably erect in spite of now wildly uncontrollable movements of the head, arms and hands. On the contrary, I was much more relaxed than a few minutes before, calmer, but with a pronounced slouch, and the beginnings of speech disturbances.

—"Not all Frenchmen are Napoleons, not all Waterloos are stinging defeats..." I began. "This gathering is a living proof that men of good will, will indeed inherit the kingdom..." I believe it was one of my finest speeches. I was very proud.

Following my speech, Jack took Marguerite and me to his house so we could rest before dinner. But the word "rest" is not in Jack's dictionary. Parkinson will never conquer some of us. First, he prepared half a dozen superb apple pies—that's his project every Friday afternoon. Then he took us to his basement where he had set up his shop and was turning out beautiful carvings. He showed off the chestnut cane he had made with his engraved initials on the pummel, the gorgeous decorative knife he was working on, and all the electronic equipment with which he repaired telephones.

But suddenly, Jack hit an off period that was sobering to witness. From one second to the next his medication stopped working, and he went tumbling on the couch, prey to a fit of

---

3 Involuntary movements of the head and limbs.

dyskinesia like I had never seen before. He anticipated our surprise.

—"Don't worry; I'll be better in 20 minutes. In the meantime, would you like to go to the living room and relax? You must be bushed. We'll leave for the restaurant at 7:00."

But the scene remains engraved in my memory, one of the many whose recurrence I hoped my walk would help prevent.

Dinner was an intimate affair, an elegant feast for six couples, each one with a Parkinsonian member. Much of the conversation centered around the walk. And when time came for coffee and dessert, Jack proposed a toast to my success, that it might bring a cure for everyone.

He addressed me expressly, with, "...and to help you reach that goal, won't you come here, my friend. I have brought something that we all want you to have. It is not intended for the APDA, but for you. It is a personal gift, for you, from us, to tell you how much we appreciate what you are doing for us, my friend. What you are doing is the work of a giant." And he reached down by his chair and came up with a splendid chestnut wood cane, engraved with the initials MM on the pummel, and with rings on the upper part. Jack explained that the rings symbolized the number of miles walked and the amount of dollars collected. When I finally turned around to address a collective thank you, big tears streamed down my cheeks. I could not stop my chin from quivering.

12

Practical Tactical Maneuvers

En Route Routine

For all the smiles, the welcomes, the warmth, the timeliness of the message and my pretending to be "in great shape," Marguerite and I were, in truth, starting to feel the strain of the expedition. Marguerite's fatigue was principally mental as she worried about her upcoming Graduate Record Exam and what she was going to do in February when the walk was over. For me, the ordeal was more of an emotional nature. Marguerite was doing her best to be attentive and our many conversations did a lot to dispel the occasional *ennui*—and so did the contacts with Patrick. But Marguerite was not a house full of kids and a sorely missed wife. I longed for the next day, a day of rest, thank God! when I would have time to call Janice. And soon we would meet in Santa Fe for Thanksgiving. Frank, we had heard, was preparing a special treat. In the meantime, I was going to soak my feet....

In our struggle to ease the strain brought on by our chaotic schedule, Marguerite and I tried as much as possible to build a routine based around two-hour blocks of time punctuated by her friendly reminders, "Michel! Time to take your pills."

The hectic demands weighed on our minds. A semblance of routine was as important for the preservation of our sanity as was my walking for the fund-raising cause. I was becoming well aware of that. The feat was not as simple as I had imagined it in the euphoria of the planning. It demanded physical endurance that I had mustered so far, but which was also wearing thin under the stress of haphazard chores on the one hand and "official" duties on the other.

Under the first category came various domestic maintenance errands: the van might need a change of oil; Marguerite might need saline solution for her contact lenses; I would need batteries for the Dictaphone I used while walking; the toilet tank in the van would have to be drained and flushed; and all the thank you notes that were accumulating, screaming to be written and sent out...

In the second category were duties, "official" duties which we could not skirt, avoid nor postpone. Those were usually phoned in by Patrick at variable times, often via Frank's intermediary. They were pleasant duties which the imp and the ham in me loved to perform. Nevertheless, they were stressful because of the flexibility they demanded of us.

—"And you say that we are expected to arrive at the city limits at 2:30 this afternoon to meet the police escort?" I asked Patrick.

—"?... ?..."

—"Can you speak a little louder, Pat? I'm at a truck stop; I can't hear what you're saying."

—"I said, 'You'd better hurry and get most of your walking done this morning cause this afternoon you have a press conference at 3:00 at the hospital.' It's two miles from the city limits. You'll have just enough time. The address is Shoreview Medical Center. The police escort will show you the way. There you're going to speak to the Parkinson patients, mostly bedridden folks. The person coordinating your visit is Joan Morrall. And, careful, you don't want to be late. She's awfully prissy."

—"Spell her name out for me, would you?"

—"...Yes, M...O...double R...."

—"Louder, please; there's a truck roaring by."

—"...Then...A...double L...You should be finished between 3:30 and 4:00. After that you're free until 5:30. That's when a Mrs. Porter will pick you up to go to dinner at the Country Club to meet dignitaries. Meet her in the lobby."

—"Wait a minute. When do I get to take a shower?"

—"I don't know, Dad! What can I tell you!... You're a big boy. Maybe you can squeeze it in while you walk this morning. By the way, they're predicting rain for the whole state, you know! Maybe I should say 'Squish it in' instead, Dad."

—"Very funny."

—"And hold on! Tomorrow is another story: the local support group is having a breakfast. Walking starts at 8:30 at Central Park...everybody is signed up to walk two miles with you. Then you can eat...while Channel 3 TV covers the event. But you'll have to eat hardy and walk fast: you're due in Kansas City Super Deluxe Hotel between 4:00 and 5:00. I'll tell you more about that tonight at the Country Club. Frank finally sent some money and I am supposed to give you half."

—"Now Pat, how's everything on your end? Is Sara holding up?"

—"Everything's under control. Sara is doing great, but you know, it's a job and a half we have. By the time we've made appointments with all the city officials; by the time we've been given the run-around by a couple of reporters; made sure that you'll be covered by at least one channel; figured out which itinerary..."

—"Yes, I know."

—"...will give you the best exposure downtown; battled with Frank to make sure that the weekly money will be waiting at the right bank before the weekend; and that there will be enough of it to quench your gas-guzzling van; and by the time I have promised all the Ms. Morralls that you will be at their hospitals on time, you know, our day is pretty well shot."

—"Yes. You are doing a first class job, Kiddo. Give Sara a big hug for me."

—"I really don't know how you would have made it without us. I, for sure, wouldn't have made it without Sara."

—"I know, I know. You two are the unsung duo of this show. But remember: your indulgences are piling up."

—"Indulgences, my foot."

—"Your foot, nothing. It's my feet at stake. Better yet: What I am leaving you is a legacy."

—"Oh, Dad, your puns sock."

—"OK, I concede this one. Thanks for the news and the banter. I'll see you this evening."

Yes, I was thankful for those chats with my son.

Routine, however, was an elusive commodity. I felt all of a sudden that the naive would-be walker who had etched this private Odyssey had turned into a very public property. At times I had the impression that I was pulled in all sorts of directions without a real direction; that I was dispatched here and there at anybody's whim; that any buffer between the world and myself had been punctured; that I was on tap at will, it seemed, for everybody to have a look at the walking Parkinson phenomenon; that I was part of a show case or the main attraction of the Frank Williams Ménagerie. At one point, I felt we were one of those mangy traveling circuses that appear out of nowhere on the village grounds attracting all the cheap thrillers gawking at the freaks and the beasties. So I dubbed the operation "The Road to Ding-ity."

Routine was also an expensive commodity. We came to appreciate any manifestation of it in our schedule so much that we invented a tea ceremony. It was a two-prong daily affair, at least when events allowed the leisure. Both parts of the ceremony evolved quite simply and naturally. One morning as I was coming back to the room after my daily morning stretches, Marguerite was stretching lazily in her bed, obviously reluctant to let go of the last vestiges of a good night's sleep.

Between two yawns she managed to communicate, "Tu sais, Michel, l'autre jour, tu m'as apporté une tasse de thé.[1] I was in such a bad mood when you brought me that tea, though—incidentally, you could try and make less noise in the morning when you leave the room or you turn on the stupid TV full blast—that I..."

—"No," I anticipated, "we will not have a shouting match..."

---

[1] —"Remember, Michel, the other day,...you brought me a cup of tea."

—"No, no, not at all. That's not what I meant. On the contrary," yawn, "what I was going to say, was that even though I did not acknowledge it" yawn, "I really enjoyed the gesture," double yawn.

—"Hold it! Don't say any more! Go back to sleep," and before I had time to reach the door, Marguerite had guessed what I was up to. I heard her order, muffled by the covers drawn over her head:

—"But this time, boy, make sure you bring a croissant along," followed by a fit of giggling.

From that day on, as long as we did not succumb to the tyranny of the numbing schedule by leaving the motel room or our hosting family in a mad dash, I made sure to bring Marguerite a large cup of hot tea, enhanced, if possible, by goodies from the neighborhood baker's shelf.

It was a good way to secure my own daily indulgences against the wrath of an untamed Mediterranean temper. Once the demon was appeased, we could serenely look at the map so that I might plot the daily course.

My natural disposition always was to plan for more than the 15 miles scheduled in order to make up for the days when I did not walk the distance. But Marguerite had been instructed by Janice and Frank that my safety and health were to be her top priorities.

—"And what do you want to prove by doing three extra miles?" she would ask. "It's not a machismo contest you're in. You're not..."

—"But...listen Maguit, I don't care. I am pledged to walk 15 miles a day. I want this walk to be a success, a true Road to Dignity Walk. For that, I have to be credible. To be credible, I must be honest with everyone and that means all the people who trust in us. I am sure you can see that. And to be able to keep the 15 mile average, I have to walk..."

—"Michel, listen. My job is to bring you safely to Los Angeles. I keep track of your mileage. You're doing fine. So it's senseless to get you overtired and risk not reaching your goal. You will be there. Why burn yourself out? Don't be more royalist than the king. Also, as we say in Italian, 'Chi va piano va sano.' Capisci?[2] Say, have you taken your pills yet?"

—"No, I'll get to it right away. While I do this, tell me what's up for today."

—"Today, for a change, is a non-neurotic day. We can be out of this place and on the road by 8:00. The newspaper reporter who missed us yesterday afternoon said he might catch us as we leave town, but somehow I don't think he'll make it. So, why don't you walk for a couple of hours for the first six miles, then hop in the van for your medicinal herb tea. Will it be mint or lemon grass, today, your majesty?"

—"Most definitely mint, today, thank you."

—"...And you can dictate some thank you notes for an hour; then at 11:00 you walk another three miles until noon. Then you hop in the van again and we drive to the McDonalds in that little town...what's it called? I can hardly read it on the map...Forest City? Yeah, Forest City. That will put you within reaching distance of the city limits where you are expected at 4:30."

—"So, today, I could conceivably go for extra mileage without deleterious effects upon my fragile health, right?"

—"I don't know about that, you sound pretty delirious to me. So forget about extra zeal. The other day on the telephone, Frank was hinting at a huge reception affair in Los Angeles/Beverly Hills for your last walking day, with people I've never heard of—of course, that doesn't mean anything—luminaries such as...oh! I forgot the names...but anyway, they are big shots from entertainment and sports."

—"I know, Maguit. I can taste it already," I've dreamed the scenario. The <u>Los Angeles Times</u> would read:

> It is January 31, and Muhammad Ali is waiting at the Los Angeles city limits for the hero of the Road to emerge from the smog. We have been monitoring

---

2   "He who goes slowly goes sanely. Understand?"

the progress made by Michel Monnot, the French professor from Carleton College, Minnesota, as he trudges his way from Minneapolis on his Road to Dignity. He undertook this walk to increase public awareness of what Parkinson disease is and to raise funds for medical research on the affliction.

Muhammad has recently been diagnosed himself as a victim of Parkinson's disease, and in an unparalleled act of solidarity, has decided to join the effort for the last few miles. All the news media have been alerted to cover the event. Everyone is waiting here at the Los Angeles city limits for this unlikely pair of heroes to meet. According to a previous interview with Michel by the Times, a last minute appearance by Muhammad walking the last five miles with Michel and carried nationwide by the media, would probably more than double the pot already raised by Michel.

The word is spreading rapidly since last night's announcement by the Ali sources, and hundreds have joined the march. At every step the crowd is getting denser. The Los Angeles Police Department is bracing for a throng to reach the Los Angeles Athletic Club where Mayor Tom Bradley will welcome the heroes. In a few minutes, Michel will be here. Muhammad cannot hide his emotions.

And suddenly, coming out of the crowd around him, Michel walks toward Muhammad Ali. The radios are blaring, Muhammad gets up to shake Michel's hand. It is a most poignant scene in this quasi-epic drama of indomitable will over mortal flesh. It surely is a historic encounter. It is a lesson in solidarity and courage from this diminutive Frenchman who has beaten the odds stacked against him, and from this great international athlete to reveal publicly the disabling symptoms of his affliction. There are banners all around sporting the APDA motto: "To Ease the Burden and Find the Cure." And now, in a gesture of mutual admiration, Muhammad lifts Michel in his arms while reporters and cameramen vie for the prime places to take the best shots.

As Muhammad puts me back on the ground, I suddenly recover my sense of reality: I have been daydreaming again, sitting on the side of my bed, waiting for Marguerite to put on her makeup and finish her tea.

Open Letter To Muhammad Ali _____

Unfortunately, my Muhammad dream never materialized. But to this day, it frequently recurs. I guess I have never come to grips with Muhammad's mutism in response to my repeated letters and passionate exhortations to "come out of the Parkinsonian closet." However, I am not likely to ever take "no" for an answer. I have not given up my quest, especially a quest of such magnitude. For this reason, dear Muhammad, I address you one more letter. This time, it is an open letter, a public appeal to you, wherever you may be.

> By going to Mexico City to check on the brain implant operation you have essentially repudiated the aura of secrecy surrounding your affliction, and accepted—whether it be a rare case of pugilistic type or any other kind—that you suffer from a form of Parkinson disease.

> With all due compassion, we welcome you into our ranks and as we gather around you, "the champ," and feel bolstered by your presence in our midst, we

have one simple question to ask of you: Will you, Muhammad Ali, the greatest fighter of all times, come out with us to wage what is possibly the greatest fight of your life?

It is not your money we beg for. What we seek is your presence at our sides to raise the money needed by research to conquer Parkinson disease. We know it is partly a selfish request. We know that there are hundreds of thousands of children in Niger and Ethiopia who are hungry, who need your help and who thrive on the hope you bring to them. Your philanthropy is known the world over and we also know you are solicited from all parts and on all fronts. Indeed, we would not be surprised if your generosity had been abused. But I am not ready to believe, I do not *want* to believe, that you choose to lend a deaf ear to our urgent plea.

Undoubtedly, you know that there are 1.5 million Americans afflicted with Parkinson, and that is more than MD, MS and ALS combined. You must know that the casualties are increasing at both ends of the demographic curve: more elderly patients are being diagnosed simply because there are more elderly people; but also surprisingly, there are more and more younger victims, like you and me, being diagnosed every day.

The phenomenon is not just American. There are 300,000 patients in Mexico, with thousands more cases unreported. And in France alone, 50,000 new cases are identified each year. The Road to Dignity Walk is over. It was an experiment. The response was a show of support reaching well beyond our expectations. Financial gifts earmarked for research poured in from everywhere. With these funds, grants were awarded to medical research teams all over the world.

However, we do not have a cure yet and more projects need to be funded. Medical science has reached a point where victory lurks around the corner. How soon we round that corner depends on how well we stoke the furnaces of scientific inquiry.

So, you, Muhammad, the charismatic athlete of the century, can make a dramatic difference. To this end, I propose a challenge: I will revive the Road to Dignity—perhaps following a different itinerary— if you will only be at my side for the last five miles— walking, wheeling, pushed—it does not matter, as long as you are there for the world to see that we are fighting together and that this latest bout may be your best and most enduring crown of glory.

As you know, every day spent with the monkey on our back is a day half lived. We know we could do so much more. All of us still have many days to fill, many nights to love, many years to live. To the hilt. That's the way we were; that's the way we want to be again.

Let us not procrastinate. Please accept my challenge.

Cordially yours,
Michel Monnot

Word War In Missouri _____

With or without Ali, the fight against Parkinson had to be carried out on all fronts. The first goal of the Road to Dignity Walk was to educate the public. Then I had to decide on which front to engage the enemy. I would identify him, stripping him of his deceptive ability to invade our bodies, undressing him of his disguise apparel. That could be done by taking part in the fight physically. That could also be done verbally, by wielding and unleashing the power of words. I felt qualified for such a sortie.

Like a young maiden lured by brawny biceps, I was seduced from a very early age by the power of words. Big words, little words. I discovered each one had its own life; some vibrating like a hummingbird, others dull like a dry ocean beach pebble; others yet, round and mute like "a globed fruit," to plagiarize Archibald MacLeish. I grew up to the music of French, to the melodies engendered by the artful blending of its euphonic elements; I was weaned on the French poets Racine, Valéry and Villon, on Baudelaire, Apollinaire and Rimbaud. While my high school classmates pursued activities appropriate to our age, I secretly got drunk learning dozens of DuBellay's sonnets by heart.[3] I felt my gestating virility triggered by reciting whole scenes of Corneille's Cid, I felt goose-pimples declaiming Cyrano. I grooved on the venomous alliterations of Orestes ("Pour qui sont ces serpents qui sifflent sur vos têtes?"[4]) and got a buzz from Phaedra's evocative flute-like assonances:

> Ariane, ma soeur, de quel amour blessée
> Vous mourûtes au bord où vous fûtes laissée?[5]

On my own, I ascribed colors to the vowels, unaware that Rimbaud had done the same three-quarters of a century before. Imagine my amazement when I discovered that he and I agreed on the color of two vowels: "i" is red, of course,

---

3   French poet, 1524-1560.

4   For whom are those snakes hissing above your heads intended?

5   "Ariane, my sister, what deadly love
    killed you on the shores where you were abandoned?"

and "u" evokes green pastures and alpine meadows. To this day, I greet the goddess Dawn for my daily dose of luck and indulgences.

But words did not yield only melodies. They could also deliver blows bigger than fists; they could be blunt and devastating as Zola's J'accuse; they could be derisively sharp and wrong-redressing like Voltaire's.

So what did the word Parkinson evoke when I heard it applied to me for the first time? What was its meaning? One thing was sure: whether good or bad, that word was going to see action on the front line of my private war. Parkinson...Parkinson disease...why not Hippocampelephantocamelos,[6] for instance, instead of Parkinson? Parkinson...so rigidly British, so neuter, so grey, so full of Albion's mists. Couldn't it have been Folamour's disease, or Dovel's palsy? No, there was no escaping subterfuge; it had to be Parkinson; nothing else would quite make it. I was stuck with Parkinson. And how in hell was I supposed to play that peach of a trump card?

Even my doctor, Dave Halvorson, suggested something more innocuous, something less telling.

—"If you prefer, Michel, let's call it Parkinsonism or let's call it by one of Parkinson syndrome manifestations like..."

—"Hey, Dave, thanks, but you know me better than that. Let's leave the double talk to Richard Nixon, and let's you and I call a spade a spade and Parkinson a hellish nuisance. OK?"

—"OK, but..."

—"OK, but what? What am I supposed to do, you ask, with that trump card? Well, you watch me, Dave. I am going to play it for all it's worth, and fight tooth and nail, with dirty punches and below the belt blows, with biting, and kicking and screaming out its vile name. Dignity may not be achieved in this round, but a gladiator's fight to the death you might

---

6   Fictitious animal in Rostand's Cyrano.

witness. It's thumbs up for me. *Ave*, Dave, *victoruri te salutant*."[7]

Yes, the monster had to be brought to the light, to the attention of the public. It had to be properly identified. It had to be recognized on sight, without any hesitation. It had to be posted on every post office FBI most wanted list.

Walking across America in that mild-weather fall of 1985 was indeed, if not a novel idea, at least an efficient way to reach people of all ages and conditions and to bring them, afflicted and care-givers alike, under the banner of our common cause "to ease the burden and find the cure."

Our van, thus labeled, was hard to be mistaken for anything else but a traveling display for the American Parkinson Disease Association. On all four sides, prominent placards announced the names of the sponsors, their addresses and phone numbers. Sharing in the credits, and deserving all my gratitude, were the Northfield Hospital—my very first source of support and encouragement—and the pharmaceutical company, Sandoz Inc., manufacturers of Parlodel™ (one of the basic drugs in the treatment of the disease).

With all these slogans painted all over it, the van looked a bit gaudy, but it served as a rallying point, a symbol which was easy to recognize for people who wanted to make a contribution, to chat, to hear, to participate in the effort by walking with me, and having the event photographed for posterity, in front of the van.

Marguerite became very good at fulfilling these requests, making sure to frame her shots in such a way that the APDA phone number was very visible over my co-walker's shoulder. Others were very serious about walking a self-imposed distance or duration. Only upon successful completion of their assignment would they feel, it seemed, worthy of giving me the envelope they had prepared ahead of time.

---

7   Adaptation of the sentence Roman soldiers addressed to Caesar before going to battle: Hail Dave, those who are going to win salute you.

We were in Missouri. Marguerite, having taken her Graduate Record Exam in St. Louis, was relaxed, free to enjoy the autumnal sun. The landscape could not have been more flamboyant, the countryside more peaceful.

The van was parked in a little clearing on the shoulder. I had walked well all morning and was quietly savoring our mid-afternoon tea ceremony, sitting comfortably at the van's folding table. Our thoughts and dialogue were punctuated by long, noisy gulps of a fragrant herb tea. Before setting out on the road, I had asked Tante Edith and her husband Robert to have their herbalist in Dijon prepare a variety of blends for me, each one specifically aimed at the improvement of one's bodily functions. Thus we had a jar for improved liver function, a jar for gall bladder treatment, a jar for digestive purposes, a jar of laxative herbs and a jar for renal function. Some of these blends, I must admit, are vile tasting—nothing like Celestial Seasonings—but others can be very pleasant, such as the digestive one, in which the sweet and blond linden underlines the mint's pungent aroma. The mixture of these two main ingredients provides a tea whose digestive properties are excellent at warding off the evils of yet another fast food lunch.

It was one of those special moments made of laziness and egotism, one of those moments you wish you could keep in reserve for a rainy day, one of those fragile soap bubble moments where all the iridescence presently toying with the sun is going to be shattered, due to explode in a matter of seconds. And when it bursts, a sprinkling of tiny droplets brings you back to the fighting reality of the present. You bolt out of your seat.

—"What could that be now?"

A car had passed us and come to a bumpy stall in the grass ahead of us.

—"It's too early to be a well-wisher," says Marguerite. "We are not expected before 5:00, and there are only three miles left before you have done your 15." The car backed up toward us.

—"Hello, we saw you on the news last night. You must be Michel. We are the Logans. This is Fred and I am Verna. Fred has Parkinson and would like to walk with you to town, if you don't mind."

The gentleman must have been in his late 60s, judging by the stooped shoulders and the fixed stare. I flashed a frozen grin to Fred, since I had been planning to rest a bit more before gobbling up the last three miles. Now, though, with a slow poke in tow, we would have to change that and leave right away. "But Monnot, you s.o.b.," pipes my conscience, "what are you here for?" I contemplated my selfishness and callousness as I noticed the old man struggling to get out of the car. The view induced a quick reversal of my mood. No, I didn't mind at all. How could I? It would be a pleasure.

I gulped down what was left of my gut soother, tied my shoe laces, and hopped out of the van by the rear door. The inconvenience of my new companion's pace was but a small price to pay for the entertainment provided. It turned out that Fred was a retired geology professor who, on two occasions, accompanied Laurence Gould on Antarctic expeditions. His lore is infinite. I am fascinated by his science. When the three miles come to a close and the city limits loom ahead, I suddenly wish the distance to walk were doubled.

And Fred is beaming.

13

Financing The American Dream, Or Footloose And Fancy Free

Gift Horses In The Mouth

Financing the walk itself became an interesting facet of life on the road. Several situations come to mind, but one in particular occurred which became comical only by its repetition. Every week or so, both Patrick and I would call Frank at home in Staten Island.

—"Say, Uncle Frank, sorry to bother you, but we are running out of money and it would be nice…"

—"Yeah, yeah, I'll see to it in the morning. What did you do with the bunch I sent you in Iowa City, anyway?"

—"Didn't you get the receipts? Marguerite sent them to you a few days ago, along with the cash and checks we collected on the road. Don't worry, we're not squandering it, but you know our gas guzzler van is never quenched, and we've been staying in motels lately because it's been cold, and I need a good mattress, etc., so please make sure we have a check waiting in Kansas City."

—"OK, OK! I'll have Jane take care of it at the office in the morning. How much do you need anyway?"

Of course, the money never arrived. Unbeknownst to us, getting money out of the coffers of APDA was such circuitous and lengthy a proposition, that on three occasions along the way we had to borrow from our hosts. In all three cases, they were most gracious and obliging, and with hindsight the incidents will be the source of good stories when we meet again with our friends in Kansas City, or Santa Fe, or San Diego. Thank you, Frank!

As it turned out, we did not need any money while in
Kansas City, our host committee having gone all out to provide us with regal accommodations. Five minutes after we
got to our rooms, Marguerite knocked at my door.

—"Knock! knock! Michel?"

—"Come in."

—"Michel, you'll never guess what's on the table in my
room."

—"Oh! I'll bet a card, a bouquet of roses and a bottle of..."

—"Ah! I see, you got the same treatment. Isn't this
fabulous? Look at these rooms," as she dances all around
mine.

—"I can't quite believe it either. Maybe there's a mistake.
Look..."

—"Oh! Yeah? How many Michel Monnots do you think this
hotel is expecting tonight? This card here is made out to you,
and the one in my room to Marguerite Sandor."

—"Look, Maguit, give me a half hour to wash up and get
dressed, then come back: we'll sacrifice one of these bubblies
on the altar of big time fund-raising." To heck with Walt
Whitman. When Marguerite came back, I sensed an immediate mood swing. The American standard of luxury in contrast
to even the most extravagant of European hotel accommodations must have shaken Marguerite's political senses into
shock, for she launched into a fiery campaign speech.

—"Listen, I don't feel right. I don't want that room with the
two immense beds and a telephone extension in the bathroom. Imagine that: three telephones for me alone! I don't
want those roses and I don't want that champagne. And I am
returning that card to the manager. You do what you want,
but I am sleeping in the van. I hate this display of riches on
me when I don't deserve it and there are children in the
world who are starving to death. This is what capitalism
fosters: the concentration of wealth at the hands of a few, and
misery shared evenly for the rest of the proletariat. Well, as
long as there are workmen striking in Oviedo and political
prisoners in Pinochet's Chile, as long as there is a famine in

Ethiopia, I refuse to eat grapes and drink wine. I refuse to wallow in these obscene and decadent displays of ill-gotten abundance. I..."

—"Hey! Wait a minute; let's retain a little sense of reality. This cornucopia of America that you so glibly accuse and dismiss did not kidnap you. You came here of your own free will, you..."

—"Oh! I see, the inane argument: love it or leave it, hey! Bravo, Michel. Frankly I expected better from you. You mean this is not a democracy and I cannot express my views if I don't love what I see? What about freedom of speech?"

—"What about it? Tell me, Maguit, is it because poverty is so much fun that your father exiled himself from Franco's Spain to capitalistic France 20 years ago? Are you not following a parallel footpath by coming to the U.S. to study computer science—l'informatique—with the best computers in the world, in the finest libraries of the best universities? Your father wanted the comforts of life for himself and for his family. But at least he had neither the impudence nor the bad taste to bite the hand that fed him...and you. You want me to tell you something? I think you and the French kids of your generation are jealous, yeah, you are plain jealous of what America's got to offer, and if you can't get it, you yell 'sour grapes.' As for your social conscience, I didn't see you take great strides toward Ethiopia to relieve her people's hunger; I haven't heard any news reports of French students storming Chilean jails; and don't tell me that you're not an avid, budding capitalist yourself. You never buy for yourself anything but the best quality things that money can buy. I give you 12 years, not one more, to have forgotten where Oviedo is, and to have fired the last three Moroccan cleaning women from your household. That's what I think of your social conscience. You can lump it...or leave it."

—"You know, Michel, you're a real bastard. Here you go wailing across the country that you need funds for Parkinson research, claiming that you want a cure, that you can't wait for it, promising that it's around the corner, provided people give you the fundamentals, and here you go, living like a king, staying in hotels I wouldn't even look at in my dreams, when you should be setting the example and living like a pauper, when you should put your money where your mouth is, instead of putting your foot in it at every step of the way. I tell you, you're one hell of a fake."

That exchange prompted me to broach Frank quickly on the subject. Marguerite was at least partially right: I felt sheepishly guilty myself.

—"You guys follow your merry way and you don't worry about a thing. I'll handle the criticism," Frank advised.

—"No, but listen, Frank, Maguit's got an important point. The question has never been put to us directly, but I have sensed it on the tips of tongues on several occasions. It's bound to pop up. What should we say?"

—"OK," said Frank. "Fair enough; I'll tell you. I'm going to give you some figures that you can use and quote. In the first place, those expensive hotel suites you got in Kansas City and that you're likely to get again as you're heading into big cities like Tulsa, Lubbock, Albuquerque, Tucson, San Diego and Los Angeles, all these are and will be gifts either of the local chapter or of the hotel itself, or both. The APDA is not one penny out of pocket for that. The integrity of your fund-raising is not affected by it."

—"But, Frank, don't you see that you could cash in those gifts and increase the pot by that much?"

—"Michel, you're green at this, so I'll let you in on a secret that every fund raiser knows, and that is: 'money begets money.' Come into town with a threepenny show and you'll sell three-penny tickets to people who cannot afford any more than that. But waltz in with a Met-class opera and you'll sell $50 tickets, and you'll get a hefty donation on top of that. Now, don't get me wrong; I don't discount small donors. They, too, have their place, but don't go around naive and starry-eyed with cockeyed ideas. How much attention do you think you would get from the press if you pulled up in a rickety jalopy, instead of this serious, I-mean-business-looking van?

Everybody wants a share of it, wants to be part of the action, see? Besides—and you're gonna hate me for saying this—but you, Michel, are our hottest commodity. We've got to pamper you. And, as you well know, charity begins at home."

—"So, in effect, you own me and I am nothing but the APDA cheap slut...or expensive whore, as the case may be."

—"Oh, come on, Michel! Let's not exaggerate. I know you're a practical man, with rational views. Do you have Parkinson, or don't you? Do you want a cure, or don't you? And I am going to tell you two more things. First, to be viable, a charitable organization's expenses cannot exceed 25% of the total budget. The APDA's expenses run at 16%. There! That's a better record than the March of Dimes. The other thing—and I'll hang up on that note—congratulations to you and your crew, my friend. As of this morning you have broken the $100,000 mark. Bye."

Soooo...the rooms were gifts! The money was coming in. The expenses were in check. What a relief! Marguerite and I looked at each other: why didn't we think of that ourselves? We could have saved a lot of money, probably, in all those little town motels. All we needed to do was ask. The worst consequence possible was to get "no" for an answer.

Shangri-La

At the peak of its color, the fall around Lake of the Cherokees takes your breath away. The main road sends out unpaved, mysterious tentacles that meander downhill on a carpet of pointillist delight down toward the finger-shaped coves and marina, so still in the sunset. Some resorts have already boarded their cabins shut. The canoes, tipped upside down, are stacked and chained to the rack. The paint is peeling on the huge neon sign that advertised the Riviera Resort, attracted tourists and fried gnats and bugs with a loud buzz on a summer's eve. It will need a new coat of paint before opening again next spring. And only an echo answers to "Anybody home?" Anybody home?

We had been told that afternoon at the shoe store of the little town we went through that somewhere on the shore of the lake was a resort we might want to take a look at.

—"It's very posh," said the salesman, "a resort for millionaires, with tennis courts and swimming pools and health club facilities, a nice place to visit—it even has its private airport—yeah, but you would not want to stay there: it's a vacation place for millionaires. It's down the road a ways. Called Shangri-La."

—"Well, now that Marguerite's got new shoes, I just don't see how we would not be welcome in a millionaire's playground, do you, Maguit?"

The setting indeed was idyllic, the lake bright blue, sailboats doing arabesques, private planes spewing their millionaire cargo from Tulsa and Oklahoma City, condominiums with acres of luxuriant lawns and an entrance motif worthy of a Tibetan Buddhist pagoda. Did people really live to be 125 here?

I requested to see the head manager.

—"Mr. Novak will be with you in a few moments. Won't you please have a seat and relax in the meantime? And can I bring you some coffee?"

—"Thank you." My hands were starting to shake, my knees felt wobbly. A door opened in the lobby. Mr. Novak appeared, headed in our direction, young, smiling, winning.

I lost no time in handing him a couple of our brochures, explaining, "I have Parkinson disease. I am walking across the country to focus attention on the plight, to develop public awareness and to raise funds—we're aiming for $1,000,000—to speed up research. Would you like to contribute to this national effort, by providing lodging and meals for the night?"

Mr. Novak took the time to let me finish my spiel, seemingly unbothered by my stammering and the decreasing volume of my voice. With an inviting motion, he led the way toward the elegant armchairs of the lobby, sat down, taking an obvious interest in the literature I had slipped him, and asked us pertinent and well-intended questions.

Then he got up, excused himself, adding, "Please, wait for me. I'll be back in five to ten minutes."

The place was indeed posh. Through the lobby's windows I could see part of the parking lot. Among all the Cadillacs and Mercedes, our van looked a bit ridiculous. On the terrace, across the pool, under indoor palm trees and tropical vegetation, preparations for a sumptuous Hawaiian luau were under way. Three chefs in toques were working over an open pit. Vegetables and fruit salads were being wheeled out from the kitchen to long buffet tables. Marguerite's hastily recalled scruples were now fully dispelled by Frank's explanations. Her desire to save money for the APDA while enjoying the comforts she craved matched my confidence that we had knocked at the right door. Indeed, Mr. Novak reappeared.

—"These are the keys to your rooms, and these are tickets for the luau tonight and breakfast in the morning. Be our guests. Enjoy yourselves!"

The next day, as we were getting ready to leave, Mr. Novak met us on the parking lot.

—"I was just about to go to your office to give you my personal thanks, and those of the APDA, for your most gracious hospitality. This was a very generous contribution to our cause."

—"Well, I was most happy to be of some help."

—"Mr. Novak? This may be an impertinent question, but I am puzzled."

—"Yes..."

—"Why, euh, why were you so, euh, readily..."

—"Well, you see, my grandfather started this resort. He died a few years ago. He had Parkinson. Unlike you, however, he never accepted it, remained in the closet and suffered. I admire your courage. Best of luck."

—"Thank you so much! It's been wonderful."

The Flip Side Of The Coin _____

Hannibal's soldiers wallowing in the luxury life of Capua
never made it to Rome. We could have become jaded by the
warm welcome, the easygoing receptions, the spontaneous
friendships, but a few sour notes here and there reminded us
that we could not take anything for granted, and that we had
to be vigilant if we were to keep up the integrity of the Road
to Dignity.

One of these warning episodes occurred in a little Oklahoma town. I had spoken to the support group. The reception was drawing to a close. The convener of the meeting, a
social worker at the hospital, came up to us and introduced
Mr. P., who had just told her he would be our host. I had noticed him and his wife sitting in the third or fourth row because during the question and answer period, he had asked
what our plans were for the night.

—"No plans as of yet. We'll likely stay at a motel."

The Mrs. was gone by now. As he was repeating his kind
offer to us, his hands became very agitated and I could not
help but think that he had initiated the offer on his own,
without his wife's approval.

When queried by Marguerite, who also smelled a rat, he
replied, "She's gone home to bake a blueberry pie." We
thanked him and we followed him home!

Marguerite's and my own suspicions were right on target.
Mrs. P. registered a look of surprise when we were ushered
into her kitchen, and obeyed reluctantly when told to show us
our rooms. She led the way; I followed Marguerite. But, pretending to get my bag, I returned to the kitchen just in time
to catch Mr. P. putting a frozen blueberry pie into the oven.
Innocently, I looked away. The blueberry pie dinner was excellent—if single-coursed—but most awkward. Mrs. P. refused to sit down, standing behind us, silent all the while.

Mr. P. felt the need to explain, "Southern etiquette, you know, the better to serve you."

—"Gee," I wondered. "How many servings of blueberry pie can you dish out for three persons out of one pie?" That evening, Marguerite and I retired very early.

The schedule for the following day, Sunday, called for a relatively short walk. I was planning to start around 2:00 in the afternoon. Mr. P. asked us if we wanted to go to church with him and the Mrs.; Marguerite used the pretext of having to clean the van and I had to write thank you notes. We would wait for them to return, then we would advise and draw up plans. Perhaps we could pop a frozen pizza in the oven. We'd see.

As soon as they stepped out, Marguerite said, "Michel, use whatever tactic you want, but get us out of here. They're driving me batty. I'm taking the van to the car wash at that shopping center over there. I'll see you in about an hour. Be ready to go."

—"We'll see," and I locked myself in the bathroom, with the Sunday crossword puzzle.

Three-quarters of an hour later, I heard Mr. P. and the Mrs. coming back from church. Then furtive footsteps in the hallway, past the bathroom door. I listened. I held my breath. Three timid knocks on each of the two bedroom doors.

—"Thank God," said the Mrs. "I think they have left! Say, George...ah! No, damn it! His briefcase is still by the sofa. George, listen to me, you're not going to invite them for lunch, I hope, because if you do, you won't see me around. I told you I didn't want extra people around here, especially more shakers like you."

—"I get so p.o.ed when you say things like that. What have you got against them? They're perfectly..."

—"I don't care what they are. I don't want any extra people in this house. You brought them here; now, you get them out. And don't you dare do that to me again, inviting people behind my back."

The van door slammed in the driveway and Marguerite was back in the house, asking how church was.

—"Oh! It was a good service," started Mr. P. But I nearly dropped my teeth on the crossword puzzle when I heard the Mrs.' two octave higher falsetto say, "Won't you have lunch with us before you leave?"

More crossed than puzzled by such hypocrisy, I bolted out of the bathroom and rescued Marguerite.

—"No, really, thank you for the invitation, but we have to leave right away. Maguit, prépare tes affaires, on part, je t'expliquerai plus tard.[1]

—"Yes, you see, I heard the weather report; there's a cold front coming in, and they forecast rain for later this afternoon. I want to get going right away. So, good bye, and thank you. It was nice meeting you. Maguit, dépêche-toi. Je suis déjà parti!"[2]

* * * * *

So, we were not welcome everywhere with the same zest! In fact, at times I had the impression that all the adulation was only skin deep, and that the success of the walk provoked resentment. Was I overly sensitive? Or too tired? Or a combination of both: depressed? (I was not yet on Deprenyl,™ that wonderful euphoriant that wipes away the blues.)

At any rate, this walk was long. Sometimes I contemplated the possibility that I had bitten off more than I could chew. As my steps resonated on the asphalt, right, left, right, left, arms swinging in parallel motion, I recalled for a laugh my smart alecky answer to a reporter a few days back.

—"Why are you walking to California?"

—"Too far to run!..."

---

1   "Maguit, get ready! We're leaving now. I'll explain later."

2   "Maguit, hurry up. I'm already out of here."

Yes, after all, this may be an overly ambitious project. Perhaps that Iowa cop was right after all. Perhaps. Some questions or comments were indeed upsetting.

At one group meeting in Iowa, a lady remarked that it must be nice to have the time and money to go around the country.

—"You see, most of us don't have the means to do that sort of thing. I wouldn't mind it myself," with a touch of envy in her intonation.

Another time, after a meeting where I had pleaded for more funds to conduct research on animal models, a lady called me up at my hosts' to inform me that she could no longer support my cause.

—"I think it is atrocious to sacrifice animals, innocent animals, defenseless, to make humans feel better. There's enough wanton carnage on this earth already. I don't want to be a part of it."

—"Well, I appreciate your feelings and your honesty. I am sorry, though, that you will no longer support us because we surely can use your help. But will you promise me one thing?"

—"And what is that?"

—"That while you feel that way, you won't have a hamburger, or a drumstick, or a walleye fillet?"

—"And why would you want me to do that, Good Lord?"

—"I'll let you think about it. Good night."

On yet another occasion, a man in his 50s walked up holding the Road to Dignity Walk brochure in front of him in true Parkinsonian fashion: hands heavily shaking and brochure already pre-opened to the place he wanted to contest. It was the "Join Him in an Act of Courage," brochure in which I state:

> My medicines—all developed in the last 25 years—
> make it possible for me to make this walk. But in a
> few years I will not be able to make such a walk. My
> hands will constantly shake. My limbs will stiffen. I
> will have difficulty walking, talking, even swallow-

ing. I will lose my strength and coordination. A normal life will become only a dream.

The man was very upset. While trying to connect an accusing right index finger to the offending text held in his left hand, he was trying to communicate the idea that the statement printed above was totally incongruous with the spirit of the walk.

—"Yes, he's so angry," interjected his wife, "that he did not even want to come and meet you. He thinks that such tear jerky pessimism is completely out of place here, where the theme should be optimism at all cost and never doubting that the cure is around the corner. He feels very strongly about that. He's had Parkinson for about 15 years now, and not once did I see him dejected or depressed or doubting that a cure would come in time for him to enjoy it. He's living for that day."

—"Well, sir, I admire your courage. I wish I had your fortitude. I wish I didn't have any doubt. Thank you for having come to the meeting anyway. And I hope you don't withdraw your support. If we are to reach that goal, we need everybody's contribution, more than ever."

There was also, in practically every group, the one Parkinsonian—or spouse of—who was on the I-am-better-than-you trip, people who get their kicks or who justify their existence from other people's misery. Some did it knowingly, others subconsciously; both to hide their own insecurity, or their subconscious feeling of superiority, and both were absolutely repulsive to me.

—"Oh, yes, George has had it for ten years, but of course, he's not as advanced as you."...

—"It must take an immense courage indeed to do what you are doing, with such a handicap."...

—"Of course, from what you say, I get by with a lot less medication than you."...

—"The way you hold your elbows up when you cut your meat is a dead give away."...

—"I am now at the stages you were about two years ago, I suppose." And so it goes.

Finally, as we forged more and more southward, the mention and invocation of Jesus in dialogues and conversations became more prevalent. Paradoxically, questions about my private life also popped up more often and became more pointed.

—"Are you married?"

—"Are you a Christian?"

—"What do you think about communism?"

—"Do you have any children?"

—"We met your son yesterday and Sara. Do you approve of their relationship?"

—"Is Marguerite your wife?"

—"Where is your wife?"

So, whenever I felt the inquisition coming on, I replied with my brightest smile that, "I would much rather talk about Parkinson and the APDA, that's what I've been invited to do." But that if they were really interested, "I would be very happy to answer their question in private later on." I had nothing to hide, but the innuendos were irritating. At what price glory? At what price research money?

14

Coping 499

Ambulation And Tribulations

Irritating or not, these incidents were part of the package. I had embarked on a long-winded venture. I knew there were bound to be some drawbacks, but I would see my way through. Besides, the benefits derived from this experience far exceeded the inconveniences. I was walking across America: my fondest dream was unfolding in front of my very eyes.

There was no question about it: the walk was a worthy enterprise on many levels, and all the means we enlisted to reach our end were equally worthy of that end. I was also doing myself good by doing others good: I considered the time I spent on the walk to be my philanthropic contribution to society. I felt the radiance of the success thus generated spill over into a rekindling of hope among our battered ranks.

However, when I became conscious of our success, I felt my head starting to spin and to increase in volume. I caught myself preaching on occasions, preaching the gospel of exercises, or the gospel of drugs, or the gospel of hope, faith and charity. I posed as a champion when I actually knew zilch on the subject. Who was I to tell other folks how to go about their business? Did I have a special case of Parkinson or a monopoly on the disease that placed me above the rest of the crowd?

A few years ago, the illness had dealt a punishing blow to my conceit and vanity. But I could feel them growing in me again as I grew used to seeing myself on the local TV news practically every night; that's right, immediately following Peter Jennings, Dan Rather or Tom Brokaw. I threw tantrums in Tulsa when the Lettermen, a singing trio, took precedence over us on the station's overbooked agenda. Ditto in Ventura, California, when all our media engagements were cancelled in favor of more newsworthy news: the space shuttle had just blown up.

Prima Donna. Conceit and vanity. Lest they engulfed me and my endeavor, I had to regain my previous composure. I worked on this problem and mulled it over like a penitent monk, in the silence and solitude of five, ten or 15 mile walks until I reached a liveable equilibrium and heard my inner voice say: do your job serenely, abnegation is self-rewarding. *Ite in pacem.* Go in peace.

Solitude and silence on the road offered a perfect context for cerebral pursuits, but during those introspective bouts, I suddenly noticed a sharp decline in my faculty to concentrate. Parkinson had been at it again. Memory lapses had become more frequent, confusion and dementia more obvious. So, when it was difficult to focus on intellectual subjects, I would switch to more mundane occupations.

I had brought with me on the walk a small soccer ball that I would kick lightly ahead of me, at least on roads with little traffic. It was an exacting proposition to jog smoothly while pushing the ball ahead with gentle and regular toe nudges, not too hard so as not to break the cadence; not too soft so as not to trip over the ball; and straight ahead, too, not too much to the right so as not to chase the ball smack into the path of oncoming vehicles; and not too much to the left so as not to have to go and retrieve the ball—as I did several times—ten feet below in the water-filled ditch lining the shoulder. I don't know how many miles I logged in this fashion, jogging slowly and carefully. I found that the novelty certainly attracted the attention of passing motorists.

I would hear a car decelerate and stop next to me. The passenger rolled the window halfway down to ask if I need help. One afternoon the face was all wrinkled, a face that had worked in the fields and taken on the earth's bronzed tone and parchment texture quality. But past the dry leather look and next to the furrowed crow's feet, deep set and smiling, her brown eyes radiated warmth and hominess.

—"Hi! What are you doing with that ball anyway? Are you training for the Olympics, or what? Or do you need some help?"

—"No thank you, nothing wrong, really, except that I've got Parkinson disease and I am walking from Minneapolis to California to raise money for research. It's a long way, but it's worth it. And I keep in shape, running behind this silly ball."

—"Oh! That's wonderful!"

The lady turned toward the driver. They whispered for a few seconds. Then, a gesture I knew by heart. The man pushed with his hands against the steering wheel and with his feet against the floor raised his right hip and with his right hand pulled out a billfold. Now with his left hand he retrieved a $5.00 bill from the billfold, which he placed between his wife's gaping index and middle fingers. Then she turned back towards me, smiled apologetically and said:

—"It's not very much, but we want to follow your lead and do what we can to help your cause, and..."

—"By all means. Would you mind distributing these brochures around you, to your friends and neighbors?

—"Of course, of course, we'd be delighted."

And she smiled a sunshine smile which rid her face of all the wrinkles and melted away all my fatigue.

In order to measure the advancement of the disease, from its inception onward, I make periodic inventories of my range of motion and commit the most important markers to memory. Thus I know that it was during my stay at the clinic in Arlesheim that I first used an electric toothbrush. Paradoxically, it was during that same period that I was complimented by Dr. Hoffmann on my penmanship. Indeed, it had not changed a bit. And it was during the following winter that my left arm was swinging so poorly that I considered it a record if I could take 40 steps before my arms swung out of phase. For some bizarre reason, eight years later, my writing has become microscopic beyond legibility, but now I can walk indefinitely with my arms swinging freely and in synchronization. I know this for a fact, because one afternoon on the lonely plains of northern Texas, I chased boredom away by meticulously counting, step after step, how many such steps I took between each telephone pole. Sixty-eight steps came back, pole after pole, with my arms swinging normally and with the monotonous regularity that I was trying to escape.

Which, after 20 such poles, led me to wonder: first, how many steps did that come to? Let's see, geez, I couldn't even come to grips with a simple multiplication by 20. I was really losing it! Second, but I would have to sit down with paper and pencil even to start thinking about how many steps it would take me to go from Minneapolis to Los Angeles.

It came back to me in a flash that at the kickoff festivities at Methodist Hospital in St. Louis Park our good friend Mary Strandness, the lady who had found the van for us, had told me that I would be in her prayers every step of the way.

—"Mary," I had replied, "that could add up to a lot of prayers."

—"Well, Michel, if you're up to taking all those steps for the cause, I guess I am up to supporting your project with as many prayers."

So that afternoon, between Wichita Falls and Lubbock, of Ava Crowder fame, I looked back to Marguerite, and signaled for her to drive up to me.

—"Maguit, do you have your calculator handy? I want to do some figuring as we go."

—"Right at my fingertip, boss."

—"Say, that's real organization."

—"The better to serve you and all that you know..."

—"Yeah, those stories where there's always a bear or a wolf or a pussy cat, also known as furry tales, right?"

—"I don't get it, but if you say so. At any rate, if you would be careful not to block the side view mirror...I am ready to compute."

—"OK. I want to figure out how many steps this walk will entail. So, I'll start with the assumption that one step measures approximately one yard, therefore, roughly, 1,600 steps to the mile. Since my daily charge is 15 miles..."

—"That brings you to, let's see, 24,000 steps a day."

—"Good! Now, I remember that when Frank and I planned the itinerary, we counted 110 walking days. So you multiply 24,000 by 110, and that gives us..."

—"OK, I get: two, four, zero, zero, zero, times one, one, zero, equals, equals...move a little closer, I can't see what's coming behind...equals two million six hundred and forty thousand steps. Wow, Michel, two million, six hund..."

—"Wait a sec. We're not finished yet. To this number, I want you to add 20 percent of the figure to make up for the fact that Parkinsonian steps are shorter than normal. So, Maguit, 20 percent of two million six hundred and forty thousand gives us?"

—"Let's see. Gives us five hundred and twenty-eight thousand, which I add to the previous total, right?"

—"Right! Bringing the total to..."

—"Bringing the total to three million, one hundred sixty-eight thousand..."

—"To which..."

—"Over three million steps, incredible, congrat..."

—"To which I add another 20 percent because I am a short Parkinsonian. And that gives us?"

—"It's not going to give us anything but a bloody mess if you keep blocking my side view mirror. OK, 20 percent," she mumbles "of...million...six...thousand, equals six hundred and sixty-three thousand, which I add up, for a grand total, Ladies and Gentlemen, attention! For a grand total of three million, eight hundred and one thousand steps."

That evening in Lubbock, in front of the mayor of the city who had just presented me with yet another key to a nonexistent door, in front of the very active APDA chapter gathered for dinner, I presented a well-received, step-by-step, leg-by-leg account of my feat.

Hello, Northfield! _____

The folks from home also wanted to hear about my progress, but as my Parkinson walked along with me, I was developing an increasingly serious case of telephonophobia—that is, my voice and speech production have become hampered so my confidence is often too shattered to call anyone on the phone. So, getting news home from the road was another source of stress.

I first noticed the symptoms of speech production difficulty in the classroom. Little by little, my early morning class, which was always oversubscribed because I made it entertaining, began to attract fewer and fewer students. More and more, I caught students hiding a yawn, then making no pretense at discretion. At first I ascribed the phenomenon to the fact that it was an early morning class and that students were just no longer what they used to be! The easy trip.... Put the blame on someone else.

Then I also realized that Janice, who used to love to have me read articles in Newsweek to her for lack of time, was no longer requesting my services; she even made excuses not to have me read when I offered. It took me a while to put two and two together, to face the truth: my voice had become a boring monotone on top of which my faulty speech production with its garbled consonants and stammering bouts, combined to make people shun my conversation. They would rather look at their shoes than risk the embarrassment of not understanding what I was saying. Add to these problems a heavy dose of a foreign accent which I have never been able to shed in 30 years of constant practice.

So, gradually, I lapsed into mutism, becoming the prisoner of my own silence. What the hell! I could always write!...and I started polishing my epistolary skills.

A by-product of this growing handicap was my increased reticence at using the telephone, especially if I knew the call was a live interview. The emotional side of Parkinson can be formidable and devastating indeed. It includes depression, paranoia, dysfunction of the parasympathetic system, with undue blushing, shallow breath, shaky voice, inability to function when watched, inability to deal with authority figures, oversensitivity bringing tears, greatly increased shaking of trunk and limbs. The more emotional the interview, the greater the pressure, the more pronounced the symptoms.

And so, as the walk became a daily public speaking forum, I classified the various possible interviews according to emotional response.

The easiest, least demanding situation was the newspaper interview: first the interview without a mike, then the interview with a mike and recorder. Next came the radio interviews; first, taped; second, live. Third were TV interviews, bad enough on the stump, but terrifying in a studio, with an audience.

When I left Northfield, I promised Jim Allen (of the local radio station KYMN) that I would call him every Friday morning for a live interview/report. I made good on my promise the first two Fridays on the road, but soon found all kinds of excuses to avoid this extra pressure; a couple of times because I did not get up on time, another time the line was conveniently busy, a fourth time Jim was out of the office.

But on my hurried nightly call to her, Janice would report, "Say, Michel, I met so-and-so at the grocery store this afternoon and she asked me 'how come we don't hear your husband on KYMN in the morning anymore. We miss his report. We wonder how his trek is going, if his feet are holding up' and I don't know what to answer. Maybe you could make a special effort to get these interviews going as originally set up. Remember, these are the people who put you on the road, they have your success at heart. I wish you could show your gratitude in some tangible manner. If the format of the radio interview is too difficult to follow, you could think of something else. I don't know, since you like to write, why not, for example, send an open letter to the community in care of the Northfield News editor."

—"Love, thanks again for your advice. I'll work on it tonight."

The next morning, I had the following letter in the mail. It kept me up most of the night, but at least I skirted my increasingly crippling telephonophobia!

Dear friends,

A drawled out "Hello" from the oak-blanketed hills of the Ozarks, and a few logbook notes for all our supporters in Northfield.

The walk is going as smoothly as can be expected from a Parkinsonian. Steps are shorter, balance sometimes difficult to maintain. But I have developed an intimate relationship with all shapes and forms of road shoulders. Some are rocky, jagged and abrupt, some are ditch-bordered or hay-lined, some are sterile, courtesy of Round-up defoliant. Some are welcoming as a bikini strap, others have a voracious appetite for the soccer ball that I kick along. Others yet hide under a thin coat of tar, and all, without exception, display dried-up remnants of decaying fur and feathers.

There also is a plague of armored-looking grasshoppers that take off in a cloud at each step, clumsily landing at all angles on the pavement. They seem to share the territory with less numerous but equally active shiny black crickets. I make an effort to avoid stepping on the crickets, but I like the crunchy/squishy noise that an erring battle-dressed, cuirass-clad grasshopper makes under my shoe. Once in a rare while, a bright metallic green/gold beetle scuttles ahead of my giant foot and lodges himself hurriedly under a stone. This morning also, I stopped and looked at a praying mantis. Her head was pivoting like a twin razor blade. She seemed fat and dazed. Must have been digesting her husband.

The Ozarks are magnificent and I promised Janice that we'd be back some fall soon to explore and roam the back roads. The crew is fine. The advance team of Patrick and Sara precedes us by two to three days doing a great promotional job. Marguerite has proven to be an intrepid van driver, once even to the detriment of its innocent dome-light which was shorn off the roof when it met with too low a canopy.

I somewhat regret the fact that we have not been able to establish a routine. As guests of welcoming committees which have pulled out all stops to make our stay a memorable one, it is impossible not to comply with the arrangements made for us even if they include a 9:30 live TV interview one day, and a fanfare and police escort at 5:00 PM the next. It is therefore up to us to adapt our schedule, and lodge five hours worth of walking whenever we can.

As I spend long hours on the road and let my mind wander, my memory never fails to bring me back to the afternoon of September 15th in Northfield. Our first welcome. I think of Maxine and Cynnie and Cliff at the hospital. I think of Paul Wellstone and his poignant speech—how much I envy his public speaking skills—I think of all the members on my steering committee whose efforts and diligence finally paid off. I think of Janice who gallantly stayed behind to cover the home front. I think of Janice and Natalie and Gigi whom I won't be able to hold in my arms until Thanksgiving. I think of my parents who might join us in Los Angeles on January 24th. I pray that this huge endeavor may not be in vain and contribute substantially to a rapid breakthrough. I thank all those who have donated, pledged, supported our cause in any way. May the road from Minnesota to Los Angeles be a true Road to Dignity, and may we all share in the success.

Until then
Michel

15

The Nature Of Courage

Of Marching Songs And Pipe Dreams

All the while, our direction switched definitely from south-ward to westward; the rich fall harvest plains yielded to the arid mile-high sierras; "the smell of buckwheat turned to smell of snow."[1]

Marguerite was discovering a new dimension to her hori-zons, amazed by the immensity of the solitude. Where in Western Europe could she drive like this, mile after mile, hour after hour, without meeting a soul, without encounter-ing a sign of life? As she was exploring the infinity of space, charging her memory batteries with new data banks of ex-periences and sensations, I was drawing on my own memory bank, trying to span two time universes: the nostalgic "then" and the new and raw "now." Only by establishing such a link-age could my two sets of identities (my French-ness and my American-ness; my youth and my middle-aged status; my past good health and my advancing sickness) be reconciled to avoid a schizoid clash. To bridge this abyss safely, I happened on a superb tool.

Before setting out on the road, I had asked my parents to send me the lyrics of old marching songs that Papa had taught us in Uxeau during physical education classes as we goose-stepped our way, two by two, from the schoolhouse to the stadium (a 60 yard track of unpaved road behind the cemetery). It was limited at the far end by a sand pit which the municipal caretaker used as his sand supply source for

---

1   From the poem "Mt. Rainier," Spring Eglogues by Ann Hyde Greet, University of California-Santa Barbara.

tomb grooming. It doubled for the occasion as the high jump and broad jump pit for our athletic accomplishments. And we would belt out those songs for the whole village to hear.

Because of forwarding mix-ups, the song package did not reach us before we arrived at the Oklahoma City Post Office—General Delivery. It was a true joy to sing those songs again on those long and deserted far west stretches of road. They carried with them the same warmth, the same emotional intensity, the same gilded velvet opulence as they had before. They carried hints of spring fever like the hot, sensual, anachronistic Chinook when it unfurls its smooth and fiery tongue from the snowcapped peaks, melting the snowy slopes down to the green grass beneath; the Chinook sower spreading summer whiffs in the smack of bitter cold winter nights. Like the howling Chinook, lyrical and nostalgic, these songs stripped loose huge chunks of memories from that earlier life when Maman's arms were the impregnable fortress and the ultimate nest; when dawn always came after a good night's sleep, night after night after night; and friends were forever.

But now, today, as I rocked back and forth on the swinging love seat on the porch of Fort Justice, in spite of these songs, I knew I was a sick man. Before I could do anything about it, my daily diet of miles had taken its toll; I felt my mind retreating to regions where my mental landscape was blurry, where I could no longer tell whether my illness was a curse or a blessing, whether my whole life had not been a flagrant paradox.

As I sank further, comfortable in the warm cocoon of the pale winter sun, I longed for a cooling off of all the passionate fires that had burned inside me. I welcomed a new quest for a simpler happiness. I smiled at passing images of my homecoming: step by step, I was approaching Burgundy. I could see the steeple of the basilica at Paray-le-Monial; I could smell the must in Pépé Monnot's cellar. A fly landed on my index finger. A reflex twitch shooed it away. I counted 3:00 being struck on the bells of the Uxeau church. I heard my mother's hands clap the end of recess in the school yard. Then I savored a circular look: the sky was so limpid in its ocean of blue where grazing cumulus mirrored their shadow upon the jigsaw puzzle of the hay fields!... I anticipated the glow of the sunset upon the golden cuts of wood neatly stacked in the clearings. I paraded through the smoothly orchestrated ballet of Spring's Fashion Festival where the hawthorn-decorated hedges were replaced by the bridal gown of the blossoming acacias, itself preparing the way for the white umbrellas of the blooming elderberry bushes.

I was staring at the cement walk in the courtyard of Fort Justice where a gust of wind blew away some candy wrappers, when Maguit's silhouette finally appeared to bring me back from my nostalgic journey.

—"It's time for your pills! And you should start walking."

I had to wake up, to forge ahead, not only to find solace to my woes, but to bring hope to all those who, along the way, had put their trust in me.

—"Michel," asked Marguerite, "do you realize that in four weeks this walk is going to be over? This is the first Christmas I've spent away from my family. I suppose that's why I feel homesick. I miss them, and I miss Andrew. Did I tell you, I got a letter from Andrew at the General Delivery in Santa Fe? He's coming to France for Easter. I can't wait."

We had just spent a month resting in Santa Fe between Thanksgiving and Christmas. Janice, Natalie and Gigi had joined us for a couple of weeks, and Patrick had backtracked from his advance post. Frank and family had also come from New York for Thanksgiving dinner at The Legal Tender, a dinner theater in Lamy, a small mining town half an hour away from Santa Fe.

And now, a few days later, somewhere between Phoenix and Albuquerque, a Basho haiku tugged at my memory:

With a hat on my head
And straw sandals on my feet

I met on the road
The end of the year

—Basho (translation by Keith Harrison)

Of Doctors And Wise Men _____

A few more steps and it would be Los Angeles. We had carried our message across the land in our own peculiar way, a blend of Thomistic self-doubt sprinkled with childish naiveté.

—"Incredible! You've made it! Glory be!" said one part of me.

—"There never was any question you wouldn't make it," would reply the other.

Little by little, as the end came in sight, whether I liked it or not, the Road to Dignity Walk had become a public entity, a standard bearer for tens of thousands of people, a chariot of hope, a vehicle of renewed pride in the hellish race to find a cure. It had become a powerful instrument to bolster teetering determinations, a loaded weapon deterring surrender. To some it represented a bold step toward the realization of a dream, to others the incarnation of a vision.

And whether I liked it or not, I had become a symbol; part of me was public property. And in some misty eyes even I could read the flattering—but how preposterous—notion that I loomed more important than my message.

I had become Dr. Monnot, a title whose use I had always studiously shunned, as I found it pretentious and misleading. Let the M.D.s be the doctors. Professor in X discipline, or expert in X field should suffice, and the confusion in people's minds will disappear.

—"Dr. Monnot," someone in the audience would ask invariably, "I would like to know what you think of such and such medication, and what kind of treatment you follow."

—"Well, let me first say that I am not an M.D. and that I have no expertise nor the right to influence your schedule of treatment or prescription. But personally, this is the combination of drugs (and their quantity) that seems to work for me. My own daily regimen consists of Sinemet,™ Symmetrel,™ and Parlodel.™ And I intend to add Deprenyl™ as soon as the walk is over and I can go to Italy to get it, since it is not approved by the FDA. Other tricks which seem to work for me: first, taking my pills between meals helps, I think; second, taking the Sinemet™ in smaller dosages but more often, seems to even out my highs and lows. But I repeat, if you have any doubt as to your schedule, by all means talk to your neurologist, or to his colleague down the street."

In the same way that hate is negative love, courage can easily be turned into cowardice, or negative courage. To be courageous, for instance, when a big, tangible reward is in sight, or to be courageous in order to avert a yet greater evil, does not really constitute an act of courage. For courage is free, selfless, unpremeditated, gratuitous. Such actions can be considered instead as nothing more than Faustian transactions with the devil. And in a sense, my Road to Dignity was paved with such egotistic intentions. I was walking all those miles, 'tis true; I was sweating; I was suffering from aches and pains; I was breathing all those exhaust fumes; yes, it seemed courageous, but if I was walking, it was really to raise money for a selfish reward. I was doing it because I saw a direct correlation between my actions and my ultimate goal: to find the cure. Helping others was a mere logical consequence, not a primary motivation.

On the other hand, Ken Mills of Tucson is a courageous man, for his actions are gratuitous. Acutely dyskinetic at times, he still manages to cope gracefully and to function satisfactorily, albeit slowly. When we met for the first time in Albuquerque's Old Spanish Town, we hit if off immediately, exchanging notes, views, jokes, poems, and philosophic considerations on our comparable states of decrepitude. He apologized for not being able to welcome us as he would have liked to, but he already shared his small apartment, he explained, with Carlton, an elderly Parkinsonian gentleman, a retired physics professor whom a year earlier Ken had rescued from solitude and despair and nowhere to go.

It was bizarre, even comical in a macabre sort of way, to watch Ken, contorted by his own erratic motions, trying to help Carlton ever so gently in and out of the car. For he took the old man everywhere with him. And at the New Year's eve that we all spent together in a Flagstaff restaurant, everyone was moved by Ken's unwavering attentions—suggesting dishes that would be easy to eat; tying Carlton's bib behind his neck; pushing his chair to the perfect angle and distance from the table. Carlton's resources and faculties were greatly diminished and impaired. At the end of the meal, we all swallowed our tears when, in an ultimate surge of willpower with lips a-trembling, Carlton tried to articulate what I lip-read as a fragmented "thank you." But only tears rolled down the stone faced mask.

A week later, we heard from Patrick that Carlton had died. Peacefully. In Ken's arms. In that sense, Ken is more than a hero. He is the best example I know of what Jean Houston, in The Possible Human, calls a 'mensch':

> A mensch is a full person. Golda Meir was a mensch. A hero is a one-shot deal. A mensch is forever. A mensch is on all levels. A mensch loves to take his children to the zoo and he does not mind doing his income tax.... When a mensch walks down the street, even the sidewalk feels good.... A mensch celebrates life...he loves to learn, he loves to laugh, he loves to listen...but a mensch also knows how to cry.

By all definitions, then, I am not a mensch. But perhaps because they saw me as a gutsy fighter, a sizable number of Parkinson victims and care-givers entrusted me with their personal complaints *vis-à-vis* their general practitioner or neurologist. Could something be done to redress the current practice of 20-minute consultations? It seemed to most of us indeed, that especially in the early stages of slow development of the symptoms, and later on in the delicate stages of fine-tuning the drug treatment, a physician simply cannot in a routine examination get a convincingly clear and accurate picture of where we "are at" nor necessarily hit upon the best suited treatment as a random salvo in a Battleship™ game. Hence the insecure impression we get of being nothing but witches' brooms at the hands of an apprentice sorcerer.

I have certainly experienced this sinking feeling upon leaving the doctor's office for not having been able to explain how I felt at certain times of the day, or for failing to describe right there and then, how that strange and episodic pull in the calf muscle affected my walking. And could he, the doctor, tell me whether that twitch was a signal of advancing Parkinsonism, or the onset of drug derived dyskinesia. He wasn't sure, would reply the doctor, he would need more time, more observation before pronouncing himself. Maybe I could help him by bringing with me at my next trimester visit a detailed list of self-made observations?

In spite of the apparent putoff, this was a worthwhile suggestion as it made me more conscious of my body's functions. At least it took care of the inevitable short-term memory failure the minute I entered the office. But in so doing, was I not looking for the wrong clues, was I not deluding myself as to the importance of such and such indices? And what kind of a help was that recommendation supposed to be to an elderly couple, for instance, without any notion of anatomy?

—"Why not, instead," I asked my trusted neurologist, "why not let me come to your office, let's say every other month, for a one full day observation session? I would come at opening time, sit in the office, roam around the clinic, watch a couple of shows on TV, go out for ten minute walks, type some letters on my take-everywhere-with-me Canon Typest*r 6. I would take my medicine regularly, and a nurse or a technician in the office could monitor my shaking or my stiffness, give me periodic handwriting tests at the beginning, in the middle and at the end of each drug intake, make note of every twitch and physical sensation I would care to bring up. And Lord knows that in the course of a day, zillions of questions pop up, some relevant, some totally asinine. But that would be for the doctor to determine and to propose an appropriate treatment."

The medical establishment raised an uproar of objections, naturally, "That would be tantamount to running a circus in the office, nurses would have to be trained, a protocol would have to be devised. And finally, we, the doctors, are already submerged by the number of patients we see everyday. How could we take care of everyone who seeks our services if we lengthened each consultation?"

So the other day, as the dental hygienist was laboring to restore some brightness to my endangered Parkinsonian smile, I was struck by an obvious analogy: why not conceive a tight Parkinson diagnostic protocol, train classes of qualified technicians who, expert in video film shooting techniques, would go to the patient's home for the day and videotape salient moments in the hour by hour unfolding of the patient's day, and edit the tape for the doctor to peruse at his leisure, before seeing the patient? Just a suggestion.

Johnny, The Reporter And The Consul _____

From Ken Mills and Tucson, it was west again toward Yuma with an afternoon detour to San Luis, Mexico; Marguerite wanting to have her French passport stamped with a Mexican visa at all cost. Then onward to San Diego, LaJolla, up along the coast to Oceanside, inland toward Palm Springs, and finally back to the Pacific; Orange County, Anaheim, Newport Beach, Santa Monica, Santa Barbara and back to Hollywood. The last few weeks went by very fast.

It was now time to take stock. Whatever my motivations had been, totally selfish or partially altruistic, did not matter much in the long run. By all accounts, we had accomplished a lot. We had reached throngs of people, both along the route and in support groups throughout the country. A magistral fund-raising campaign, simultaneously launched from the APDA national office, had yielded an unexpected amount of money and promises for more. On that score, we had no reason to complain. However, a whole lot more needed to be done in the realm of education, both of the masses and of the victims and their care-givers.

I felt there was an ocean of despair out there whose surface we had barely scratched; I knew that overt and covert reactions of hostility, uneasiness, embarrassment, even of simple curiosity from the public still greeted us wherever we went outside the Parkinsonian community. But from the turnout at speeches and meetings, I could tell that huge segments of the Parkinsonian population itself were still living in the closet, victims of needless shame, guilt and self-pity. While studies showed that the illness cuts across all segments of the population regardless of race and sex, I found that the vast majority of the afflicted who came to these support group meetings was composed of white males. Many fewer white females, hardly any black males and I do not recall having met a single black female victim. Why should it be that way? Why such a waste?

Yes, public education had a long way to go, both among the population at large (to foster a minimum understanding of our handicap) and among our own ranks (to console and cajole and quiet our fears). Personally, I was still reeling against that myopic Carleton dean—I wonder if there will ever be a spot in my heart to forgive him—for his smug ignorance of my condition and his crass unwillingness to step out of his tower and learn something new for a change.

Another example I used to illustrate my speeches had taken place about six weeks prior to the beginning of the walk. In order to be my van driver, Marguerite had applied

for a visa of unusual purview, and she had been summoned
by the American Consulate in Lyon to appear in person and
justify her request. She had asked me to come along. I remember the scene vividly.

The appointment was for 2:15 PM. We arrived shortly after
2:00. The waiting room was almost full already and more
people were still coming in. The room was a small rectangle
with a window in the back wall overlooking the mighty
muddy Rhône. This window was swept at irregular intervals
by the Mistral[2]-whipped tail of a Stars and Stripes hanging
from the balcony one floor above. The two side walls of the
shoebox shaped room had no opening. For decoration, only a
cheaply framed photograph of the President on one side; on
the other, a clock—to keep track of the speed of the
bureaucratic immobility, I mused.

The chairs had been neatly arranged as in a traditional
classroom, six rows deep, five chairs abreast, all facing the
front wall—the better for everyone to observe the newcomers
who walked in the door on the right, and the better to
listen—when not drowned by babies' cries—to the private
business being conducted on either side of a huge bulletproof,
two-way radio equipped glass window on the left. Behind
that window, in the aquarium-like office, an armada of
various size fish periodically came to the light and retreated
into the shadows.

A frisky guppy would undulate to the mike and announce
in a shrill voice, "Monsieur et Madame Archambault?" (Ah!
Newlyweds going to Disney World for their honeymoon!). Or
a fat cigar-smoking zebra fish would weave itself to the fore
among the desks, all the while keeping a vigilant eye on the
fauna out there in the waiting room.

—"Miss Sandor?" bubble, bubble, and ring of smoke
bubbles, "The vice consul will see you in half an hour."

---

2   The Mistral is a powerful wind which blows in the Rhône valley from
     Lyon to Marseille.

A flip of the mandible and without ceremony, he turned his back on Marguerite who had sprung out of her chair.

Soon everyone had become privy to everyone else's business. There was the oversize backpack toting, hippie looking American student who had been rolled in a seedy part of Marseille the night before and needed to call home for money. He probably did not know that he would have to go to Paris immediately for issuance of a duplicate passport.

There were the newlyweds, anxious to make that American Airlines connection in Orly the next morning. After all, it was not their fault if the travel agency had kept their passport until yesterday.

There was also the ubiquitous Assistant Professor of French on sabbatical from his post at Stanford University and recipient of a one-year Fulbright Fellowship who wanted to know what limitations were placed on traveling to North Africa (Algeria and Tunisia). He was a specialist in Francophonia and he just thought he would visit these two countries for two weeks before he started his tenure at Lausanne. But was it safe for him? You see, his name happened to be David Siegelman....

And there was the widow who was going to Cincinnati for her yearly visit at her daughter's, the war bride, and her grandchildren, only this year she had applied for a six-month visa instead of the usual two-week one when her husband was alive. Because this year also, she was going to meet the latest arrival, a great-granddaughter in Tucson, Arizona. Oh! My, she'd never traveled so far away. But what a way to spend the winter, she'd been told.

Finally the vice consul appeared at the glass pane.

—"Miss Sandor?"

—"Yes."

Marguerite got up making the mistake to sigh while looking at her watch. I followed her to the window.

—"I believe I only called one person to the window..."

—"That's right, sir," I said, "but I'd like to speak to you about Ms. Sandor's appli..."

—"Could you speak up, please?" he shouted in the mike for everyone to hear.

—"Precisely, Sir, I would like to speak to you in private." My voice was growing fainter. "You see, I have asked Ms. Sandor...."

—"Look, Sir," he said, "you'll simply have to speak louder. We have a lot of applications to process this afternoon..."

—"OK," I shouted with a touch of anger, and my legs started to shake. "I would like to conduct this interview in private. I have difficulty standing; I would like to talk while sitting down." Now I was shaking and in addition, my speech was modulated to a decrescendo of uneven syllables. He sensed something was wrong. I sensed his split second hesitation.

—"Are you feeling all right?"

I had the advantage.

—"No, I am not feeling well. There must be a place around here where I can present my business comfortably, sitting down, and where I don't have to shout my problems to the four winds." I just did not want the whole world to know that I had Parkinson....

—"I am sorry; we're simply not equipped in this office to hold private interviews, but please, Sir, just a minute. I will call the consul. Who should I say..."

—"Monsieur Monnot and Mademoiselle Sandor. We had an appointment for 2:15."

The consul appeared, debonair, holding the Sandor folder in one hand and some papers in the other. I recognized at a glance the French newspaper clippings which related my proposed walk: "héros local, va faire la traversée des Etats-Unis à pied pour combattre la maladie de Parkinson."[3] I had sent them to Marguerite at the beginning of the summer to complete her dossier. From that point on, it was a breeze. The

---

3   Local hero will undertake walk across the U.S. to fight Parkinson disease.

consul was urbane; he was prompt with congratulations and also with apologies for the inhumane reception, "But with all the rampant terrorism, I am sure you will understand…"

Another example I liked to use to illustrate the ignorance of the public *vis-à-vis* our illness, even when coming from well-intentioned people, refers once again to Muhammad Ali. It was in Palm Springs. After a long interview, Lynn Simross of the Los Angeles Times had invited us for dinner. The conversation was a natural extension of the interview. Lynn volunteered that she had been at a social gathering about six months before. Ali was there among the guests and it was obvious something was drastically wrong, but it was not until someone asked for the champ's autograph that Lynn concluded he had lost all his faculties.

—"Imagine," she said, "there he sat, with pen and paper in his hand, for a good three minutes before he could write his name. Imagine that! Muhammad Ali, unable for three minutes to remember his own name."

It took me the rest of the evening to convince Lynn that this was NOT the case, that Muhammad was as sharp in the head as he had ever been, that he had not "lost it" as she said, but on the contrary, that his delayed reaction was due to a symptom well-known of Parkinsonians, namely, the inability to initiate movements.

Herein lies the crux of our education program: the difficulty to explain the elementary, to demystify the obvious.

How do you carry the message across, for instance, that you are not drunk as you go teetering down the street, or slam your shoulders into doorjambs? Are you credible to your interlocutor over the phone when your voice starts shaking and diminishing and you sound more seethingly furious at him than helpless at controlling your own voice? Do you not feel childish having to stop in the middle of a joke and explain to your assembled dinner guests why your breathing becomes so erratic and you have to send eyebrow signals for your wife to deliver the punch line? And why do you need three tries to slam a car door shut? Working up a sweat by simply tying your shoelaces is another interesting proposition—when you are not the subject of such an experience yourself. And why does your elbow constantly slip off the edge of the table, or your butt off the edge of the sofa?

But scarier by far is the panic that grabs you when you periodically realize that you've come down another notch because you can no longer do the little wrist exercise that you could still perform six months ago. The world seems to do a slow meltdown all about you. Suddenly, nothing is sure anymore, all your past points of reference (like your family status, your professional rank, your religious convictions) become moot points. Do you remember that sinking feeling you felt the first time you were stuck in the bathtub, and your wife was at work and the telephone kept ringing? Or the first attack of hastening movements that sent you tumbling on the uneven shag carpet, while you ticked off in your mind all the other symptoms yet to come? And what happened to your macho self-image the first time that your stiffness and clumsiness overpowered your desire to make love to your amorous and welcoming wife? The shock was so great you even wrote in your diary as an apology:

> The intensity of my desire for you is matched only by the force of inertia dragging down my limbs, and by the sorrow of being unable to translate this desire into long and languorous caresses or powerful embraces which, frustrated and frozen in mid-gestation, do nothing but clutter my mind.
>
> Willpower disintegrates into palsied velleities which have nothing in common with the pulsations I used to know and which now haunt me. All my sap seems to have dried up. All my shivers turned into sobbing fits. If this is life, I prefer to die.

And you rehash in your mind scenes of the most powerful movie you have ever seen, <u>Johnny Got His Guns</u> starring

Timothy Bottoms. Johnny gets his gun all right. Johnny goes to war. Johnny comes back home without his arms, or his legs, or his face. All Johnny can now do is hear what goes on around him and blink his eyelids to say "yes." He can think clearly, he can hear his attending VA medical team split over what to do with him—euthanasia or keep him on the breathing machine for the rest of his life? He's got a ways to go: he's only 22. Who knows if he's not brain dead already? And what's left of Johnny's body is frozen stiff in his mind, inert, stumped, unable to initiate speech or any action.

And you know that if another Fleming, or Pasteur, or Cotzias does not come to the fore very soon with a new drug or a miracle treatment, you may be the next Parkie-got-his-fun on vegetable row. Not a savory prospect.

So you pack your bag and you take to the road. Not with a missalette but with a beggar's cup. Not to escape, but to help. To help yourself, to help others. It really does not matter.

16

Hail To The Chiefs

Take The Ball And Run!

The message is clear. One has to be a realist. No one suffering from Parkinson has ever been cured. Unless there's an unreported miraculous case. But that would come under "divine intervention," not medical case history. Most of us have to contend with the rule, rather than with the exception. So, it is very likely that all of us who have Parkinson today will die with Parkinson. In order to survive as long and as well as possible without losing our minds to impatience, we must maintain a healthy dose of skepticism. Yes, a cure may be announced in tomorrow morning's Los Angeles Times, but let's not wait with bated breath. We know! It's happened before.

A few months ago, for instance, the airwaves came alive with the news that a Mexican medical team had performed successful adrenal cell brain implants in humans. Only long enough, however, for the medical world and the patients' universe to burn like a wild bonfire, as bright and promising as it was short-lived. New feedback is just now coming in, which calls for extreme caution, four of the eleven patients having died.

As we are reeling back from the disappointment, we cannot but heed that caution. We have to be realists: adrenal cell brain implants may not quite be the answer yet. We have to be skeptical, patient, realistic. But not pessimistic. We all have to find our individual *modus vivendi,* an accommodation principle whereby we understand that, while we cannot yet shake loose the dragon's clenched teeth from around our necks, we can clearly give him an excellent run for his money.

When I was on the Walk, I was disappointed by what I considered a setback one day. In Kansas City a foul rain storm made havoc of the reception committee's calendar of events. The march was cancelled, as was a part of the activities that had been projected with the Kansas City Chiefs. We did visit, however, the locker room where I knew I would feel like a dwarf in Gulliver's house, and Otis Johnson graciously led a tour of the Chiefs' owner's apartments. Unfortunately, because of the soggy field, I missed the chance of a lifetime at one of my dreams. It unfolds like this:

I am a meek, humble, bespectacled professor who does not understand why he has been fingered out by the Fates to lead his students and colleagues out of the beleaguered field of foreign language teaching. All he knows is that the situation is desperate and he has but one try to do it. Then he gets all dressed up in a gaudy football uniform, there's a loudly cheering throng, the quarterback is Tarkenton who yells at him numbers he cannot understand, but that's OK because the name on the #10 jersey fades away to be replaced by Parkinson, and there are defensive backs out there as big as houses ready to make mishmash of him.

But suddenly the corset/uniform loosens, his cemented feet in the ground are miraculously freed, a flea-flicker combination gives him the ball that he catches on the fly, and he runs...oh, boy! Can he run! He's suddenly the best running back in the league. He fakes; he dodges; he's got the first down; the crowd goes wild; coach Madden pours himself out into the frame of Frank Williams; he eludes the defensive backs who have never seen such nimbleness; they miss him and go crashing into each other, thudding their sparse brains into oblivion; 25 yards down, 15 to go; someone grabs him by the jersey, he trips over a body. Is he down? Is it over?

The crowd comes down from the bleachers, emptying onto the field. He fakes a slip but goes into a somersault instead and he goes on; ten yards to go; the goal line is in sight; eight yards to go; he's about to enter the Health Hall of Fame; seven, he knows he can't look back; six, immortality is at hand; five, it's Pandemonium on the field; four, three more steps; a diving leap would carry him over the line; better not, though; two, the flash of a white shoe in his stride, a crashing hammer blow on his elbow; the ball shoots up in the air as he spins around and falls. Fumble!... Everything recoils in his mind like the air fluttering out of a balloon. Everything disappears: the French students and the student teachers, the Vikings and Tarkenton, the Chiefs and Parkinson, and the fumbled cure has become the burden.

Except, this time around, with the Chiefs using the spot as a public service announcement, we were going to make it across the finish line, like the man in the MONY life insurance ad on TV. Damn that rain.

The Jock

There exist, of course, other avenues of defense. One that I perceived immediately and instinctively to be of the utmost importance was a real exercise regimen. Being a Parkinsonian jock isn't just a dream. Rigorous and regular exercises make an enormous difference in my daily life. For example, my program includes, (ideally) every morning: 20 minutes of stretching exercises, many of which were shown to me by various physical therapists; a combination of alternate walking and jogging, for a total of at least one and a half miles; a session in the weight room, where I hang loose from the horizontal bar for a couple of minutes to rest my back and shoulders, and then catching my breath, I gather and concentrate my strength on a half dozen chin-ups. Next, for no more than ten minutes, I harness myself to the Universal machine for a toning session of light weight iron pumping and a set of sit-ups. I then switch over for a few minutes to the arm building station where I stretch my fingers, rotate my wrists and build up forearms, biceps, triceps and deltoids.

Finally, if I am not too tired by then, I go to one of Carleton's six squash courts located above the track. In my first years teaching at Carleton I used to play squash there with my colleagues Wolf Chamberlain and Ted Hunt. But Wolf has been gone now for over seven years and I have become too slow and too clumsy to give Ted a good game. So now I only pay him tribute and thanks here for having been—for several years into my progressing incapacitation—a patient friend and a needed trainer, pacer, game mate and cajoler on the numerous days when the will was weak and determination deterred.

To remedy the lack of playing partners—necessity being the mother of invention—I devised quite naturally a solitaire game which I call "toe ball" or "mono-ball" and which is really soccer with a tennis ball in a squash court. Alone in the court with only a yellow tennis ball to suffer my grand slams, I chase and kick said ball all over the court, practicing the accuracy of my kicks, a skill much easier to attain with a soccer ball than with a tennis ball. But a soccer ball would be too big and unwieldy for the court and a squash ball is not resilient enough. And I kick and I kick, left foot, right foot, exterior shot, inside shot, knee control, head control, drop kick, set kick, an occasional countervolley shot, and very rarely, an attempted reverse scissor kick, most of the time missed because of the fear of landing on my back. But this kind of workout I find a bit too harsh nowadays.

While in the squash court I also practice throwing the tennis ball against the far out wall, baseball pitcher style, right arm, left arm, scooping up the ball with the left hand, throwing with the right hand, switching procedures then basketball hookshot style, etc. The combinations are endless.

I know. It's not easy to persevere in such a program. Winter morning, 6:00 AM, 20 degrees below zero, snow two feet deep on the ground, who would not be tempted to pull the blanket over his eyes and let the alarm ring...and ring...and ring. It is hard, indeed, but there are rewards, not the least of which being—as you pull down on your face mask to adjust

the hole for optimum breathing—the thought and the faith
that spring some day will be back and you'll swallow the first
spring gnats and bugs as you go running into the arboretum!
Delicious, crunchy, bugs!

In the meantime, George, your colleague and running
partner who has just woken you up with the one ring telephone code, is already waiting for you in the street, warming
up with stretching exercises, and will start on his own if you
don't get a move on. Of all the formats I have devised to insure a continued and steady running/jogging program of last-
ing value—as difficult to find as a diet you can stick to—is the
simple program George and I used. One of us (alternating
each month) would telephone the other at 6:30 AM sharp,
with a one ring call. The caller, having gone through the
trouble of setting his alarm, of waking up and calling across
the street, had already invested too much diurnal energies to
go back to sleep. The recipient of the call, aware of his neighbor's heroic efforts, could not in good conscience disregard
this beckoning offer. And both our wives, knowing that they
could turn a deaf ear to that noninvading one ring prod into
their oniric domain, could gleefully and noncommittally
nudge their reluctant marathon man out from under the
covers.

Our partnership ran for three years. Then George and
Beth and Ann and Rachel moved to Palo Alto. Perhaps just as
well for my ego, for already, toward the end of that third year,
it became evident that I was losing ground and it would have
been a chore for George to wait up for me on those increasingly frequent mornings when my legs would stiffen and my
ankle joints would jam tight. The point that I missed then,
and that I think is very important for my fellow Parkinsonians, is that, in all sincerity, George probably would NOT
have minded waiting up for me, even if he would have had to
compensate by running on his own for five extra minutes at
the end of our daily jaunt.

I should have been more receptive to the fact that George
enjoyed helping me, I should have been less self-critical, and

more open to the helping hand—and feet—of my devoted neighbor. We, the patients, are not usually as bad off or as useless as we might think we are. We must never let the bulb of our self-worth glow dim. If only past, our accomplishments and feats are part of us. They cannot be dissociated from our present makeup and they may even be the source of emulation for our children and generations to come.

So I have learned not to be shy or self conscious. With or without a partner, go to the next gym and start walking, or go to a health club, sign up for a squash court, and start kicking that tennis ball. Incidentally, toe ball has no rules, just instinct. You can play alone or with someone. Actually, I get a better workout when alone: more kicks, less dead balls per minute. In no time at all, I have broken into a healthy sweat. That's it! Lean on the ball. There's a good bounce, gracious parabola. My legs work smoothly like mighty pistons. I have never felt so good; elation. Who says I have a debilitating disease? Then, split second of inattention; right leg not moving fast enough to reach the point where right foot should step; ankle caving under, whole body lurching forward. Yet the saving reflex—reflex responses are not affected in Parkinson disease—of twisting back and tucking head in, sending only the shoulders crashing into the wall. I have Parkinson all right. But still, while I can kick, I WILL kick and kick; and keep kicking. And go home today with Richard Simmons' exhortation: "If you can move it, use it."

17

Road Reflections

Flashback To Muskogee

The drive back from the airport to Northfield was dreary. The three-foot-high snow banks along the side of the road were a constant reminder of the final five weeks of the walk in California when the temperatures were in the 80s, the beach in Santa Monica golden and burning and the future a world without disease. One memory leading to another, I reminisced about that fall afternoon approaching Muskogee, Oklahoma.

Our advance team told us we were to stay in Muskogee for one night only. But when we met our host family, Rallie and Jack Bishop, we learned that plans had been changed and we were to spend the entire weekend with them. Rallie, a woman of about 50, had taken over the operation in her own inimitable way, a blend of authoritarianism and compassion. It was easy to see she had suffered, but she had also pugnaciously won her fights. That did not mean she was home free. Like everyone she still battled with the problems of a sick husband and a mother whom she visited every day at an old folks' home. But she tended both of them with maximum zeal, love and efficiency. Why she wanted to be saddled with the extra burden of this odd marching couple for the weekend is beyond me...but proof enough of the well-tempered steel will of the woman.

In a sense, Rallie is symbolic of all the people we met on the walk: either tough-fighting patients or no less determined spouses and mates. They all have hope, they all have spent hours of insomnia together, trying to alleviate the symptoms of the crippler, crying together wondering what the future holds in store for them, calculating the impact that

a disability salary will have on their present finances, on
their oncoming retirement, reading the medical literature,
separating the genuine doctors from the charlatans, dread-
ing if, after all, the disease might be hereditary, and if little
Susannah, their first grandchild, will not be the next target.
Rallie is no exception, but she is a model, and during that
weekend, she will have taught me, the supposed peddler of
hope, what faith and love really are.

Thus I reminisced driving home from the airport warding
off the approach of another snow storm slaughter. Lovely
people indeed. How was I so lucky to meet so many of them
on my trek across country? The welcoming hands, the care,
the interest, the generosity, the hospitality put me back 28
years ago, when, at 17, I came to spend a year in the U.S. as
an AFS (American Field Service) exchange student. This second Odyssey, on which I had now embarked, was just as promising, just as fruitful, just as much of a turning point in my
life and career, just as formative as my first. A new education
had started on September 15, 1985.

The Creative Mind _____

And there were many others like Rallie. Since the Road to
Dignity was a communal effort to benefit all Parkinsonians,
there were various manifestations of that coping creativity
which were given to me along the way. First this exhortation:

Don't Quit

When things go wrong as they sometimes will,
When the road you're trudging seems all uphill,
When the funds are low and the debts are high
When you want to smile, but you have to sigh

When care is pressing you down a bit,
Rest, if you must—but don't you quit.

Life is queer with its twists and turns,
As everyone of us sometimes learns,
And many a failure turns about
When he might have won had he stuck it out,
Don't give up, though the pace seems slow—
You might succeed with another blow.

Often the goal is nearer than
It seems to a faint and faltering man,
Often the struggler has given up
When he might have captured the victor's cup.
And he learned too late, when the night slipped
down,
How close he was to the golden crown.

Success is failure turned inside out—
The silver tint of the clouds of doubt—
And you never can tell how close you are,
It may be near when it seems afar;
So stick to the fight when you're hardest hit—
It's when things seem the worst that you mustn't
quit.

A model of lyricism it certainly isn't, but I cherish that big print poster because of its ever reinforcing gut message. And I cherish it because it was given to me at an emotion-filled farewell party by fellow Parkinsonian Doris Evans, President of the Sedalia, Missouri APDA chapter. Here is one courageous wisp of a lady, fighter *emerita*, energy-packed leader of a peppy little group. Upon hearing that she had Parkinson disease, she vowed that the illness would not deter her from doing anything she wanted to do. She signed up for classes in an esoteric branch of karate and quickly became a black belt. She also entertained the APDA chapter presidents

at their biannual meeting in New York last September, doing
back flip somersaults on the stage. In a constant testing of
her will, last January she went on a severe drug holiday
which I would not recommend to anyone. I would not want to
try it myself.

Within two weeks she had totally quit all medication, and
then spent the rest of a hellish four weeks flat on her back.
Her daughter Stephanie and the couple of friends who kept
unrelenting watch over her day and night for a month were
under orders from Doris not to obey her or give in should she
ask for her drugs before the due date. Instead, what she
begged for during the whole last week of her near complete
paralysis, was to be put to sleep. How she survived the ordeal
borders on the miraculous. The last time I saw her, she was
eagerly waiting for the morrow: it was her day of the week for
skydiving. I think the APDA ought to produce a brochure to
honor this woman's willpower and use her accomplishments
as a showcase of possibilities open to Parkinsonians. Dear
Doris, Dear Doris Evans, Dear Doris "Don't Quit" Evans.

Neale Oliver of Kansas City is another live wire of a
Parkinsonian. With a different style. Neale looks at you with
his big brown round eyes while he orates an endless stream
of witticisms. You'd want to howl, point your finger and
scream, "Cynic" if you did not know that Neale and his lovely
wife Sara are the kindest, gentlest, most endearing couple in
the world. Gracefully cynical Neale, gratefully not embittered. With his permission, a few of his gems:

Parkinson's: Its Fringe Benefits

With apologies to Sidney Dorros, whose book
Parkinson's: A Patient's View has been an inspiration to all of us Parkinsonians, I proceed boldly
ahead to enumerate some of the left unsaid in that
tome.

"You have all the symptoms of Parkinson's disease." That little phrase emanating from the lips of your family doctor is initially more devastating than the news of Pearl Harbor, your condemnation to the firing squad, or even more than "Dear John." If that has happened to you, cheer up! There's good news ahead! Once the initial shock has passed and you have learned to accommodate the malady—you'll discover some pleasant surprises.

You always look great! The limited knowledge of Parkinson's and the accompanying mystery of the disease lead many friends and acquaintances to expect the worst, and you are usually greeted with "You have never looked better," or "Gosh, you look great!" What a salve to the old ego. You seem to acquire a bravery which heretofore has gone unnoticed.

Dining takes a turn for the better. Since your movements are much more deliberate, your manipulation of knife, fork and spoon slows considerably, and the intake of calories is reduced accordingly. The result—overnight you change from a "gourmet pig" to a "disciplined diner," and your belt and collar suddenly feel more comfortable. There is another benefit related to eating. What is more awkward than trying to cut into what you believe to be a Kansas City strip when actually you find that your hostess has selected the smaller New York cut. Help is on the way in the person of a compassionate dinner partner who supplies the elbow grease, and you proceed to devour the bite-sized morsels with a facility never before demonstrated and your plate is soon empty.

Parking and public ramps and staircases no longer
are a handicap. Everyone hates supermarket parking lots! Is there any experience more annoying
than lugging your weekly supply of groceries to
your automobile, parked somewhere in the next
county, when the comfort index is either 103
degrees or -12? Of course, you can always use a
grocery cart, but who wants to return it across that
desert or frozen tundra? Your handy handicap
decal or license plate eliminates these discomforts
as you ease into the spaces nearest the entrance;
and upon your departure there is invariably someone to carry your bundles.

Or consider the endless winding ramp to the upper
levels of the football stadium. Edgar Allen Poe, in
his wildest alcoholic delusions, never experienced
such a maddening maelstrom! Once again, it's
Parkie to the rescue, as you show your special pass
and ascend comfortably to your level in the elevator
provided.

An exciting new vocabulary. Pity the poor non-
Parkinsonian who will never be able to drop such
words as dyskinesia, carbidopa, thalamotomy, bro-
mocriptine, festination, levodopa, dopaminergic,
and my favorite: bupropion hydrochloride.

Mask for middle/old age symptoms. Now you can
disguise many of the telltale symptoms of middle
age and senior citizenry without revealing your
true age. Just think, all forgetfulness, tremors,
slower movement, shortness of breath and other
characteristics can be attributed to the malady. If
the researchers can come up with a medication for
Parkinson's that eliminates liver spots, your age
will be a secret forever.

So cast off all the deep funk and consider the Parkinson's fringe benefits. After all, it could be poison ivy!

—Neale Oliver

Finally, An Ode to Mr. Parkinson, by Mr. Joe Griffey, a member of the Central Ohio Parkinson Society.

An Ode to Mr. Parkinson

Good morning, Mr. Parkinson, how do you do?
I have some new information just made for you;
For twelve long years you've been messing up my life;
You've stolen the respect of my kids and my wife;
You've slowly taken over like a constricting snake;
Well, I've had about all of you I care to take.
You don't play fair as you make up all of the rules;
But now sir, I have access to some brand new tools.
What are these brand new tools? You might desire to ask,
Well, they are strong and ready for their given task.
One of these tools is called new medication;
And a second new tool is more information.
A third tool is support from my Parkinson peers;
You're losing your grip as I am shedding my fears.
Through all of these years you have had things your own way,
But you've had little opposition 'til this day.
Now you've got real problems that are certainly not fake;
So wake up and smell the coffee, you sickening snake.
You made a big mistake trying to conquer me,

I am no longer afraid of you, don't you see?
This time, Mr. Parkinson, and I tell you true,
You have really bitten off more than you can chew.

There are, of course, endless ways to handle our problems, to cope with difficulties for which we were not prepared, to struggle and flail about and still manage to keep our chin up and our neck above water. Each patient must find his own way based on his own makeup. The person with an athletic background will emphasize sports in his therapy, while the electrical engineer may want to spend his recently found extra time developing a body dryer, for example. A third person will want to use her business and organizational skills creating a support group for Parkinsonians. A fourth will channel his Parkinson induced speech impediment to another communication skill and discover an innate talent for writing. My friend Elliott Rudenstein did when he started editing his group's newsletter. He has not missed one issue since its inception several years ago.

In the same way that we exhale our oxygen-burnt waste products and inhale unsoiled oxygen, so must our final goals be to shun shame, guilt and self-pity and pursue hope, faith and charity.

E Pluribus Unum

It is no secret that one common denominator for all Parkinsonians is the idiosyncratic onset of the symptoms, their helter-skelter development, the varied individual reaction to the medications, the diversity of the progression in each patient, and for each symptom, the wide-ranging intensity. All these combine to make a totally chancy prognosis. In other words, although we are all in the same boat, there are not two of us alike. We would almost be tempted to say *Vive la différence*, if it were not for the complications wrought in the treatment of the syndrome. In my case, I have been remarkably free of problems with legs and feet...although I have had occasional warnings, subtle enough not to jeopardize my ability to finish the walk, but definite enough to give me a fairly good idea of what to expect in the near future. Indeed, in a few instances, I have felt a menacing tightening in the back of my right knee. At some other times I have been visited by shuffling and by quickening of movements. I have also had a couple of bouts with a case of leaden feet, when starting to walk with a half turn. So, if my evolution seems slow when it comes to legs and feet—an appreciable reprieve for anyone crossing the United States on foot—the same cannot be said, unfortunately, about my voice and speech production.

Just as there are no two Parkinsonians with the same set of symptoms, there are likewise no two identical Parkinson support groups. I should have known that from my classroom experience, where each class has its own qualities and faults, where each section of the same level class has its own set of dynamics. The same is true of a concert or of a theatrical production: each performance has its own identity with idiosyncratic variations which depend as much on the audience as on the teacher/performer.

In this light, the Columbia, Missouri group was business oriented. I took great pleasure facing the camera in the company of the mayor and savoring the delicious Red Delicious, for which Columbia is the self-proclaimed world capital. My appearances on the local media also were sponsored by a well-known local sporting goods store whose owner had me photographed bedecked in his logo-ed T-shirt, walking up and down Main Street, entering and leaving the store.

On the other hand, the Sedalia, Missouri group, headed by Doris (Don't Quit) Evans was colorfully dramatic. Almost single-handedly she organized a dinner for 200, complete with music and song, including an unforgettable rendition of the Man of La Mancha's "To Dream the Impossible Dream" which had everybody in tears.

On that same occasion, using the Road to Dignity Walk passage through town as an excuse, Doris had the guts to organize a grippingly dignified parade along Main Street, where about 40 people at various stages of advancing Parkinsonism, with a good dozen patients in wheelchairs, held up the rush hour traffic, attracting wide attention and compelling the shopkeepers to come out and clap in admiration for this motley group.

Images of medieval pilgrims entering St. Jean Pied-de-Port and images of the Benediction of the sick today in Lourdes flashed through my mind. I am sure that that noteworthy exhibit of Parkinsonians, replayed on the local 6:00 PM and 10:00 PM news, did more to put Parkinson on the city's map and in the public cortex than any single event I can think of.

Different yet, the Lubbock group was Texan-ly congenial: amusingly conceited about their state perhaps, I thought at first, when I noticed the shape of the state of Texas on the template of wall clocks: unduly narcissistic, I was sure when I found the motif repeated in the design and shape of our hotel bathroom sinks.

—"Michel," Marguerite came knocking at my door, "did you check out the shape of the bathroom sink?"

—"Yeah! Interesting, isn't it?"

—"Interesting?" She balked, "I can't believe my eyes! 'Totally unclassical' I would say!..."

—"Well, I wonder what you will say when you find a toilet stool in that shape..."

—"Oh! Shut up! Your bad taste matches the sink."

—"You mean: how can I sink so low?"

Unclassical as the Texas designers may be, it is in Lubbock that we met one of the classiest ladies on the trip. Ava Crowder, just out of the Parkinsonian closet that she had called home for five years, was re-establishing her bearings based on a new consciousness: she had finally acquired the courage to face the hard fact and, in so doing, she was discovering with delight that she could still function at a very high percentage of her potential. She was becoming more and more aware that there were other people in the same boat, and that life was better lived in the living room than in the broom closet. There, at least, was more legroom for her tall Texan structure.

She confided at the next day's lunch that she was now enjoying meeting people. She put her gregarious nature to the service of our cause by taking an active role in the affairs of her chapter, by visiting fellow Parkinsonians in hospitals. She was also booked on two upcoming cruises. She said life had never been so promising and she was now ready and looking for some way to channel her energies, talents and resources into positive actions. Just a few months later, Ava, an extremely articulate woman, had parleyed these natural gifts into the presidency of her APDA chapter and into an APDA Ambassadorship at Large.

Before we left town, feeling she had found a mirror image in my positive outlook, she invited us to her house to meet her daughter and husband, and had made me promise that we would go together to receive the cure wherever and whenever it was announced.

The Road to Dignity was indeed a huge melting pot of people from all walks of life, a warm and caring extended family of individuals who one day had been compelled to look Truth in the eye and to start a new life from scratch. There were no longer phony barriers and social differences.

To wit, a topflight engineer who had worked at the Jet Propulsion Laboratory and designed the landing gear for the moon probe was now intensely listening to the advice freely dispensed by the unassuming but genuinely concerned caregiving housewife.

—"Now, take Ralph here," she proudly explained, "he does much better on half doses of Sinemet,™ but taken twice as often, don't you, dear?" as she turned to Ralph. "You ought to try it, too."

Or vividly etched in my memory is the recollection of the young man who had moved, carefree, to Albuquerque two years before, lured by the big city glitter, and who was now faithfully going back to Roswell every weekend to take care of his rapidly failing father whom he nursed lovingly.

Or the Hollywood producer's wife who had just made the acquaintance of the helpless, recently widowed war bride and was discovering in Erika's story the solace she needed to face her own recently diagnosed symptoms.

—"Parkinson by itself on a single Social Security check is no fun," Erika was lamenting. "But now, with Christmas approaching, it is going to be doubly difficult to face the stark reality alone."

Then she burst out, half out of compassion, half out of despair, "Why wouldn't you come and spend a few days with us in Los Angeles? We have a big empty house. We'd love to have your company."

Or that funny French professor from Minnesota, usually so conscious of etiquette and decorum, who could not believe what he had just done: "Mo," he said, "it sure was a great pleasure for me and a source of pride for all of us that you joined our crusade and walked with us into Tucson this morning. I appreciate it all the more, knowing the hectic schedule you maintain. You look splendid; I would never have guessed that you were one of us."

—"My God, Monnot!" I shouted inwardly, "Do you know what you just did? Shame on you! What would your mother say if she heard you? Have you lost your head? Yes, I know. I can't believe I just called a man who's ten years older than I, who's a foot taller than I, who's a U.S. Congressman from Arizona, who ran for his party's nomination for president, I just called that man by his first name."

This breaking down of barriers, more than anything else, symbolizes the spirit of liberation shared by people in the same lifeboat, fighting for the same good cause. As the artificial barriers come tumbling down, a familiarity develops which does not breed contempt, but rather engenders respect and dignity.

Now for all the members of this huge family to congregate, a network of supporting relatives, friends, advocates and professionals must operate constantly with vigor, understanding, and efficiency. These brothers and sisters in need are the doctors and neurologists, the Parkinson Disease Information and Referral Centers' directors and the chapter and support group presidents, whether they belong to the APDA, the PEP (Parkinson Education Program) or the PSGA (Parkinson Support Groups of America). They paved my road with meaning and dignity, for they were the catalysts who enabled me, the hope peddler, to extend my message to all the afflicted.

Among many of equal warmth and efficient help were a daughter, mother and grandmother team at the Joplin, Missouri clinic. Susan Emke in Lubbock, Liz Parmenter in Tucson, Joan Claussen in Tulsa, Kay Chisholm in Albuquerque, Ellen Moscinski, in San Diego, Lupe Beaver in Los Angeles, Ruth Flugel in Minneapolis, John Foss in Ames and Jack Perry in Waterloo; Warren Haven in Rochester; Ann Kirkland and Neale Oliver in Kansas City; Don Moore and Zada and Nita in Tulsa; Fred McGarret in Lubbock; Les Ansberg and Richard Allen in Sante Fe; Ken Mills in Tucson; Norma Peabody, Shirley Krims and Kathleen Cooper in Los Angeles; Carole Wolken in Tucson; and Laura Watt in Denver. The list is endless and any absence from it is due entirely to my short-term Parkinsonian memory.

Cementing the bond of kinship were also all the meeting convenors and social workers at hospitals, all the nurses and candy stripers, the physical therapists, who made us feel welcome, who took pleasure and pride in showing us their facilities. Salient in my mind is the memory of a hospital administrator in Miami, Oklahoma who insisted that I take with me as a souvenir, since I had expressed my admiration of it, a carved replica of a Sooner Schooner, one of those prairie wagons used by Oklahoma settlers.

Equally touching and still fresh in my mind is the memory of the rousing surprise reception that was organized by the hospital in Anaheim. It was totally unsuspected. When Patrick and I, panting heavily from the last mile that we had jogged instead of walked, entered the lobby, we were greeted with fanfare, balloons and a standing ovation. How difficult to fight back the tears! And to reminisce today without nostalgia!

I would like to think that one of the biggest bonuses of the Road to Dignity Walk was an attempt at bringing together extraordinary individuals whom I am proud to count as my friends, but who by design or even by chance happen to espouse slightly different approaches in our common effort to find a better life. Each of us pursues his own means to ease the burden and find the cure. Among those leaders I was privileged to meet were author and artists Peter and Irene Stern, Charlotte Drake of PEP who took the time to give us a grand tour of the PEP offices and to take us to lunch. Mary Willis and her group in Whittier, and Phyllis Marks and Leona Bivens in Los Angeles are more; Elliott Rudenstein is another; Mariette Bell of Denver and Bev Stewart of Santa Barbara also, as well as Russ Alstrom of Mankato, and right here in Northfield, without forgetting my initial sponsors, Maxine Lamm and the unaffiliated Northfield support group.

18

Going Places

Kudos

...And five months later I arrived in Los Angeles. I might as well have walked around the globe. It truly felt like an eternity. During all that time, my thoughts, my ideas, my values had all done somersaults in my mind, liberating their youthful energies and leaving my body a sanctified urn of decanted fluid.

This is a time for joy and rejoicing. Oh! I know I will be castigated for having succumbed to depression at times, to negative anticipations.... Too bad for my critics. Having never encountered the darkness of failure, they must not know the color of joy. So, today, we celebrate. Freely.

Janice and Natalie arrive with a delegation of Northfield admirers who this morning unfurl a giant banner signed by hundreds of well-wishers at home. And the procession is off from the Santa Monica Miramar hotel where princely suites have been put at our disposal; up along Wilshire Boulevard, direction: the Los Angeles Athletic Club. The walking is less dignified than I would have wished: I limp and have to walk with a cane. Two days ago while kicking my soccer ball along the San Juan Capistrano beach, I pulled a thigh muscle. Afraid that it would jeopardize our fund-raising efficiency, I apologized to Frank for my stupidity.

But he is quick with a soothing word and a Machiavellian grin, "I'm sorry you're hurt, Michel, but as a fund raiser, I know that your limping will play havoc on the heart strings of would-be donors and contributors. So, forgive me for appearing so callous, but if I were you, I wouldn't worry one bit about fund-raising at this point."

He was right. I caught glimpses of compassion from passers-by on the sidewalks, while TV cameras focused on my uneven gait punctuated by the click-click of my Jack Perry cane.

Dick Saunders had been the instrument of our invitation and celebration at the Los Angeles Athletic Club. As such, he had also enlisted the participation of luminaries in the fields of sports and health. Present and walking next to me were Rafer Johnson, the decathlon world record holder; Tim Daggett, Olympic gymnastics champion. He looked so young that I mistook him for a wandering high school student who had spontaneously joined the crowd, and focused my attention instead on the feminine charm of TV personality Barbara Valentine, hostess of Heart of the Nation show. George Mills, my old running partner, had come down from Palo Alto for the occasion; my former student Larry Bahr was there, accompanied by his Samoan wife; Beth Moran, one of the students we took on the first bicycle trip to France was there with her husband and two lovely children. Representatives from Sandoz Inc., the manufacturer of Parlodel™ and contributor to the purchase of the van were there. The various Parkinson groups from all around the region were also represented. Richard Simmons of If-you-can-move-it-use-it fame was there too.

At one point Frank moved up to Janice and me and said, "Here's someone I would like you to meet. This is Ralph Edwards. Perhaps you remember Ralph was the host of the TV show This Is Your Life. His wife Barbara has recently been diagnosed with Parkinson and he has just agreed to be APDA's National campaign chairman. As such he will introduce you after lunch."

—"Delighted to meet with you, but sorry that your wife's misfortune is the cause of my pleasure to meet you."

—"It's a great joy to meet you, too. What a fantastic adventure!..."

It was mayhem in the Club's dining room. Huge round tables had been set. I caught a glimpse of Natalie chatting with

Patrick and Sara. I was introduced to Barbara Edwards long enough for a Ronsard poem to surge from the depths.

But what can the matter be with Marguerite? There she sits, brooding in one corner of the room, forlorn. I instinctively know what it is, but I am not given a chance to do anything about it, as short-clad and curly-haired Richard Simmons gently takes my hand to have me meet his new facilities manager. All the while, Dick Saunders and his jazz band softly blew old swing tunes. And it was a warm handshake from Walter Erlich; a "congratulations" from the Rosens; and a neat little gift wrapped present from the Rosenbergs; a quick "hello" to the Peabodies; a raised glass and a cheer to Lupe and Gerry Beaver; until a rolling of the drums announced that lunch was served. Each subsequent speech at the podium extolling the virtues of the feat we were celebrating was punctuated by a toast. By the end of the third speech, the mixture of alcohol and flattered ego made its way to my head. I have to gain control of myself. It will soon be my turn at the podium. Remember—joyous, I can be; undignified, I may not. Dessert had already been served, and with a crescendo of lyricism on the part of the two M.C.s, Frank Williams and Ralph Edwards, various awards and plaques of recognition were distributed, each one underlined by the rippling sound of the cymbals. And now Ralph asks me to join him. A pat on the shoulder from Frank as I walk past him.

—"Michel! aaah, Michel," begins Ralph as he tugs at some notes stuck in his inside coat pocket. But they won't be dislodged. Unflappable, he turns to Frank and asks for the proclamation. "Michel, I have here a special document I want to read to you. Mayor Tom Bradley could not be here to greet you, but he asked me to present you with this proclamation which makes you, as of today, an honorary citizen of Los Angeles." And he deployed a beautiful illuminated parchment worthy of the best medieval manuscripts. "But that's not all," he warned. By now, he had managed to extract the notes and as I passed the proclamation around for everyone to admire, I heard him intone:

So, three cheers for Michel Monnot,
indomitable, unrelenting Michel,
through hailstorm, rain, wind and snow,
walked a nation
that all Parkies might get well.

Professor Monnot,
single-handedly
you have lit a candle;
no, you have lit a skyrocket.
Finally, for Parkinson's
an explosion!

You sir, the first, the bravest,
the most creative and productive,
Frustrated with no headlines for Parkinson's;
no explosions;
you decided that if the mountain would not come to
Michel,
Michel would come to the mountain.

It took unbelievable physical stamina;
Mr. Nobody, coming from nowhere
wrenching your way over trails
a healthy guy wouldn't have tackled
into headlines for Parkinson's.

If ever a man succeeded in what he wanted to do,
you did!
Michel Monnot, your feat has brought newfound inspiration to this cause.

—"So for all of us to show our admiration and appreciation,
the APDA offers this tribute which I am honored to present
to you. Frank, would you please bring the plaque?" Under my
eyes Frank uncovers an immense walnut plaque which he
hands to Ralph. Oohs and aaahs, applause.
    —"Let me read you the inscription:

TO MICHEL MONNOT,
FOR HIS EXTENSION OF FUNDAMENTAL
HUMAN VALUES—FOR THE BETTERMENT
OF HIS FELLOW PARKINSONIANS—FOR
HIS INSPIRATION & VIBRANT COURAGE
IN COMPLETING THE ROAD TO DIGNITY WALK
AND IN FOSTERING THE IDEALS
OF ALL AMERICANS
JANUARY 25, 1986
BOARD OF DIRECTORS
THE AMERICAN PARKINSON DISEASE
ASSOCIATION

—"Congratulations, Michel."

It's now my turn. I am a bit winded. Quick, three deep breaths while the applause continues.

—"Thank you, thank you." Circular look at the audience. I am just a tad overdosed. Things will be fine.

—"Thank you Ralph, thank you Frank. Thanks to all of you for being here, lending your time, donating your money, throwing your support to this good cause that we may find relief very soon. Indeed, I want to thank you for having been extraordinarily supportive of this effort. Some people called it a feat. In that case, I guess that makes you arch-supporters." Laughter. "Incidentally, I tried Dr. Scholl's for a donation for that one. But no response! I guess that makes him a heel! And we don't want a heel. We want a cure. Right?" More laughter. "Kidding aside, it is my turn for accolades. First of all, to Frank Williams, the architect of this adventure, the father of the slogan 'The Road to Dignity Walk,' an astute manager, best of all a good friend. Also at the top on the list, thank you to Janice who has been supportive of this undertaking since its inception and without whose benediction this trek would not have taken place. Thank you to my children Natalie, Gigi and Patrick for having understood my plight in moments of darkness. Thank you to my initial committee and to the Northfield Hospital who first pledged, then raised the money to see this idea off the ground. Maxine Lamm, Cynnie Buchwald, please take a bow.

—"Thank you to Dr. Felix Zwiebel of the Parkinson Clinic at Methodist Hospital in St. Louis Park for his care, concern, understanding and science and for giving me the formal authorization to go ahead. I wish he would have been riding in the van that day in Iowa where an obtuse highway patrolman told Marguerite: 'This guy there is not fit to be on the road.'

—"Thank you to the Carleton College administration, Dean Roy Elveton who understands my plight and agreed to keep my position open for the day when a cure is found. Thank you to all my colleagues at Carleton and friends who banded together to offer me an IBM-PC upon my going on disability. One of them even took two days off from his job at Palo Alto to come and walk the last few miles at my side. Thank you George. Won't you please stand up?

—"Thank you to my road crew, my son Patrick and friend Sara who formed the advance team and prepared the way by making sure that everything was ready for me in each town I went through (contacts with the local group, the press, the mayor's office, the police station) and who did all this by taking a semester off from their studies at the University of Wisconsin at Madison.

—"Thank you to all the members of the press who, throughout the journey helped spread the word about Parkinson, and especially to Diane Rossi and Rusty of Channel 11 in Minneapolis/St. Paul who covered the event from the beginning and who are now reporting live from this room to Minnesota.

—"And finally, last but certainly not least, my warmest thanks to Marguerite Sandor for four and a half months of lively exchanges of views and opinions. Maguit, by driving the van so expertly, by administering my medications so unerringly, you kept me safe. By your good cheer, your loyal defense, your fabulous organizational skills, you kept me sane. Without you, Maguit, I would still be spinning my wheels somewhere in the middle of Iowa. All our best wishes on your return to France. We shall miss you.

—"However, I would be remiss not to address a few last comments to Ralph Edwards. Ralph, I want you to know that meeting you and Barbara has been a real pleasure. And I also want you to know that your TV show This Is Your Life was an integral and formative factor in my Americanization process. You see, when I was a young college student at St. Cloud State College 25 years ago, I had a standing invitation from my landlady to come up to her living room once a week to watch your show. I loved it. I never missed it. You were one of my American heroes. The show was homey, warm, generous, optimistic—we would say today 'upbeat'—it epitomized for me what is good about this country. I thought of you as a good spirit, a modern reincarnation of Merlin the Enchanter as you created one fairy tale after another. So today among all days of my life, I could not have hoped for a more perfect host. It is a good omen. I am blessed. Perhaps I have done something right. Perhaps this glorious day was predestined to be the converging point of all my life's journeys, from the Old World to the New; from Minnesota to Los Angeles; from shame, guilt and self-pity, to faith, hope and charity; from Rage to Courage. Perhaps the gods are with us now."

Good-bye Marguerite

—"All passengers for Northwest flight #61, nonstop, Minneapolis/London please report to gate #22 on the Gold Concourse."

This is it, I thought. The very last plug has been pulled. The Road to Dignity Walk, which had been scheduled to end on February 2nd, has lingered on for ten more days while Marguerite stayed with us in Northfield, preparing for her return trip to France while I reaccustomed myself to being at

home. But now, this is the true ending and the walk has come
to a grinding halt.

In fact it is deceased, dead, it is over. It is no more. It feels
like striking the set after the last performance of a play. The
walk has now embarked on the journey of "memories only,"
detached from the tangible, oblivion-bound into eternity. For
a very short while yet, it will remain programmed on the precarious neural connections of a few individuals' brains, then
it will inexorably decay.

The airport was jammed. Marguerite, standing in a long
line of waiting passengers, had an assortment and a quantity
of luggage that betrayed 18 months of accumulation. She is a
well organized inveterate pack rat. She saves everything
and, miracle of miracles, remembers exactly where she puts
every piece of her ambulatory collection. But in this instance,
the result of her acquisitive mania forced her to accomplish
an erratic juggling act to keep all her bags and purses in
equilibrium on her shoulders. Passport and ticket tightly
gripped between her teeth, she stepped out of the line,
flashed a clenched smile, and we fell into each other's arms.
The five months together on the road created a deep and
genuine friendship, hammered out of countless trials, tribulations and shouting matches, but also out of many happy occasions. All in all, the Road to Dignity Walk was very
successful, and so this good-bye was a moment of shared
warmth, sadness and joy. Our embrace reflected those feelings.

The line had moved. It was Marguerite's turn. The clerk
tinkered for a second with a keyboard, prodding the monitor
to spew back information. She scribbled something on the
boarding pass and returned passport and ticket to Marguerite.

—"Here you are, ma'am. Non-smoking section, seat 37.
And this is your boarding pass. We'll be boarding by section.
Have a good flight and thank you for flying Northwest."

Walking toward the gate to say good-bye was Rusty, the
TV cameraman. He had probably come to the airport to give

Marguerite another token of his head-over-heels fall for her. He and Diane Rossi, medical reporter for the same station, had covered the Road to Dignity Walk since the inception. I remembered gratefully that Diane was the first TV reporter to interview me.

I also recalled how assiduous Rusty had been in his courtship of Marguerite. First, in Santa Monica it was a pair of earrings that she could not wear because she does not have pierced ears; then, a week ago in Northfield when he came down from Minneapolis to show us the video he taped in San Juan Capistrano—in particular the sequence where Patrick, Marguerite and I play soccer on the beach and I writhe in pain for pulling a muscle—that time, the gift was a pair of delicate mother-of-pearl earrings with a matching pair of barrettes.

What can it be this time? I caught a furtive thrust of white into Marguerite's purse. An envelope with a card, perhaps? But I had the feeling this may well be his last gift: Marguerite was a bit reticent toward him. She was also not wearing the mother-of-pearl earrings and barrettes. Rusty is no fool, he seems to understand the finality of the situation. Tomorrow she will be in Paris! Suave enough in his prospective discomfiture, he had the graciousness to pay his respects gallantly and leave. Only a few minutes left. A last embrace.

—"Now boarding, seats 30 to 48, please have your boarding pass ready." The embrace lasted a little longer.

—"Thank you, dear Maguit. Have a safe trip and don't forget to send me your thoughts on the book..."

—"I won't! And 'thank you,' to you. Take good care of yourself, you can do it, the cure is at hand. You know that, don't you? It is just a matter of patience. I know you will be OK. Straighten up your shoulders, lift up your chin, don't let this damn thing drag you down. Remember, if somebody can shake it off, *you* are that somebody. You are strong, you are young, you think young, you have energy 'galoore.' You're working for a good cause. Frank Williams and a million supporters are behind you. You may be on disability for teaching

French, but not for teaching guts and courage. And I'll be thinking of you. How could I ever forget this experience!"

—"Maguit, you dear, you very dear," and tilting my head back I feigned a frown, "so you think I can 'shake it off'? Now who's being macabre?"

—"All right! It's your bad sense of humor and your sick jokes that are rubbing off on me," as she took a step back. "That's the proof that it is high time for me to go back to France."

—"And oh! One more thing Maguit," I put on my most innocent air, "in American English we do not say, 'energy galoore,' we say 'energy galore!' "

She burst out laughing, "Tu es vache![1]...Don't worry, I'll have my revenge." For five months, in a caring case of the blind leading the blind, I had been trying to correct the very few mistakes she made in English, while she was helping me revamp my academically aging French.

And so it has gone with our relationship, mutually respectful, warm, acerbic, honest, sarcastic, erratic, sisterly, brotherly, easygoing.

—"This way to the plane, ma'am, and please sir, could you move a few steps back?" A last look at her before the airship's cavernous entrails swallowed her up. She turned around, readjusted the shoulder straps of her bags, a wave of the hand, she was gone.

First Class Travel

As I stared at the empty space where Marguerite had stood just seconds before, I remembered that extraordinary day at Orly Airport in Paris.

---

1   "You're such a jerk!"

Orly. El Al and American Airlines counters were heavily guarded. It felt like a ratio of one machine gun per passenger. All the pieces of luggage had been taken to a room on another floor and passengers had to select which pieces were theirs. Any piece left unclaimed was a prime suspect for further investigation. The airport attendant escorting me led me through shortcuts, with "won't you step this way, Mr. Monnot," and "Please follow me, Mr. Monnot." I smiled inwardly. That's OK, I don't mind the attention. Besides, I asked for it. On that day, too, just as I was on the Road to Dignity Walk, I was spoiled, surrounded by solicitous and generous people everywhere. Granted, we cannot live as if there will always be someone at our beck and call—even with Parkinson disease. But in the few instances where help can make the difference between success and failure, such as in catching or missing a plane connection, there is no need for false pride in requesting and accepting help which is already built into the financial structure and available for the asking.

When I travel I am sometimes alone. So I have elaborated a system to ease the burden and face the world. I have with me at all times a note to flight attendants, usually typed on yellow paper to attract attention, which says who I am, what I have, what my medical problem is, and what type of help I may need during the course of the trip. (See Appendix A.) I can vouch for its efficacy. When I come up to an airline counter at any airport, it is not always obvious that I have Parkinson disease. It is therefore somewhat surprising to the attendant that I should ask for the privilege of preboarding or for the use of a wheelchair.

It is indeed paradoxical that I can walk 15 miles a day but that I cannot stand in line on my two feet for more than five minutes without shaking noticeably and most uncomfortably. By saying that the disease is neither hereditary, contagious nor fatal, I reassure the flight attendants: they need not be concerned for their health, and by listing the symptoms, I tell them what to expect.

'Tis true, I'd much rather remove the plastic or aluminum foil off the dinner tray myself than having the flight attendant do it for me—incidentally, it seems some companies take a sadistic pleasure in keeping Parkinsonians out of and away from their products by wrapping an impregnable shield of plastic or aluminum foil around them—but I reason that if we cannot get help for the little things, we will not get help for the important ones either.

Of course my list can be changed to include pertinent personal variants.

When the counter attendant has read my sheet—I can be sure this has been done by watching the attendant's facial expression as he or she reads—I ask for it back and repeat my action with the cabin official greeter and again with the attendant assigned to my seat. I have only praise for the system. Never once, since I have put it into practice, have I waited unnecessarily on my legs, nor been frustrated by a stubborn aluminum lid on a cup of orange juice. I've had help with my bags stuck under the seat, help in feeding paper into my portable typewriter. I've been saturated with pillows and blankets, and best of all, I've been treated without the fake smiles and artificial bonhomie we are accustomed to.

To anyone who may be envious of this apparent favoritism, my answer is simple: "Eh, Bud, you haven't got Parkinson disease but if you have some condition equally debilitating, an equally preferential treatment is there for the asking."

So much attention lavished on the passenger is not, however, without its minor drawbacks. Once I had just landed in Dallas. It was one of those airline logic specials where in true crow flight fashion, the most direct line between Minneapolis and Paris went through Dallas...and I had a four-hour layover. I had made plans to find myself a cozy little spot in an uncluttered area of the open waiting room; I would pull out my portable jewel, the Typest*r 6, and snug and smug in my independent bubble I would write the definitive novel. At least I would catch up with a couple of thank you notes.

I soon discovered the gratuity of such plans. Dallas airport personnel, bless their souls, had other plans.

—"Mr. Monnot?" I heard a shrill voice ask as I stepped out of the plane, "We have a wheelchair here, ready for you. Please sit down. You have a long wait before your next departure. We are going to take you to room E3 where you can rest."

Too surprised by the peremptory tone, I could only stammer some inaudible monosyllables, which Ms. Bonaparte interpreted to her convenience. Never mind that those grunts of mine were strong objections to the treatment and to the program of action prescribed. In the first place, I don't need a wheelchair and just because it says on my ticket that I may need help does not mean that I cannot walk to the terminal. In the time it took to clear my throat and prepare an intelligible riposte, she was at it again.

—"Please step right in, that's it, back up a step or two more, easy, easy, plop. OK fine, now lift your feet and put them on the footrest. I'm going to whisk you to our Special Needs and Rest Center, Room E3. There, you can rest quietly, someone will bring you sandwiches and something to drink. You'll want to watch TV I am sure, and someone else will pick you up later to help you board the plane."

These were too many things I did not want to do.

So I raised my finger, schoolboy fashion, and said, "Miss? May I go to the bathroom instead?"

Behind the shrill voice there was a good sense of humor. She looked at the childish, impish, pouting face I had managed to contrive for the occasion, hesitated a split second, then burst out laughing.

19

Epilogue

It's now been two years since the end of the Road to Dignity Walk and we still do not have the cure that I was promising along the way. But there's a lot to be boasting about. And more than ever I look toward the future with increasing optimism. I just know that the years remaining before we have a viable cure can be counted on the fingers of one hand. Medical advances are moving by leaps and bounds, and all around us there is ferment afoot that something big is gestating in the wings, preparing to make its front stage appearance—an explosion, as Ralph Edwards said.

Oh! I am no fool. Pollyanna, my name is not. I have learned to temper my boyish enthusiasm with patience and humility. I know full well that Parkinson has gained some territory in my private war: since the end of the walk I have experienced my first fall, tripping over the pants I was trying to put on. I have felt the shuffling pitter-patter of incipient festination. (A new word I learned from the Latin verb *festinare*, to hurry, to hasten. Compliments of Funk and Wagnall dictionary, and Parkinson.) I have suffered episodes of incarceration, unable to extract myself from bed, from the tub and from the car. Those are indeed terrifying jolts.

Equally abrasive on my sense of dignity, paradoxically, is the fact that I can no longer aspire to the vanity of wearing contact lenses: I shake too much to put them in for one thing. For another, my ophthalmologist refuses to outfit me with a pair: he claims that the diminished blinking caused by Parkinson increases the chances of scratching the cornea. Also, on account of the shaking, I have given up bird watching as holding binoculars steady is a greater nuisance and source of frustration than the enjoyment derived. In addition, for safety's sake, I have been forced to trade my macho ten-speed racer for a less showy woman's frame bike; it has the redeeming advantage of letting me get on and off without stretching my right leg over the seat and the back wheel, a most welcome feature. Finally, my handwriting has become illegible.

But man is a remarkably adaptive and resourceful beast, and there's always one way or more of skirting the obstacle, of inventing a solution be it ingenious or obvious. Coping becomes second nature. Darwin had a point: adapt or die; flourish or perish.

The most poignant illustration of this strategy that I know can be found in Giraudoux's Tigers at the Gates. Hector and Andromaque wonder what the future holds for their expected son:

> Andromaque: He will not be a coward. But I will have cut off his right index finger.[1]
>
> Hector: If all the mothers cut off their sons' right index fingers, the armies of the universe will wage war without index fingers...And if they cut off their sons' right legs, armies will be peg legged...and if they gouge out their eyes, armies will be blind, but there will be armies, and in the mêlée, they will grope for each others' throats or Achilles heels."

Waging our individual as well as collective war on Parkinson requires similar dogged determination. So look not toward the future with fear of old folks' homes and wheelchairs, for negative anticipation is ruinous. Turn your face instead to the rising sun with your mind taut with hope, with confidence oozing out of every pore of your skin, knowing in your heart that a cure is at hand.

---

1   So he won't go to war because he cannot shoot a gun.

In the meantime, consider that doctors around the world and around the clock churn out data leading piece by piece to the completion of the puzzle; research is diversifying to explore all avenues of possible progress; surgeons are refining their techniques and sharpening their tools to probe into the brain.

What keeps me especially hopeful is the variety of options that cannot but succeed in cornering and trapping Parkinson very soon. So the adrenal cell transplant was not what we expected? Then the fetal cell implant will be the answer! So the research on fetal cell implant has to be abandoned because of the ethical issues involved? Then *in vitro* cell harvesting will be the answer. Already a doctor in Denver is about to isolate a defective protein in Parkinsonian patients. Another doctor at the University of Pittsburgh is making breakthroughs in the study of PHMO, nerve growth factor.

There is a multitude of scientists, research teams, and pharmaceutical companies in North America and Europe working in a frenzy to develop new drugs and new ways to administer them.

The public's education program is gaining momentum and spreading. The Road to Dignity Walk has spawned two annual series of fund raising walk-a-thons throughout the country which have netted $100,000 to $250,000 respectively. A young man is Tulsa is about to bequeath $25,000,000 to research.

Hope is moving in the right direction. Meanwhile, this reminder is still apropos:

Thou shalt not judge a man by his handshake.

Appendices

Itinerary (September 1985 to January 1986)

MINNESOTA

Minneapolis	9/15
Northfield	9/15
Faribault	9/16
Waterville	9/17
Mankato	9/18
Waseca	9/20
Owatonna	9/21
Rochester	9/22
Austin	9/24

IOWA

Mason City	9/25
Waverly	9/26
Waterloo	9/27
La Porte City	9/29
Cedar Rapids	9/30
Iowa City	10/2
Grinnell	10/3
Ames	10/4
Boone	10/5
Des Moines	10/7

MISSOURI

Trenton	10/8
Kansas City	10/9
St. Louis	10/11
Columbia	10/14
Sedalia	10/15
St. Clair	10/16
Rolla	10/17
Lebanon	10/18
Springfield	10/19
Monett	10/21
Neosho	10/22
Joplin	10/23

OKLAHOMA

Miami	10/25
Vinita	10/26
Pryor	10/27
Claremore	10/28
Tulsa	10/29
Coweta	11/1
Muskogee	11/2
Warpec	11/4
Wilburton	11/5

McAlester	11/6
Holdenville	11/8
Ada	11/9
Pauls Valley	11/11
Lexington	11/12
Chickasha	11/15
Lawton	11/16

TEXAS
Wichita Falls	11/18
Abiliene	11/21
Lubbock	11/22

NEW MEXICO
| Roswell | 11/23 |
| Santa Fe | Christmas |

ARIZONA
Flagstaff	12/29
Prescott	12/30
Phoenix	12/31
Tucson	1/3
Yuma	1/6

CALIFORNIA
Mountain Springs	1/8
San Diego	1/9
Carlsbad	1/14
Palm Springs	1/16
Anaheim	1/19
Newport Beach area	1/20
Laguna Beach	1/20
San Juan Capistrano	1/21
Los Angeles	1/24

Note To Flight Attendants

Dear Flight Attendant,

Hello! My name is Michel Monnot and I have PARKIN-SON disease.

It is neither hereditary, fatal nor contagious. The symptoms are: shaking, rigidity, and slowness of motion. Because of these, I'd appreciate it if you could help me in the following areas:

- Getting things in and out of the overhead compartment.
- Getting things in and out of my handbag.
- Food tray: removing the food wrappings and cutting the meat.
- Clothing: helping me put on and take off my jacket.
- Possibly help from a male flight attendant for loosening and fastening my clothes in the restroom.
- Seating: preferably an aisle seat, please, and if in a Boeing 747, in the center section with no seats in front.

Thank you for your help! And have a good flight!

Appendix C

Works Of Similar Appeal

Bergland, Richard, *The Fabric of Mind*, Viking, 1985.

Cousins, Norman, *The Anatomy of an Illness*, Norton, 1978.

Cousins, Norman, *The Healing Heart*, Norton, 1983.

Dorros, Sydney, *Parkinson's Disease: a Patient's View*, Warner Books, 1981.

Duvoisin, Roger, *Parkinson's Disease*, Raven Press, 1984.

Fletcher, Colin, *The Man who Walked Through Time,* Vintage, 1964.

Gray, Martin, *Au Nom de Tous les Miens*, Laffont, 1971.

Gray, Martin, *Le Livre de la Vie*, Laffont, 1973.

Gray, Martin, *Les Forces de la Vie*, Laffont, 1975.

Hallum, Boen, *My Fading Full Moon*, PEP, 1984.

Jenkins, Peter, *A Walk Across America*, Fawcett Crest Books, Ballantine Books, 1979.

Jenkins, Peter and Barbara, *The Walk West*, Fawcett Crest Books, Ballantine Books, 1981.

Kunst, David, *The Man Who Walked Around the World*, Morrow, 1979.

Monnot, Michel, *Selling America: Puns, Language & Advertising*, University Press of America, 1981.

Pitzele, Sefra, *Chronic Illness*, Thompson, 1985.

Peale, Norman Vincent, *Imaging, The Powerful Way to Change Your Life*, Guideposts, 1981.

Rousseau, Jean-Jacques, *Les Rêveries du Promeneur Solitaire,* 1783.

Stern, Peter, *The Parkinson's Challenge: a good life in the slow lane*, 1988.

Vaughan, Ivan, *Ivan: Living with Parkinson's Disease*, Macmillan, 1986.

ORDER FORM

Please send me _____ copies of Michel Monnot's *From Rage to Courage — The Road to Dignity Walk* at $10 per book.

Note: 10% of proceeds automatically credited to APDA.

_____
Name

_____
Address (not a P.O. Box)

_____
City   State   Zip

_____
Telephone Number

Add $2.50 for first book and $1.00 for each additional book for shipping. Minnesota residents please add 6% sales tax.

I am enclosing my check for $_____ for _____ copies of *From Rage to Courage* including $_____ for shipping and $_____ for tax.

Make check payable to:
St. Denis Press, P.O. Box 442, Northfield, MN 55057